Personal Fitness for You

Roberta Stokes
Sandra L. Schultz

Hunter Textbooks Inc.

ISBN 0-88725-317-2

Photo Credits:
Corel Professional Photos, Big Box of Art Photos and Clipart, Ablesoft.Com Photos, and photos from the
Miami-Dade County Public Schools taken by Sandra Schultz, Paula Fitzpatrick, Jay Flinchum, Paula
Raflowitz, and Lisa Spinosa. A special thanks to Mark Anthony Bailey at Miami-Dade College-North for his
assistance.
*Life*ART illustrations used with permission of Williams & Wilkins.

Inquiries should be addressed to the publisher:

Hunter Textbooks Inc.

701 Shallowford Street
Winston-Salem, NC 27101
visit our website at www.huntertextbooks.com

Printed in the United States of America.
1 06

Acknowledgments

The authors of the text would like to acknowledge the many outstanding physical education teachers who have contributed their time and effort in the development of this book. Many teachers who have used previous editions of the text provided ideas, suggestions, and comments as we prepared this new edition.

In particular, we would like to thank the following teachers for providing evaluations and comments from their students:

Cynthia Strauss
G. Holmes Braddock High School
Miami, FL

Laly Albalate
Coral Gables High School
Coral Gables, FL

Lisa Spinosa
Felix Varela High School
Miami, FL

Paula Raflowitz
South Miami High School
Miami, FL

Michelle Torres
Felix Varela High School
Miami, FL

Donna Neuweiler
Turner Tech High School
Miami, FL

Barbara Speights
Hialeah-Miami Lakes High School
Miami Lakes, FL

Manny Rodriguez
Miami Coral Park High School
Miami, FL

Cindy Snyder
Crooms Academy of Information Technology
Sanford, FL

Judy Kubit
Felix Varela High School
Miami, FL

Additional thanks to Tim Andexler, Miami-Dade County Public Schools, for his assistance with the information on working with special students and to Cookie Rosell for her invaluable instructional units for using stability balls, exercise bars, and resistance bands.

Roberta Stokes
Sandra L. Schultz

How to Use the *Personal Fitness for You* Student Resources

This student textbook will serve as the core for achieving the course objectives. It provides fundamental information on the principles and concepts of physical fitness. Each chapter includes learning aids which will assist you in understanding the chapter topics, provide mini-assessments, enrichment activities, and guide you in becoming an independent learner. Each chapter has the following learning aids:

Chapter Topics   *Test Your Knowledge*
Chapter Objectives   *Remember This*
Kay Words   *Did You Know?*
Suggested Physical Activity   *For Your Information*
Healthy People 2010   *Family Activity*
Lesson Checklist   *Stress Stopper*
Chapter Projects   *Web Site*
Behavior Change Evaluation   *Safety Tips*
Critical Thinking

In addition to the student textbook, you will receive a *Personal Fitness for You* **Student CD**. The information on the CD will provide additional mini-assessments, tutorial programs, remediation activities, and enrichment activities. Some of the items you will find on the CD are:

- Individual fitness plan forms called MAP – My Activity Plan
- Laboratory Activities for each chapter
- Chapter Summaries (in English and Spanish)
- Chapter Reviews
- Chapter Practice Test Questions
- Chapter Study Guide (in English and Spanish)
- Vocabulary Flash Cards
- Spanish Resource Materials (glossary, MyPyramid, Dietary Guidelines, etc.)
- Workout Schedules
- Video about the Personal Fitness Course
- Additional resource information for each chapter

Use these resources to increase your knowledge of personal fitness and wellness and gain the motivation to make physical activity a lifelong pursuit!

Contents

Chapter 4: Evaluating Your Health-Related Fitness..... 54

Chapter 5: Evaluating Your Skill-Related Fitness 88

Chapter 6: Training for Fitness.. 102

Chapter 7: Nutrition and Your Fitness 120

Chapter 8: Planning a Diet for Fitness and Wellness 144

Chapter 9: Managing Your Weight 164

Chapter 10: Handling Stress 194

Chapter 11: Understanding the Cardiorespiratory System 214

Chapter 12: Achieving Cardiorespiratory Fitness 236

Chapter 13: Understanding the Muscular System...... 272

Chapter 14: Achieving Muscular Fitness 284

Chapter 15: Achieving Flexibility 314

Chapter 16: Designing Your Fitness Program 334

Chapter 17: Becoming a Wise Consumer 352

Chapter 18: Lifetime Personal Fitness 380

Preface

Personal Fitness....For You!

If you are like most teenagers, you are concerned with how you look. Your appearance is important to your self esteem and to obtaining peer acceptance. Hopefully you also understand the role that diet and physical activity play in developing the body image you desire and the energy you need for daily activities.

This text will guide you in reaching and maintaining a weight that is right for you and the muscle development to look your best. It will help you achieve a level of fitness that means you are healthier and have improved energy. This text will also assist you in learning valuable skills that can help you now and in the future. You will be challenged and guided in learning life skills such as goal setting, time management, and responsible behavior.

As with any course you take, your results will be in direct proportion to the effort you put in to attaining the objectives. This course and the text are designed to help you achieve *Personal Fitness for You*. However, achieving your fitness goals will require a commitment to following the principles presented and completing the many student activities. You are encouraged to strive for your optimal level of health and fitness – your personal best – rather than being satisfied with minimal standards or comparing yourself to others. Only you can make the commitment to good health – only you can make the choice to seek personal fitness! The decision is yours! Go for it!

Only you can make the choice
to seek personal fitness!

Why Personal Fitness?

1

Chapter Topics

- Fitness Habits of Students
- Fitness in America
- Health, Wellness, Physical Fitness: What Do They Mean?
- Factors Determining Your Level of Fitness
- The Decision Is Yours!
- Fitness and Your Lifestyle

Chapter Objectives

After completing this chapter, you will be able to:

- Identify reasons why fitness is an important state and national concern.
- Define health, wellness and physical fitness.
- Identify each of the health-related components of physical fitness.
- Identify each of the skill-related components of physical fitness.
- Describe the factors determining your level of fitness.
- Describe the relationship between fitness and lifestyle.

Key Words

behavior
emotional fitness
environment
health
health-related physical fitness
heredity
intellectual fitness

maturation
physical fitness
sedentary
skill-related physical fitness
social fitness
spiritual fitness
wellness

Suggested Physical Activities

In preparation for the fitness evaluation which will be administered as a part of this course, perform the following activities:

◆ Stretching exercises such as the sitting hamstring stretch, Achilles tendon stretch and the hamstring stretch (see Chapter 15)
◆ Muscular strength and endurance exercises such as curl-ups, push-ups and leg lifts (see Chapters 4 and 14)
◆ Healthy heart activities such as walking, jogging, swimming and cycling (see Chapter 12)

Use the *Personal Fitness for You* Student CD for:

◆ Lab 1-1: Pre-Exercise Medical History Form
◆ Lab 1-2: Lifestyle Profile
◆ Lab 1-3: Your Fitness Image
◆ Chapter Practice Test
◆ Chapter Study Guide
◆ Chapter Crossword Puzzle
◆ Vocabulary Flash Cards
◆ Chapter Power Point Review

Achieving personal fitness is important for everyone.

In this course you will be involved in a new experience in physical education. The course is designed to be a *personal* course which focuses on you as an individual. By following the guidelines suggested in this book, you can achieve these benefits of personal fitness:

- A better looking you!
- A firmer you!
- A stronger you!
- A more energetic you!
- A healthier you!
- A happier you!

This textbook will assist you with a variety of topics related to health and physical fitness. You will learn how to assess your own fitness levels and, based on that information, you will be able to design your own personal fitness program to achieve lifetime personal fitness. Now is the time to take charge of your health.

Why Healthy People 2010?

Healthy People 2010 is a comprehensive set of disease prevention and health promotion objectives for America. These national health objectives were designed to identify the most significant preventable threats to our health and establish national goals to reduce those threats.

The program is designed to reach two major goals:

Goal 1: Increase quality and years of healthy life. This goal is to help individuals of all ages to increase life expectancy and improve their quality of life.

Goal 2: Eliminate health disparities. This goal is to help our nation eliminate health disparities among different segments of our population

The following Leading Health Indicators were identified as 10 high priority areas for the Nation's health:

1. Physical Activity
2. Overweight and Obesity
3. Tobacco Use
4. Substance Abuse
5. Responsible Sexual Behavior
6. Mental Health
7. Injury and Violence
8. Environmental Quality
9. Immunization
10. Access to Health Care

Each of us can benefit by gaining the knowledge and level of health encouraged by the individual objectives for each of these focus areas. Specific objectives will be listed at the beginning of each chapter which relate to that health topic.

The personal fitness course will help you make the lifestyle choices to achieve many of the Healthy People 2010 goals.

Fitness Habits of Students

Have you ever wondered why a course in personal fitness is necessary? The main reason is that the current American lifestyle fosters a lack of fitness. The increased use of mechanical devices and technology has decreased the need for physical activity in our daily activities. We spend most of our day riding, sitting and watching. As a nation, our population is becoming more obese each year. Seats in football and baseball stadiums have been widened to allow for a change in our physical size.

Research shows that an inactive lifestyle places one at high risk for many diseases. To avoid this, however, we know that:

- An active lifestyle during childhood has a direct benefit to health in later years.
- Those who are active as children tend to be active as adults, which lowers their risk for disease.

The situation among high school students is very disturbing. For instance, the National Center for Chronic Disease Prevention and Health Promotion states:

- Nearly half of American youths aged 12-21 years are not vigorously active on a regular basis.
- About 14 percent of young people report no recent physical activity. Inactivity is more common among females (14%) than males (7%) and among black females (21%) than white females (12%).
- Participation in all types of physical activity declines strikingly as age or grade in school increases.

An active lifestyle during childhood directly affects health in later years.

Do you watch a lot of TV or play video games? Too much time sitting actually can make you feel tired and lazy!

Family Activity

Have a Family Olympics at a picnic or reunion. Play games such as tennis, horseshoes, volleyball and basketball.

Did You Know?

Get Moving!

The average young person watches 28 hours of television each week. Watch less and move more!

More people are becoming aware of the importance of physical fitness.

In addition, studies show that:
- Most teenagers have poor eating habits, eating foods that are high in fat, salt and sugar.
- Blood pressure readings among teenagers, on average, are higher today than they were twenty years ago. High blood pressure indicates a greater risk for cardiovascular disease (diseases of the heart and blood vessels).
- The percentage of overweight adolescents ages 12-19 tripled from 5% to 15.5% between the late 1970's and 2000.

One goal of this personal fitness course is to assist you in developing a lifelong habit of physical activity.

Fitness in America

The good news is that Americans are now becoming increasingly aware that inactivity and poor health habits are linked to illnesses and early death. There has been a widespread trend to health and fitness during the past ten years. More people than ever before are becoming aware of the need to change their lifestyle.

There are many exercise programs and devices from which to choose. Many colleges, high schools, hospitals and businesses have wellness centers on site. Sales of home workout machines (rowers, bicycles, ski machines, treadmills, etc.) are on the rise.

The bad news is that not enough Americans are exercising and changing their lifestyle. A national survey indicates that only about 10% of adults perform the amount of activity recommended to achieve fitness, and as many as one-fourth of adults have no leisure time physical activity at all.

Great advances have been made in the medical profession in the prevention, treatment and cure of diseases. Many major health problems are caused by the way we live—our lifestyles. Poor nutritional habits, inability to manage stress, tobacco, alcohol and drug use contribute to what are called the lifestyle diseases: heart disease, high blood pressure, stroke, diabetes, cancer, emphysema and cirrhosis of the liver.

It is clear that by including physical activity in our lifestyle, we can positively influence many other individual behaviors. The following facts support this claim.

- Regular exercisers are more likely than non-exercisers to quit smoking, eat less fat, cut down on caffeine, eat low calorie foods and drinks, lose weight and cut down on salt and sugar.
- Physically fit individuals are at less risk of early death than inactive people.
- Physically fit individuals are less likely to die from cancer or coronary disease than unfit persons.

Fitness is a strong state and national concern, but it must also be a strong individual concern.

Health, Wellness, Physical Fitness: What Do They Mean?

It is important to understand the relationship and differences between health, wellness and physical fitness.

Health

Health refers to a state of complete physical, mental and social well-being that enables you to function at an optimal level in many areas of your life. While it suggests an absence of disease, health is certainly more than that. Don't believe that if you do not have a cold or the flu, are not in pain, or have limited functioning that you are therefore "healthy." Health involves many dimensions. Your goal should be to go beyond simply "not being sick" to reach your highest potential for functioning in all areas of your life.

Each person must develop his or her own plan for achieving wellness.

Remember This ☑

You are responsible for your health and well-being.

Wellness

Wellness is another way of describing the quality of your life. Wellness suggests not only that your health is good but that you can also function at a high level in other areas of your life. The essential components of wellness are intellectual, physical, emotional, spiritual and social fitness. These are described on the next page.

Each person must develop his or her unique pathway to wellness. A key factor to doing this is developing an integrated and balanced lifestyle.

Each element of wellness is related to the others. One element will frequently affect another. For instance, if you are not well due to illness (physical), it may cause you to avoid participating in activities with your friends (social), and that could lead to a feeling of being "down" (emotional).

The importance of a high level of wellness cannot be overemphasized. The impact of a lack of wellness is evident by a lack of vitality, inability to achieve your potential, loss of energy, and inability to contribute effectively to society.

There are certain signs that serve as indicators of your level of wellness. To determine your level of wellness, ask yourself the following questions:

- Do you have a high energy level at various times during the day—when awakening, after lunch, after school?
- What is your general appearance—skin, hair, eyes?
- Is your enjoyment of life at a good level—feeling of satisfaction and purpose on most days? Are you in good spirits most of the time? Do you feel that living and life itself are worthwhile?
- Is your appetite good?
- Do you have the ability to relax and sleep soundly?
- Are you able to do what you want and what you need to do at the appropriate time?
- Are you able to cope with and overcome a variety of types of stress in your everyday life?

Intellectual Fitness

Ability to think critically about issues; having an active, curious mind

Emotional Fitness

Ability to deal with stress, to maintain a positive self-concept and to adapt to changes in life

Social Fitness

Ability to develop meaningful relationships with family, friends, co-workers and others in the community

Spiritual Fitness

Finding meaning and purpose in life whether through religion, meditation or other methods

Physical Fitness

Assuming personal responsibility for one's health by exercising, eating healthy foods; observing measures to avoid illness and injury

Being fit helps you feel better about yourself.

The Internet is a great resource for information about health, fitness, and wellness.
To learn more about health, visit the following web site:
//medlineplus.gov

Your behavior is the key to achieving your optimal level of fitness.

Create a clear picture of what changes you may need to make to raise your level of wellness. Set realistic goals and expectations as you attempt to take control of your life. Why go through life with unnecessary handicaps which will make your life more difficult? Make a goal to live life with all the best going for you.

Strive to reach your maximum levels of intellectual, physical, emotional, spiritual and social fitness so that you experience the highest possible quality of life. To obtain a high level of wellness, you must take responsibility for all areas of your life.

Physical Fitness

Physical fitness (and personal fitness) refers to the ability to attain certain physical attributes. To some people it means being able to successfully participate in a sport such as tennis, softball or basketball. The most commonly accepted definition of physical fitness is a state of physical well-being that allows you to:

- perform your daily activities with vigor.
- reduce your risk of health problems related to lack of exercise.
- establish a fitness base for participation in a variety of physical activities.

Physical fitness is generally classified into two types: **health-related physical fitness,** which includes those attributes that contribute to disease prevention and health promotion; and **skill-related physical fitness,** which includes those attributes that contribute to the ability to participate successfully in physical activities such as a variety of sports.

The skill-related components form the basis for successful sports performance. Although skill-related components are important, they do not contribute to overall good health. You do not have to be a great athlete to be considered physically fit. On the other hand, the health-related components are vital to a person's lifetime well-being.

The Two Types of Physical Fitness

Health-Related Physical Fitness

- Cardiorespiratory Fitness
- Flexibility
- Muscular Strength
- Muscular Endurance
- Body Composition

Skill-Related Physical Fitness

- Coordination
- Agility
- Reaction Time
- Power
- Speed
- Balance

Because of their importance to health and wellness, this course will focus on the health-related fitness components. In Chapter 4 these components will be described in detail.

How would you rate your health, wellness, and physical fitness? No doubt you have areas that need improvement. This course will give you the information you need to make those lifestyle changes. You can develop the body image you desire and have the energy you need for daily activities. You can be proud of your appearance and maintain an appropriate weight. You can enjoy each day more and feel better than ever before. Health, wellness and physical fitness are goals you can achieve!

Achieving optimal levels of fitness is important for your life now and in the future.

What Exercise Can Do for You Now

- Improve appearance
- Increase energy level
- Help you cope with stress
- Improve sleep

Heredity, behavior and environment influence your fitness.

Factors Determining Your Level of Fitness

While it is possible for everyone to achieve the benefits of fitness, there are several factors which determine the extent to which you will be able to achieve your optimal level of fitness. These factors are described on the next page.

As you consider each of the factors, notice that your **motivation and behavior or lifestyle** are key factors to achieving a healthy fitness level. Although heredity, environment, and maturation may set some limits, you can overcome many limitations by becoming motivated and changing your behavior. Take advantage of the things you have going for you and avoid the behaviors which you can control (tobacco, alcohol, drugs, etc.).

The Decision Is Yours!

No matter how intelligent you are or how much information you acquire, it will be of little value unless you use it. The final choice as to whether you achieve and maintain a state of fitness depends upon you and no one else. Why not start today to make the healthy choice? Do it not just to live longer, but to enjoy each day to its fullest and to look and feel better. Make fitness a part of your daily life, not just something you do in your physical education class. Fitness is a lifetime commitment!

Factors Determining Your
Level of Fitness

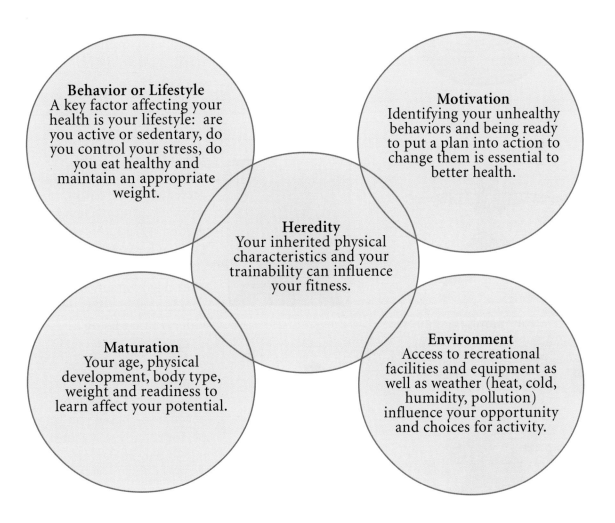

Behavior or Lifestyle
A key factor affecting your health is your lifestyle: are you active or sedentary, do you control your stress, do you eat healthy and maintain an appropriate weight.

Motivation
Identifying your unhealthy behaviors and being ready to put a plan into action to change them is essential to better health.

Heredity
Your inherited physical characteristics and your trainability can influence your fitness.

Maturation
Your age, physical development, body type, weight and readiness to learn affect your potential.

Environment
Access to recreational facilities and equipment as well as weather (heat, cold, humidity, pollution) influence your opportunity and choices for activity.

Fitness and Your Lifestyle

Think about your behavior – your lifestyle. Does it contribute to a high level of wellness? Check your responses to these questions.

Do you think you consume a healthy diet?

Are you flexible enough to avoid basic injuries and to participate in daily activities?

Have you maintained an acceptable level of body weight?

Do you regularly include physical activity (walking, recreational activities, working around the house, gardening, etc.) in your day? Do you have a **sedentary** (inactive) lifestyle – most of your day is spent sitting, watching television, playing video games, using a computer?

Is your muscle development sufficient enough to enable you to perform daily tasks and participate in various activities?

Do you manage your time and deal with situations in ways to control your level of stress?

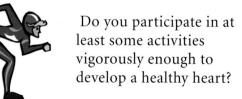

Do you participate in at least some activities vigorously enough to develop a healthy heart?

Lifestyle Changes You Can Make

- Take an exercise break—get up from your desk or while watching television stretch, walk around and relax your mind.
- Use the stairs instead of the elevator—if you can't make it up several flights, do what you can and take the elevator the rest of the way.
- Park further from the campus, classroom or store and walk the rest of the way. If you ride a bus or other public transportation, get off one or two stops early and walk a few extra blocks. Walk wherever possible.
- Avoid using the remote control for your television or VCR—focus on getting up and moving, not sitting.
- While talking on the phone, stand or walk around (a cordless phone makes this easy).
- If you walk your dog, try walking a little faster and a little longer. If you don't have a pet, walk a neighbor's dog.
- Try "heart healthy" shopping—wear comfortable shoes and put in an extra lap or two around the mall.
- Substitute an activity (bowling, miniature golf, skating, etc.) for going to a movie.
- Encourage adults in your life to participate in some form of physical activity.

Summary

This course is designed to help you achieve the many benefits of health, wellness, and fitness. Achieving your optimal fitness will help you improve your appearance and your energy level. The text will help you understand why achieving fitness is important, guide you in designing an exercise program and motivate you to seek the highest level of health, wellness and personal fitness.

Looking at the health risks associated with a lack of physical activity, it is clear that Americans who are not yet regularly physically active should become active. Everyone can benefit from physical activity. The activity need not be strenuous to be beneficial - moderate activity can provide great health benefits.

It is clear, however, that maintaining personal health and fitness is a matter of individual choice. Many of the health problems we develop result from things which are under our control - things we can do something about. How we live determines to a great extent how long and how well we will live. The decision to be healthy and fit is within your reach. You can establish a lifestyle which enables you to achieve your optimal fitness level.

Chapter 1 Review

Lesson Checklist

- Can you define fitness, health, wellness?
- Do you know why maintaining optimal fitness is important?
- Do you know the health-related components of fitness?
- Do you know the factors which determine your level of fitness?

Chapter Projects

Write a response to each of the following:

1. State examples of how heredity might set limits on your potential to achieve a goal.
2. What have you done in terms of behavior which could affect your physical fitness?
3. List the lifestyle changes you need to make to achieve fitness.
4. Research the cost-savings of a local business which has a physical activity program as part of its employee wellness plan. Does your school have a wellness program? Interview the school administration and find out why or why not. Write a report on your findings.

Behavior Change Evaluation

Review the following items to see if you have gained an understanding of fitness and wellness. On a piece of paper briefly state how you will make these changes.

- I will work to make changes in my lifestyle to achieve improved wellness.
- I will make healthy choices and make fitness a part of my daily life.

Critical Thinking

Based on what you have learned about fitness and wellness, describe the areas which you believe are limiting your achievement of a high level of wellness.

Chapter 1 Review

Test Your Knowledge

Read the questions below and select the best possible answer for each.

1. The factor most responsible for your level of fitness is
   a. your parents
   b. the government
   c. how much money you make
   d. your behavior

2. Which of the following is a set of comprehensive disease prevention objectives?
   a. Health Related Fitness
   b. Healthy People 2010
   c. Skill Related Fitness
   d. Wellness Goals

3. Which is a skill related component of fitness?
   a. muscular strength
   b. flexibility
   c. agility
   d. muscular endurance

4. Which area of wellness enables you to perform daily activities with vigor?
   a. spiritual fitness
   b. intellectual fitness
   c. emotional fitness
   d. physical fitness

5. Which is a health related component of fitness?
   a. flexibility
   b. coordination
   c. reaction time
   d. speed

6. What are the key factors determining your fitness level?
   a. heredity and behavior
   b. behavior and maturation
   c. environment and heredity
   d. motivation and behavior

7. The three leading causes of death in the United States are
   a. AIDS, suicide, cancer
   b. Heart attacks, diabetes, AIDS
   c. Stroke, heart attacks, liver disease
   d. Cancer, heart disease, stroke

8. Which of the following statements is NOT true?
   a. most teenagers have poor eating habits
   b. teenagers today have more body fat than teenagers of 20 years ago
   c. the overall fitness of young people has declined over the past 20 years
   d. most teenagers get too much exercise

9. What is true of regular exercisers?
   a. they are more likely to smoke
   b. they are at less risk of early death than inactive people
   c. they are more likely to die of cancer
   d. they are more likely to die of a heart attack

10. The ability to deal with stress, to maintain a positive self concept and to adapt to changes in life is known as
    a. Social Fitness
    b. Emotional Fitness
    c. Physical Fitness
    d. Intellectual fitness

Let's Get Moving!

2

Chapter Topics

- What Physical Activity Can Do for You—Now!
- Lowering Your Risk Factors for Disease
- Developing a Positive Attitude
- How Much Physical Activity Do I Need?
- Make Physical Activity a Lifelong Habit
- The Activity Pyramid

Chapter Objectives

After completing this chapter, you will be able to:

- Describe the benefits of participating in a regular personal fitness program.
- Identify the ways physical activity helps lower your risk for disease.
- Identify negative attitudes you may have toward physical activity.
- Describe the amount of physical activity needed to achieve health and fitness.
- Identify ways to make physical activity a lifelong habit.

Key Words

exercise
metabolism
moderate physical activity

optimal fitness
physical activity
vigorous physical activity

Suggested Physical Activities

Plan a family activity such as walking around the neighborhood after dinner at least three times during the week. If family members can't participate, get a neighbor to join you.

Healthy People 2010 Goals

- Improve health, fitness and quality of life through daily physical activity.
- Increase the proportion of adolescents who engage in moderate physical activity for at least 30 minutes on 5 or more of the previous 7 days.
- Increase the proportion of adolescents who engage in vigorous physical activity that promotes cardiorespiratory fitness 3 or more days per week for 20 or more minutes per occasion.
- Increase the proportion of adolescents who participate in daily school physical education.
- Increase the proportion of adolescents who spend at least 50 percent of school physical education class time being physically active.
- Increase the proportion of children and adolescents who view television 2 or fewer hours per day.
- Increase proportion of people who perform physical activity that enhances and maintains muscular strength, muscular endurance and flexibility.

Use the *Personal Fitness for You* Student CD for:

- Lab 2-1: Making Physical Activity a Habit
- Lab 2-2: Fitness on the Internet
- Chapter Practice Test
- Chapter Study Guide
- Chapter Crossword Puzzle
- Vocabulary Flash Cards
- Chapter Power Point Review

Did You Know?

Participation in physical activity enhances your opportunities for social interaction with members of your family, your peers and your coworkers.

If you already have an active lifestyle, you are probably aware of how regular activity makes you feel better. You know what it means to feel totally alive, have enthusiasm and energy to enjoy life to the fullest, and to feel good about your self image. For those who don't participate in regular physical activity, you can gain these same benefits by getting active NOW! In addition to the long term benefits of an active lifestyle, some of the immediate benefits of becoming active and achieving your **optimal fitness** level include:

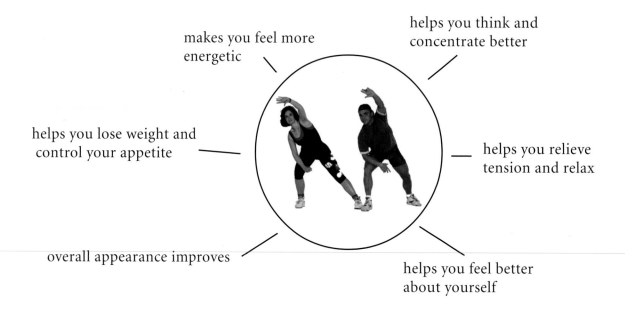

makes you feel more energetic

helps you think and concentrate better

helps you lose weight and control your appetite

helps you relieve tension and relax

overall appearance improves

helps you feel better about yourself

Lowering Your Risk Factors For Disease

Physical activity plays a significant role in lowering your risk for many diseases.

The information which follows describes how your participation in this personal fitness course—which focuses on improving cardiorespiratory fitness, muscular fitness, flexibility and body composition—can help you enjoy higher levels of wellness today and in the future.

Achieving cardiorespiratory fitness—a strong heart and healthy lungs—can:
- reduce the risk of heart disease.
- lower blood pressure.
- burn body fat and increase lean muscle mass.
- raise the "good" cholesterol levels.
- strengthen your immune system.
- reduce risk factors for some cancers.
- reduce stress.

Achieving flexibility—the range of motion of your joints—can:
- reduce the risk of injury.
- decrease muscle soreness.
- maintain ease of everyday movement.
- reduce stress.

Achieving muscular fitness—muscular strength and endurance—can:
- strengthen bones.
- maintain and increase lean body mass.
- reduce body fat.
- prevent back pain.
- improve posture.

Did You Know?

Studies show regular exercisers are:
- 50% more likely to quit smoking.
- 40% more likely to eat less red meat.
- 30% more likely to cut down on caffeine.
- 20% more likely to eat low calorie foods and drinks.
- 200% more likely to lose weight.

Source: President's Council on Physical Fitness and Sports.

When you exercise you actually get more energy.

Achieving appropriate body composition—the ratio of lean body weight to fat weight—can:

- reduce the risk of heart disease, high blood pressure, obesity, diabetes, cancer, stomach and intestinal disorders.
- improve metabolism efficiency. **Metabolism** refers to all the body processes that allow the cells to function.
- increase energy levels.

Developing a Positive Attitude

Maybe you do not have a good outlook on exercise and fitness. This may be due to exercising using incorrect technique, failing to follow the principles of training, injury problems or poor results. In any case, it is important to develop a positive attitude and overcome any negative thoughts about physical activity. Use the chart on the next page to identify any limiting or negative thoughts you may have toward physical fitness. Acquire the positive attitude that will help you establish physical activity as a part of your daily lifestyle.

STRESS Stopper

Spend thirty minutes this week participating in some type of recreational activity—cycling, playing volleyball, badminton, racquetball, etc.

How Much Physical Actvity Do I Need?

The evidence is clear that becoming physically active is worth the effort. But you may be wondering how much activity is enough to realize these benefits.

The 1996 Report of the Surgeon General of the United States reports that:

People who are usually inactive can improve their health and well-being by becoming even moderately active on a regular basis.

Physical activity need not be strenuous to achieve health benefits.

Greater health benefits can be achieved by increasing the amount (duration, frequency or intensity) of physical activity.

Attitudes Toward Physical Activity

Negative Attitudes	Positive Attitudes
I do not have enough time to exercise.	Exercise gives me a break from work, study, problems, and helps me work more efficiently.
I'm too tired to exercise.	Exercising helps me feel more energetic.
I don't need to exercise—I'm okay.	I want to reach my optimal level of fitness—I know there is room for improvement.
I'm too out of shape—there's no hope.	I can reach my goal if I take it one step at a time—every bit of improvement is important. I can enjoy the challenge.
I do not have the skill or coordination to do fitness activities.	There are many fitness activities which I can enjoy—walking instead of jogging, step aerobics, exercise to music, etc.
I don't have a place to exercise or exercise equipment.	There are many exercises I can do at home or in the neighborhood.
I don't like to exercise alone, but I can't afford to join a health club.	I can find a partner (school friend, neighbor, relative) to exercise with me. Exercise is also a good way to meet new people.
Exercise is inconvenient.	I can identify a variety of exercise activities that are interesting and enjoyable.
Exercise is boring.	I can establish an exercise program that is fun and fits into my schedule.
I don't want to get my hair messed up and get sweaty.	I can allow enough time to clean up after exercise, because I know the workout is important.
My friends don't like to exercise.	I can find an activity that my friends might enjoy.
I will start exercising tomorrow.	It is important to start today to achieve my fitness goals. Exercise can help improve my appearance and health, so I should start now.

Did You Know?

There are 1440 minutes in every day. Start now to schedule 30 of them for physical activity.

You can do your activity all at one time or spaced out over the day.

WEBSITE

Visit the following website to log and track your physical activity participation and earn the Presidential Active Lifestyle Award:
www.presidentschallenge.org

This is good news for the many people who are inactive or have tried an exercise program but got discouraged. The **Exercise Guidelines for Adolescents** are:

- an accumulation of **30-60 minutes** or more of **moderate intensity** physical activity on most days, preferably every day of the week
- to achieve higher benefits, strive for three 20 minute sessions of continuous moderate to vigorous activity per week
- **45-60 minutes** a day (200-300 minutes per week) of moderate intensity physical activity is recommended to **prevent weight gain** and facilitate weight loss
- participation in a variety of activities from the Activities Pyramid is recommended

Moderate activity can be easily achieved in a variety of ways. Select an activity you enjoy and fit it into your daily schedule. Since the amount of activity is directly related to the time and difficulty of the activity, perform moderately intense activity such as brisk walking in a longer session and more strenuous activity such as running in a shorter session. If your time available for physical activity is limited, participate in activities that are high intensity for a short amount of time. Accumulating exercise throughout the day is also beneficial. That means you can do ten minutes of activity in the morning, ten at the middle of the day and ten in the evening.

The chart on the adjacent page provides examples of vigorous to moderate amounts of activity. These activities use approximately 150 calories of energy per day or 1,000 calories per week.

The Surgeon General's Report emphasizes the importance of exercise for health rather than "fitness." Attaining general health benefits requires only moderate intensity activity, but to achieve cardiorespiratory fitness more effort is required. Chapter 6 will describe the principles to follow in order to reach a higher level of fitness.

Stay Physically Active

Activity	Duration	
Walking stairs	15 min.	
Shoveling snow	15 min.	
Running 1.5 miles	15 min.	**More Vigorous, Shorter Duration**
Jumping rope	15 min.	
Bicycling 4 miles	15 min.	
Playing basketball	15-20 min.	
Playing wheelchair basketball	20 min.	
Swimming laps	20 min.	
Water aerobics	30 min.	
Walking 2 miles	30 min.	
Raking leaves	30 min.	

More vigorous, shorter duration

	Duration	Activity
	30 min.	Pushing stroller 1.5 miles
	30 min.	Fast social dancing
	30 min.	Bicycling 5 miles (10 mph)
	30 min.	Shooting basketball baskets
Less Vigorous, Longer Duration	35 min.	Walking 1.75 miles
	30-40 min.	Wheeling self in wheelchair
	30-45 min.	Garden work
	30-45 min.	Playing touch football
	45 min.	Playing volleyball
	45-60 min.	Washing windows or floors
	45-60 min.	Washing and waxing a car

Source: Center for Disease Control Prevention

Remember This ☑
Families need to include physical activity in their daily routine.

Can you commit to a TV free day?
How much screen time do you get each day? Screen time is time spent watching TV or videos, playing video games or using the computer. Replace your screen time with activity time! Avoid sitting for more than 30 minutes at one time!

Less vigorous, longer duration

Physical activity – bodily movement that is produced by the contraction of skeletal muscle and that substantially increases energy expenditure.

Moderate **physical activity** – activities that use large muscle groups and are at least equivalent to brisk walking.

Vigorous **physical activity** – rhythmic, repetitive activities that use large muscle groups at 70 percent or more of maximum heart rate for your age. Examples include jogging/running, lap swimming, cycling, aerobic dancing, etc.

Exercise – planned, structured, and repetitive bodily movements performed to maintain and improve physical fitness.

Family Activity

Ask family members to join you for a daily walk. Take your dog along too!

Make Physical Activity A Lifelong Habit

- Involve family, friends, or neighbors.
- Try a variety of activities.
- Make activity a habit - a part of your life.
- Work out to music.
- Exercise while watching TV.

Choose one activity from the list of moderate or vigorous activities on the previous page and develop your activity plan —your MAP to get moving!

My Activity Plan (MAP)

My goal is to do the following activities:

Activity	Number of Minutes per Day	Times per Week
Cleaning house	75	1
Bicycling	20	4
Swimming laps	30	2

Refer to the student *Personal Fitness for You* CD for the *My Activity Plan* form.

The Activity Pyramid

Refer to the Activity Pyramid on the adjacent page to see how you can make activity a lifelong habit.

As you move from the everyday lifetime behaviors to include aerobic activities, exercises for flexibility, strength and endurance exercises, and special recreational activities in your regular routine, you will begin to receive the maximum health benefits and find yourself functioning at an optimal level. It doesn't take much time or effort, so start today to become active for a lifetime.

The Activity Pyramid

SPEND LESS TIME

Watching TV, playing video & computer games, just sitting

2-3 TIMES A WEEK

Strength and Endurance

Use weights and resistance exercises, curl ups, push ups

Recreational Activities

volleyball, tennis, golf

3-5 TIMES A WEEK

Aerobic Exercise

swim, power walk, cycle, jog, step aerobics

Flexibility Exercise

stretch, gymnastics, yoga

DAILY ACTIVITY

Lifetime Behavior

Stay active—keep moving, walk as much as possible, use the stairs, do yard work, house work. Take extra steps whenever you can

Summary

Once you are aware of the many health benefits of an active lifestyle and how easy it can be to get the activity you need, it is up to you to make it happen. Only you can decide what activities you will enjoy and how you can work them into your daily routine. Then you can use the Activity Pyramid to achieve an active lifestyle.

Chapter 2 Review

Lesson Checklist

- Can you list five of the health benefits of participating in a regular personal fitness program?
- Can you identify the ways physical activity helps lower your risk for disease?
- Can you describe the amount of physical activity needed to achieve health fitness?
- Can you describe the activity which forms the base of the Activity Pyramid?

Chapter Projects

Write a response to each of the following:

1. Explain six specific benefits from achieving an optimal level of fitness.
2. Evaluate your attitudes toward physical activity and make a list of those that are negative and those that are positive.
3. Examine the Activity Pyramid and describe the specific activities you will use at each level to strive for an active lifestyle.
4. Review the many ways in which physical activity can lower your risk for disease. Describe the ones which have most meaning and concern for you.

Behavior Change Evaluation

Review the following items to see if you have gained an understanding of fitness and wellness. On a piece of paper briefly state how you will make these changes.

- I will accumulate thirty minutes or more of moderate intensity physical activity every day this week.
- I will take steps to develop a more positive attitude toward regular physical activity.

Critical Thinking

Based on what you have learned in this chapter, describe an activity program you will follow for one week that involves moderate as well as vigorous activity. Indicate the type of activity, the amount of time you will spend on it, and how it would meet the guidelines for regular daily activity.

Chapter 2 Review

Test Your Knowledge

Read the questions below and select the best possible answer for each.

1. Achieving cardiorespiratory fitness can
   a. increase resting heart rate
   b. reduce stress
   c. prevent back pain
   d. improve posture

2. Which statement is true about achieving muscular fitness?
   a. Increased muscular fitness will decrease lean body mass
   b. Increased muscular fitness will increase risk of back pain.
   c. Increased muscular fitness will weaken bones
   d. Increased muscular fitness will improve posture

3. Achieving appropriate body composition can
   a. decrease metabolism
   b. increase energy levels
   c. increase obesity
   d. increase blood pressure

4. How many total minutes of moderate intensity physical activity are recommended daily?
   a. 30 to 60 minutes
   b. 10 to 20 minutes
   c. 20 to 60 minutes
   d. 120 minutes minimum

5. An example of a vigorous exercise is
   a. Jumping rope
   b. Gardening
   c. Walking at two miles per hour
   d. Washing a car

6. Achieving flexibility can
   a. Reduce risk of injury
   b. Help you lose weight
   c. Increase your stress
   d. Cause muscle soreness

7. What are the body processes that allow the cells to function?
   a. respiration
   b. fitness
   c. health-related
   d. metabolism

Portfolio Idea

Physical Activity Assessment

Record the results of this activity in your personal portfolio or follow instructions from your teacher, Using the chart "Attitudes Toward Physical Activity" on page 23, complete the following assessment by listing the positive and negative attitudes you have toward physical activity.

Attitudes Toward Physical Activity

My positive feelings toward activity:_____

_____

My negative feelings toward activity:_____

_____

Exercising Safely

3

Chapter Topics

- Safety First!
- Selecting Exercise Clothing
- Exercising in Hot Weather
- Exercising in Cold Weather
- Exercising in Polluted Air
- The Sun and Skin Cancer
- Other Precautions
- Common Problems Associated with Exercise
- The Biomechanical Principles of Exercise

Chapter Objectives

After completing this chapter, you will be able to:

- Identify proper procedures and benefits of warming up and cooling down.
- Describe how to select appropriate clothing and footwear for exercise during hot and cold weather.
- Identify precautions to be taken when exercising in hot weather.
- Explain methods of maintaining proper fluid balance during physical activity.
- Identify signs of heat-related disorders.
- Identify precautions to be taken when exercising in cold weather.
- Identify precautions to be taken when exercising in polluted air.
- Identify precautions to be taken when exercising in the sun.
- Identify common problems associated with exercise.

Key Words

biomechanics
cool down
dehydrated
diaphragm

heat cramps
heat exhaustion
heatstroke
hypothermia

lactic acid
PRICE method
shin splints
warm-up

Suggested Physical Activities

As you begin your exercise program, pay careful attention to your warm-up and cool down. Practice taking your pulse before, during and after exercise. Take your recovery pulse five and ten minutes after completion of exercise.

Healthy People 2010 Goals

◆ Increase the proportion of persons who use at least one of the following protective measures that may reduce the risk of skin cancer: avoid the sun between 10 a.m. and 4 p.m., wear sun-protective clothing when exposed to sunlight, use sunscreen with a sun protection factor (SPF) of 15 or higher and avoid artificial sources of ultraviolet light.
◆ Reduce the rate of melanoma cancer deaths.

Use the *Personal Fitness for You* Student CD for:

◆ Lab 3-1: Exercising Safely
◆ Lab 3-2: Evaluating a Sport Drink Label
◆ Chapter Practice Test
◆ Chapter Study Guide
◆ Chapter Crossword Puzzle
◆ Vocabulary Flash Cards
◆ Chapter Power Point Review

Safety First!

It is very important to use common sense when you are exercising. Listen to your body. Start slowly if you are out of shape. This chapter describes how to prevent problems before they occur, how to exercise safely, and how to treat some common exercise problems.

In order to participate safely in an exercise program, it is important to remember the following:

- Follow the principles of training which are described in Chapter 6.
- Always use correct technique
- Remember fitness cannot be rushed - shortcuts and "hurry up" programs usually result in injury.

Warm-Up First

Your muscles work better when they are warm.

- You will perform better and have less chance of injury.
- The body has time to redirect blood to the muscles that are active.
- Your heart has time to adjust to the exercise.
- The fluid within your joints spreads and helps protect from injury.

For most people, 5 to 10 minutes is sufficient, but the time can vary depending on the type of activity and fitness level.

You should perform low intensity movements similar to the activity that you will be performing. Walking slowly before beginning a walk/run workout, swinging a bat or golf club before playing ball or golf, and jogging slowly before a running workout are examples of warm-up activities.

Cool Down After Exercise

It is very important to cool down properly after exercise to allow the body to return to its pre-exercise state.

- The body needs time to redirect the blood from the working muscles to the other areas of the body and also blood flow to the heart and brain needs to be maintained; otherwise dizziness and/or blood pressure problems could occur.
- During the 5 to 10 minute cool down, the heart rate and breathing rate returns to normal as you gradually reduce your speed or exercise intensity.
- You should cool down until your heart rate is below 100.
- Some people prefer to stretch **after working out,** when their muscle temperature is elevated, enabling them to stretch further with less risk of injury.

Selecting Exercise Clothing

The type of exercise activity and the weather should influence your selection of clothing and shoes. Shoes that do not fit properly can result in poor performance and possibly injure your feet. Clothing that is not suited for the weather can cause serious health problems.

Clothes

When exercising in warm or hot weather, select cotton clothing because it is light and allows air movement to help evaporate perspiration, thus cooling your body. Nylon tends to trap perspiration, slowing down the transfer of body heat to the air. In cold weather, wear layers of clothing that are easy to remove as your body heats up. Exercise clothing has become even more beneficial with the development of new synthetic fibers that are lightweight, allow air movement and are made specifically for hot or cold weather.

Choose exercise clothing that is comfortable and allows for freedom of movement.

To avoid blisters, wear socks which fit well.

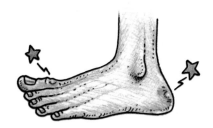

Family Activity

Share your knowledge of how to exercise safely with others in your family.

Wear athletic shoes when exercising.

Comfortable, loose-fitting clothing is best for most exercises as it allows for freedom of movement. However, for some activities such as swimming, skiing or bicycling, it may be desirable to wear form-fitting clothing which cuts down on air or water resistance.

It is best to wear light-colored or white clothing in hot weather, since these colors reflect rather than absorb the sun's rays. If you exercise at night, wear white or reflective clothing, so you will be seen easily.

Socks

It is important to have socks which fit well or blisters may result. Some people prefer to wear two pairs of socks for extra protection. Cotton and wool socks absorb perspiration. Make sure your socks are clean and dry to guard against the fungus known as athlete's foot.

Footwear

Today there are athletic shoes designed specifically for almost every sport. Before you purchase shoes, consider the following:

1. **What is the main type of activity for which the shoes will be worn?** Do you plan to use them for walking, running, tennis, aerobic exercise indoors or basketball? Remember that running shoes are designed for straightforward movement and should not be used for activities such as tennis, racquetball, volleyball or basketball which require lateral (sideways) movement as well.

2. **Know your foot type.** Step in water, then on a concrete surface. Look at your footprint. If you have a thin line connecting the heel with the ball of the foot, you have a high arch. If the entire footprint is filled in, you have a flat foot. A normal foot falls somewhere in between. It is important to select a shoe that is designed for your type of foot.

3. **Regardless of price, if shoes don't fit you and are uncomfortable, they are not a bargain.** Take a pair of athletic socks with you when you go shopping for shoes. Try the shoes on late in the afternoon or early evening when your feet are swollen from standing on them all day. Walk or jog inside the store; stop suddenly and make sure that the shoes are long enough and wide enough for your feet. The shoes should be comfortable the minute you put them on. Don't believe that they will "stretch out."

4. **Consider the type of construction of the shoes.** Make sure they have good arch supports and well-cushioned inner soles. The heel cup should fit your heel and hold your heel securely. Make sure the soles are appropriate for the types of surfaces on which you will be exercising.

Another important thing to remember is that your exercise shoes will lose about one-third of their ability to absorb shock after fifty miles of use. This shock absorbent quality will sometimes disappear long before the soles or uppers show wear. If you do about ten hours of running and jumping each week, then you should do a close inspection of your shoes every six months.

Exercising in Hot Weather

When you exercise in a hot, humid environment, your muscles produce heat. It is very important that this heat be removed from your body. If not, you could possibly suffer a quick and dangerous rise in body temperature. When warm blood from the muscles moves closer to your skin, and your body sweat evaporates, this causes your body to cool.

However, after you have exercised for several hours in a hot climate, your body tends to become **dehydrated** and blood volume decreases, causing less blood to move toward the skin to be cooled.

HOT WEATHER SAFETY TIPS

- *Drink 2 to 4 glasses of water per hour while exercising*
- *Wear lightweight, light-colored clothing*
- *Apply sunscreen with an SPF of at least 15*
- *Wear a wide-brimmed hat*
- *Avoid hot foods and eat light meals*

REMEMBER THE KEY IS PREVENTION OF HEAT RELATED DISORDERS!

Did You Know?

About Sweat

Sweat is composed of water, sodium chloride (common salt), potassium salts, urea (waste product containing nitrogen), and lactic acid (waste product from glucose and fat metabolizing). The primary purpose of sweating is to cool the body; it also eliminates a small amount of wastes. A person usually sweats very little in cold weather but in extreme heat, sweating may increase to about three pints per hour. A person who is well acclimated to extreme heat may sweat as much as eight pints per hour.

Dehydration:

when body tissues lose fluids, particularly water.

Plan your outdoor activities to avoid the hottest part of the day.

Did You Know**?**

Fruit juices, caffeine-free soft drinks and sports drinks can be used to replace carbohydrates after exercise.

This decreases the amount of heat lost by this type of cooling. Even though you might be a physically fit person, your body requires time to adjust to hot weather conditions. You can only increase your ability to withstand heat by regularly exercising in hot weather. If you participate in outdoor sports such as cycling, tennis, beach volleyball or athletic team practice, you should remember the following guidelines:

- Plan your workout for the coolest part of the day.
- Cut back on your workouts, both in length and intensity, until your body adjusts to the heat.
- Wear a light-colored, perforated hat or head covering to protect your head from the sun.
- Never wear rubber suits or anything that prevents the escape of body heat.
- Drink plenty of fluids, especially water, before, during and after exercise.
- The use of salt tablets is not recommended.

Fluid Replacement

Don't wait until you are thirsty to begin drinking! You may have lost three to four percent of your body fluids before you feel thirsty. It is a good idea to drink a couple of cups of water an hour or two before you exercise. While you're exercising, drink a cup of water every fifteen minutes for a total of one quart per hour. After exercise, continue drinking a cup of water every fifteen minutes.

If you are exercising for less than sixty minutes, cool water is recommended. You have sufficient sugar stored in your body to replenish the needed energy. However, if you're exercising for more than sixty minutes, it is recommended that you replace fluids with a commercial sports drink.

Heat Index

High humidity makes the effects of heat worse. The National Weather Service uses a heat index, which combines temperature and relative humidity, resulting in a temperature indicating how hot it "feels." For example, if the actual temperature outdoors is 85° but the relative humidity is 90%, the temperature "feels like" 102°, a temperature which can be dangerous. Texas, Florida and Louisiana are the states which typically have the highest heat index. Even though you may be used to hot weather, you should be aware of the risks when the heat index is high and take appropriate precautions.

Heat Index Chart

% Relative Humidity

		0	5	10	15	20	25	30	35	40	45	50	55	60	65	70	75	80	85	90	95	100
A	140	125																				
I	135	120	128																			
R	130	117	122	131																		
	125	111	116	123	131	141																
T	120	107	111	116	123	130	139	148														
E	115	103	107	111	115	120	127	135	143	151												
M	110	99	102	105	108	112	117	123	130	137	143	150										
P	105	95	97	100	102	105	109	113	118	123	129	135	142	149								
E	100	91	93	95	97	99	101	104	107	110	115	120	126	132	138	144						
R	95	87	88	90	91	93	94	96	98	101	104	110	114	119	124	130	136					
A	90	83	84	85	86	87	88	90	91	93	95	96	98	100	102	106	109	113	117	122		
T	85	78	79	80	81	82	83	84	85	86	87	88	89	90	91	93	95	97	99	102	105	108
U	80	73	74	75	76	77	77	78	79	79	80	81	81	82	83	85	86	86	87	88	89	91
R	75	69	69	70	71	72	72	73	73	74	74	75	75	76	76	77	77	78	78	79	79	80
E	70	64	64	65	65	66	66	67	67	68	68	69	69	70	70	70	70	71	71	71	71	72

Locate the **air temperature** along the left column and the **relative humidity** along the top. The cell where the two intersect is the **heat index**. Exposure to full sunlight can increase values by up to 15 degrees Fahrenheit. The chart below explains the meaning of the index.

Temperature Risks with Physical Activity and/or Lengthy Exposure

Heat Index	General Effect of Heat Index
80° to 89° - Very Warm	Fatigue possible with prolonged exposure and/or physical activity.
90° to 104° - Hot	Sunstroke, heat cramps, and heat exhaustion possible with prolonged exposure and/or physical activity.
105° to 129° - Very Hot	Sunstroke, heat cramps, or heat exhaustion likely, and heatstroke possible with prolonged exposure and/or physical activity.
130° or Higher - Extremely Hot	Heat/sunstroke highly likely with continued exposure.

Heat-Related Disorders

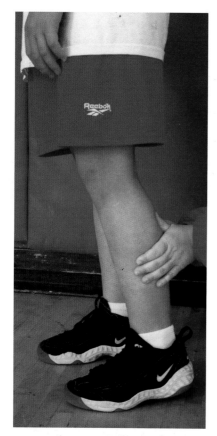

If you have a heat cramp, massage the muscle.

Heat Cramps

Heat cramps are not usually a serious problem but can be very uncomfortable. The affected muscle usually occurs in the legs but can also occur in the abdomen and arms. It will contract violently and uncontrollably. Some of the symptoms of a heat cramp include: thirst, nausea, clammy skin, chills and/or increased heart rate.

First Aid Procedures:
1. Stop activity, and move to a shaded area.
2. Massage the muscle. If it is a muscle in your leg or foot, standing on it often helps. Gradually stretch the muscle as the cramp subsides.
3. Replace fluids by drinking half a cup of water, clear juice or a sports beverage every fifteen minutes.

Heat Exhaustion

Symptoms: headache, nausea, dizziness, cool and clammy skin, pale skin, heavy perspiration, weakness, rapid and shallow breathing.

First Aid Procedures:
1. Stop activity, move to a cool shaded area, apply wet towels.
2. Drink large amounts of fluids, preferably water or a sports drink.
3. Seek medical attention.

Heatstroke

Heatstroke is a response to heat that results in an elevated body temperature above 103° F. When a lot of water has been lost, the brain shuts down the sweating mechanism to prevent additional water loss.

Symptoms: hot, dry, flushed skin; very high body temperature; strong and rapid pulse, sudden collapse and possible impaired mental state and loss of consciousness.

First Aid Procedures:
1. Seek immediate medical attention
2. Get the victim out of the heat.
3. Loosen or remove clothing.
3. Apply ice packs around neck, groin, under arms and knees (where blood flow is the greatest).

When exercising in cold weather, wear layers of clothing for maximum warmth.

Exercising in Cold Weather

Conserving body heat is a major consideration when exercising in cold weather. You must take into account the factors such as air temperature, wind chill, dampness and fatigue which can combine to significantly lower the body's temperature. If the right combination of these factors occurs, **hypothermia** (the breakdown in the body's ability to produce heat) will result. Symptoms of hypothermia include a drop in body temperature to below 95° F, shivering followed by a loss of coordination and difficulty speaking. As the body temperature continues to drop, shivering stops, muscles become rigid and unconsciousness occurs. Immediate medical attention is necessary.

When exercising outside on cold days, observe the following rules:

- **Wear several layers of light clothing, rather than one heavy layer.** Dressing in thin layers of clothing allows you to remove or add clothing when the temperature changes. Polypropylene is good for the inner layer next to your body. Fleece or wool is a good choice for the middle layer because it insulates even when wet.

*F*or *Y*our *I*nformation

Should you exercise when you have a cold?

If your symptoms are *above* the neck (runny nose, sore throat), it is usually safe to exercise. However, after ten minutes of exercise, if discomfort increases, you should stop. If your symptoms are *below* the neck (body aches, vomiting, stomach aches, no appetite), you should not exercise. Also, if you have a fever or swollen glands, discontinue your workouts until you have fully recovered.

Did You Know?

Myth: Hot drinks keep you warmer during cold weather.

Fact: Research shows that you would have to drink a whole quart of hot liquid at one time to generate body heat. Hot liquids can cause blood vessels in the skin to dilate, which makes you feel warmer but can lead to a small amount of heat loss. It really doesn't matter if you drink hot or cold liquids when you are outside in cold weather, the important thing is to keep drinking fluids. However, cool drinks (40-50°F) are absorbed more quickly than lukewarm ones.

Myth: You need to eat more in winter to keep warm.

Fact: If you spend a lot of time indoors and dress warmly when you go outside, you won't need any additional calories. If you exercise vigorously, you will increase the number of calories burned and need to eat more; however, this is true any time.

This material should allow perspiration to evaporate so that the clothing next to the skin does not remain damp or wet. The outer layer should repel water and be windproof and breathable.

- **Wear one layer less than you would if you were outside but not exercising.** If you are too warm, you will perspire excessively, causing your clothes to become wet. A good rule is to feel a little chilly when you first go outside. After about five minutes, you should warm-up to a comfortable level. Even in cold weather, if you exercise hard enough, you sweat. Don't forget to drink enough to replace fluid loss.
- **If it is snowing or raining, and your clothes become wet, you will lose body heat at a faster rate.**
- Since about 40% of your body's heat is lost through the neck and head, **wear a head covering.**
- **Wear shoes with good traction and shock absorption when running on frozen ground.**
- **Try wearing a mask or scarf to keep the cold air from triggering asthma or irritating bronchitis.**
- **Wear sunglasses** when exercising in the snow on a bright day to prevent snow blindness.
- Remember that it is much easier to pull a cold muscle in colder weather, so a **brief warm-up** just before going outside will help. Cool down and stretch indoors when you have finished exercising.

Wear sunglasses when exercising in the snow on a bright day.

- Get used to exercising in cold weather gradually.
- **Exercise with a friend.** Your friend could notice signs of frostbite or hypothermia before you do.

Exercising in Polluted Air

More than half of the people in the United States live in areas that fail to meet national clean air quality standards. The air we breathe contains all kinds of gases, some of which may be harmful. If you bicycle, jog or walk in a polluted environment, you need to be concerned about the levels of harmful gases in the air. Try to schedule your exercise route so that you pass through major intersections where there is heavy traffic in the early morning before traffic builds up or the sun gets too high. When air pollutants combine with heat, they can be even more harmful. Radio, television and newspapers report air quality indexes. If the pollutants are too high, consider moving your workout indoors. This is especially important for those with respiratory problems such as asthma and bronchitis, because vigorous exercise speeds the rate and depth of breathing, increasing absorption of pollutants.

Try to avoid exercising in a polluted environment.

The Sun and Skin Cancer

The sun is a serious problem for anyone who either works outside or who participates in outdoor sports. The American Cancer Society states:
- One in every seven Americans will develop some form of cancer in his or her lifetime.
- One serious sunburn early in life doubles the chances of developing skin cancer later in life. Sun exposure is an accumulated risk with effects that may not show up for **ten or twenty years**.

For **Y**our **I**nformation

Consider your clothing when spending time in the sun:

Tightness of weave. If light shows through when the garment is held up to a light bulb, it is loosely woven and will let ultraviolet radiation through to your skin.

Color and thickness of material. Dyed material blocks UV rays better than undyed. Thicker fabric also offers better protection.

To learn more about sports medicine, visit the following web site:
www.mspweb.com

- Three-fourths of all deaths from skin cancer are caused by malignant melanoma, a tumor which usually begins as a mole—a growth or a dark or discolored spot or mark on the skin. This type of cancer has doubled in the last ten years. If current rates continue, one out of every hundred Americans will be diagnosed with this form of cancer.

The American Cancer Society has a simple tool to remember for early detection of this cancer. It is called the ABCD way. See a doctor immediately if you have a mole with any of the following characteristics:

A stands for asymmetry. This means that one half of a mole does not match or look like the other half.

B is for border. The edges are irregular, ragged, notched or blurred.

C stands for color. The color of the mole is not the same all over, but may have differing shades of brown or black, sometimes with patches of red, white or blue.

D stands for diameter or size. The area is larger than 6 millimeters (about 1/4 inch - the size of a pencil eraser) or is growing larger.

Some people have a higher risk of developing skin cancer. These people include:

- Those who have fair skin and red or blonde hair.
- Anyone who sunburns easily.
- Anyone who has a family member who has been diagnosed with melanoma cancer.
- Anyone who spends a great amount of time in the sun.

It is strongly recommended that you **wear a sunscreen** whenever you are outside. Sunscreen with a sun protection factor (SPF) of 15 protects you for about five hours. The sunscreen should be applied at least thirty minutes before going into the sun and repeated if you are swimming or perspiring heavily. It is important to wear a sunscreen even on a cloudy day and to remember that the sun's rays can penetrate into three feet of clear water. In extremely intense sunlight,

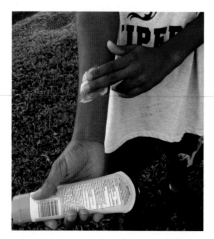

It is important to apply sunscreen before going out in the sun.

use SPF 30. Since the active ingredient in sunscreens has a short shelf life, replace sunscreens after a year.

If possible, avoid direct sun between the hours of 11:00 a.m. and 2:00 p.m. Wear a wide-brimmed hat and clothing that covers your neck, arms and legs when outside.

People living in the sunbelt states should use sunscreen year-round because the incidence of skin cancer is higher in this area. For maximum protection use sunblock.

Other Precautions

Lightning Strikes

Each year about 100 people die from lightning strikes and many more are injured. If you are exercising in open areas, mountain tops or lakes, be alert for darkening skies, flashes of lightning and thunder.

If there is a threat of lightning, stay away from metal objects such as golf clubs.

- Count the seconds between the flash of lightning and thunder; every five seconds equals one mile. If the lightning is three miles or closer (fifteen seconds), take precautions.
- Stay in a safe shelter or automobile.
- Avoid standing under an isolated tree.

- Avoid high terrain and open fields; if caught in an open field during a storm, find a low spot and lie down.
- Get out of lakes, rivers and pools.
- Stay away from metal objects—poles, golf clubs, fences.

Using Hand, Ankle and Vest Weights

Walking with weights increases intensity of effort and calories burned per minute. Additional benefits include improved strength, endurance and muscle tone. Because weights can affect your rhythm, form and balance, you should not wear ankle weights during aerobics or running.

There are risks associated with weighted walking. Weights increase physical strain. This additional strain combined with repeated motion over an extended amount of time can increase the risk of bone, joint and connective tissue injuries.

The increase in intensity from walking with weights is significant. Walking at three and a half to four miles per hour with one pound weights increases calorie use about 5-10%, increasing to as much as 40% with five pound weights.

Using hand weights increases intensity of effort and calories burned per minute.

To reduce your risk of injury while wearing hand or ankle weights:
- Begin with one pound weights. Increase weight slowly.
- Use hand weights one day; ankle weights the next day; no weights the next day.
- Start at a slow pace so your body adjusts to the weight.
- Do not carelessly swing your arms while using hand weights as the momentum can stress your shoulder and elbow.
- An extra shoelace or string can be used to tie the weights together and carry them over your shoulders in case you experience joint pain while walking.
- Vary your arm motions to reduce risk of injury. Try punching, pumping, raising arms sideways, etc., which works different muscle groups while other muscles rest.

Ankle weights increase calories burned by 20-25%. Using both hand and ankle weights increases the effect. Weighted vests (or backpacks) also increase intensity with less risk, but you have to carry much more weight (up to fifty pounds). The reason you have to carry so much more weight is leverage. A fifty-pound backpack is carried close to your body, while hand or ankle weights are at the ends of your arms or legs, making one to five pound weights feel heavy.

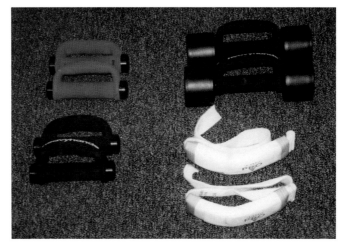

Various types of weights.

Common Problems Associated with Exercise

Seventy percent of all fitness injuries start out small and gradually become worse. An injury may begin as a small pain you feel at the end of a workout. Then the next time you exercise, it occurs again, hurting a little more. This pattern continues until even everyday activities cause the pain and you have to stop exercising.

Most of these injuries are caused by overuse—changing your exercise or increasing intensity or time without giving your body time to adapt.

To avoid injury, remember to:
1. Start slowly—warm-up correctly.
2. Be careful when switching shoes, exercise surfaces (wood to concrete, grass to pavement) and equipment (tennis racquets).
3. Be especially careful at the end of your workout when your muscles are very tired.
4. Make sure you cool down correctly and stretch after exercise to improve flexibility.

To avoid injury, start slowly and warm-up correctly.

Muscle Soreness

Muscle soreness is unfortunately one of the universal outcomes of vigorous exercise. This is particularly true when exercising after a long period of inactivity or unfamiliar exertion. Soreness is probably due to tiny tears in muscle and connective tissue and the resulting swelling.

Gentle stretching and limited usage are the best means of easing muscle soreness. In addition, cold applications, gentle massage and warm baths seem to give some relief. After recovery, resuming participation in the exercise will not result in as much soreness.

Gentle stretching is a good way to ease muscle soreness and relieve cramps..

Muscle Cramps

Muscle cramps (charley horses) are powerful involuntary muscle contractions. Causes include:

- dehydration—caused by exercise or excessive heat
- electrolyte imbalance—loss of potassium and sodium from excessive sweating
- injury—surrounding muscles may contract to protect an injured muscle or joint
- inadequate physical conditioning
- overexertion

Relieve muscle cramps by gently stretching the muscle which activates nerve endings in the tendons and helps prevent further muscular contractions. Ice applied during stretching (or heat in cold weather) can help if an injury is the cause of the pain. Massage can also help to increase blood flow.

Stitch in the Side

A stitch or sharp pain in the upper abdomen may occur to anyone at any time. However, it usually happens when first beginning a conditioning program. While the exact cause is unknown, there are a number of theories.

Overexertion is one of the causes of muscle cramps.

1. Muscle cramp theory. The stitch in the side is caused by vigorous exercise (especially running or walking) before the abdominal muscles are warmed up and/or breathing incorrectly. Thus the muscles do not get enough oxygen, and **lactic acid** (the waste product produced during anaerobic exercise) builds up. The muscles then go into spasm (uncontrolled contraction).
2. A spasm in the **diaphragm** (the muscle above the abdomen) caused by rapid breathing due to unaccustomed activity.
3. Too much lactic acid in the diaphragm.
4. Reduced blood flow to the area because of other body demands.

Solution: Slow down or stop; take deep breaths; stretch the muscles on the side of the abdomen—raise your arms and bend sideways away from the pain; press your hand on the pain.

Injury Treatment

When you are injured, you need to decide how serious the injury is and whether you should seek medical attention. If you observe deformities, significant swelling or intense pain, you should immobilize the area and get medical help.

To relieve pain from a stitch in the side, bend away from the pain.

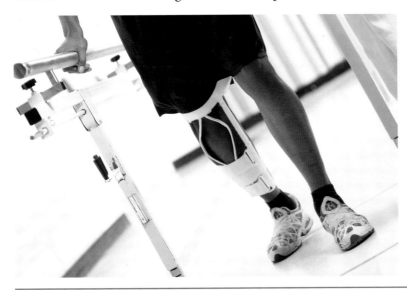

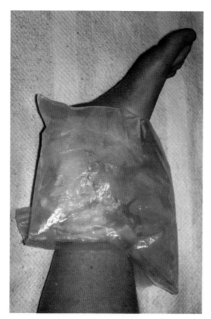
Ice reduces inflammation and pain.

The best treatment for a minor injury is the PRICE method.

P **Protect** from further injury by using splints, pads or crutches.

R **Restrict** activity - rest the injured part for 48 to 72 hours in most cases, which will allow the healing process to begin.

I Apply **Ice** to reduce inflammation and pain. Apply cold packs or cold ice water immediately to the injured part for 15-20 minutes, every hour to hour and a half.

C **Compression** or pressure reduces blood flow and swelling. An elastic bandage is excellent way to apply compression, but do not cut off circulation by applying it too tightly. It should be only as tight as a snug sock.

E **Elevate** the injured area. This helps decrease internal bleeding and swelling, especially if the injured part can be elevated higher than the heart.

Heat may be applied to most injuries after 48 hours of the PRICE treatment method. Heat increases blood flow and nutrients to the injured tissue. Heat applications reduce pain, stiffness and swelling. Heat should be applied for 15 to 20 minutes, one to three times per day.

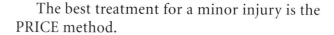

Remember This ✓

Protect
Rest
Ice
Compression
Elevation

Heel Pain

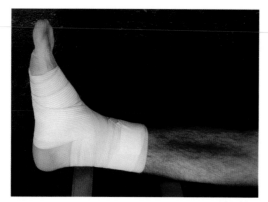
An elastic bandage is a good way to apply compression, as long as it is not too tight.

Heel pain, sometimes called a "stone bruise," usually occurs in the center or outer edge of the fat pad of the heel. The injury occurs because of repeated pounding of the heel on a hard surface, causing a swelling of the tissue lying between the fat pad and the bone of the heel. Standing for long periods of time or being overweight can also add to the pressure.

To prevent this problem wear shoes that are adequately cushioned and avoid running on hard surfaces.

Placing a special heel cup or donut pad in the shoes provides additional cushioning and helps to reduce shock to the heel area. Apply ice immediately after running to reduce swelling. This injury does not heal quickly. Switch to exercises that do not stress the heels, such as cycling or swimming, until the injury heals.

Shin Splints and Hard Surface Running

It is usually best to run on soft surfaces such as grass, because this reduces stress on the joints. Proper footwear also aids in absorbing the shock of running.

Prolonged running on hard surfaces sometimes causes an inflammation and tearing of the muscles and soft tissues of the lower leg. This condition, commonly called **shin splints**, usually responds best to the PRICE method, stretching and complete rest of the legs for a period of time. If the condition is not serious, use stretching exercises before and after a workout to gain relief.

Sprains

Sprains are injuries to the ligaments or the capsule-like sac that surrounds a joint. Sprains are caused by movement of the joint beyond its normal range of motion or trauma, which overstretches the tissue. While severe sprains may not be distinguishable from a more serious fracture except by x-ray, the PRICE method will reduce pain and speed recovery.

Muscle Strains

When a muscle is forced into unaccustomed exercise, it may overstretch. These pulls or strains can tear muscle fibers. The muscle will contract, swell and stiffen. With rest, the torn fibers will heal. However, if the fibers are torn completely (ruptured), surgical repair and physical therapy are often necessary.

To Prevent Shin Splints:

- Wear well-cushioned shoes.
- Avoid running on hard surfaces.
- Stretch calf muscles before running.
- Strengthen and stretch the legs.
- Increase workout intensity gradually.
- Consult a podiatrist to see if an orthotic (shoe insert) will help.

Sprains are caused by movement of the joint beyond its normal range of motion.

Family Activity

Gather items for an "Exercise First Aid Kit." Include items such as cold packs, ice bags, bandages and muscle pain relievers.

First aid for mild muscle strains is the PRICE method followed by moist heat and stretching exercises. If pain persists, see a physician.

The Biomechanical Principles of Exercise

Biomechanics is the study of human motion and the effect that forces have on the body. Awareness of these principles as you perform various movements will help you to avoid many of the injuries described in this chapter and will enable you to perform movement more efficiently. For instance, many vigorous movements put high demands on the joints, muscles and skeletal system. If performed incorrectly, these movements put additional strain on the body—performed correctly the force is reduced and there is less chance of injury.

In this book you will learn activities for cardiorespiratory fitness, muscular fitness and flexibility. The movement pattern for each activity described will use the proper biomechanical principles. Learn and follow the correct techniques for each activity.

Following correct biomechanical principles will lesson your risk of injury from vigorous activities.

Be sure to follow these safety guidelines when exercising as well as doing everyday activities related to lifting:

- Keep your body close to the object.
- Keep your feet shoulder-width apart to have a solid base.
- Bend knees and keep back straight. Do not bend at the waist.
- Tighten your stomach muscles.
- Use your leg muscles to lift the object.
- Hold the object close to your body as you walk.
- Try not to twist your body as you lift—instead, point your feet in the direction of your turn.
- Don't try to lift an object that is too heavy.

Summary

Exercising can be done safely and without fear of injury if certain precautions and guidelines are followed. The selection of proper clothing is an important part of beginning an exercise program. The environmental conditions of the exercise location should be considered.

The importance of drinking water before, during and after exercise cannot be emphasized enough. Knowledge of heat-related disorders can prevent their occurrence.

The quality of our air and the relationship of the sun's rays to cancer are ever-increasing concerns to outdoor exercisers.

Knowing how to treat common problems such as sore muscles, side stitches and sprained ankles will speed your recovery.

The primary responsibility for safe exercise participation and achievement of optimal results rests with you. Once you have the knowledge, the next step is to put it into action.

Exercise can and should be enjoyable!

Chapter 3 Review

Lesson Checklist

- Do you know how to select appropriate clothing for exercise in all kinds of weather?
- Do you know how to exercise safely in hot or cold weather?
- Can you describe the differences between heat cramps, heat exhaustion and heatstroke?
- Do you know precautions to take when outdoors during lightning strikes?
- Do you know why it is important to maintain a proper fluid balance while exercising?
- Can you explain why you should use the PRICE method when you are injured?

Chapter Projects

Write a response to each of the following:

1. You have a muscle cramp. What should you do?
2. What are the symptoms of heatstroke and why is it so dangerous?
3. You have sprained your ankle. What should you do?

Behavior Change Evaluation

Review the following items to see if you have gained an understanding of fitness and wellness. On a piece of paper briefly state how you will make these changes.

- I will dress appropriately for exercise during both hot and cold weather.
- I will select exercise footwear that fits correctly and is designed for the activity or exercise in which I plan to participate.
- I will apply a sunscreen with at least 15 SPF every time I go outdoors.
- I will use the PRICE method for injuries.
- I will make sure that I drink enough fluids before, during and after exercise.

Critical Thinking

1. Describe what you would wear if you were going to exercise outside when the temperature is 36° F. Also describe how you would warm-up and cool down.
2. Describe how you will prepare for exercising in 85° F weather on a hot, sunny day. Include clothing, fluid needs and sunscreen.
3. You get a pain in your side as you jog. What could be the cause and how will you stop it?

Chapter 3 Review

Test Your Knowledge

True or false?

1. The best time to purchase exercise shoes is in the morning.
2. Dark-colored clothing is best for exercising in hot weather.
3. Cooling down properly helps prevent sore muscles.
4. When you exercise on very humid days, your perspiration evaporates faster and you cool down quickly.
5. You should not drink water during exercise.
6. Heatstroke can be a life-threatening condition.
7. When exercising during cold weather, it is best to wear one heavy jacket over your regular exercise clothes so that you can keep warm.
8. A large percentage of body heat is lost if your head is uncovered during cold weather.
9. It is not necessary to wear sunscreen unless you are out in the sun all day.
10. You are generally more flexible after exercise during your cool down period than before exercise.

Read the questions below and select the best possible answer for each.

1. Heat exhaustion symptoms include
   a. heavy perspiration
   b. pale skin
   c. nausea
   d. all of the above

2. Heat stroke symptoms include
   a. cold, wet skin
   b. loss of body heat
   c. weak pulse
   d. high body temperature

3. Which heat related disorder is the most serious and often requires medical attention?
   a. heat cramps
   b. heat exhaustion
   c. heat stroke
   d. heat fatigue

4. Which of the following statements is NOT true about an acute minor injury?

   a. You should apply heat as soon as possible to relieve the pain
   b. Ice will help keep swelling down
   c. Elevating the injured area will help keep swelling down
   d. Cold packs or ice should be applied for 15-20 minutes, every hour to hour and a half

5. Which is true about fluid replacement while exercising?
   a. You can drink before, during, and after exercise
   b. You should never drink water while exercising
   c. Caffeinated drinks are good fluid replacements
   d. It is necessary to drink sports drinks before you exercise

Evaluating Your Health-Related Fitness

4

Chapter Topics

- Health-Related Fitness
- Evaluating Your Health-Related Fitness
- Understanding the Results of Your Tests
- Personal Profile Information
- Evaluating Your Cardiorespiratory Fitness
- Evaluating Your Flexibility Fitness
- Evaluating Your Muscular Strength and Endurance
- Evaluating Your Body Composition
- Health Fitness Standards
- Setting Realistic Goals

Chapter Objectives

After completing this chapter, you will:

- Understand and be able to describe the health-related components of fitness.
- Understand why it is important to know your current level of health fitness.
- Know a variety of tests and activities that can be performed to determine your level of health-related fitness.
- Know how to interpret the results of your health fitness tests using criterion-referenced standards.
- Understand how the results of your health fitness tests can help you set personal goals.

Key Words

aerobic capacity
bioelectrical impedance analysis
body mass index
caliper
cardiorespiratory fitness
carotid artery
criterion-referenced
essential fat
flexibility
joint

lean body weight
maximum oxygen uptake (VO_2max)
muscular endurance
muscular strength
non-essential fat
pulse
radial artery
resting heart rate
skinfold
triceps

Suggested Physical Activities

Do a thirty-minute workout which includes brisk walking as a warm-up, stretching, short jogs alternated with walking, curl-ups and push-ups (regular or modified).

Use the Personal Fitness for You Student CD for:

◆ Lab 4-1: Your Health Fitness Test Profile
◆ Lab 4-2: Your Resting Heart Rate
◆ Lab 4-3: Blood Pressure Check
◆ Lab 4-4: Charting Your Progress
◆ Lab 4-5: Contract for Change
◆ Chapter Practice Test
◆ Chapter Study Guide
◆ Chapter Crossword Puzzle
◆ Vocabulary Flash Cards
◆ Chapter Power Point Review
◆ Fitness Score Sheet
◆ Health Fitness Standards

Just as the term suggests, the health-related components of physical fitness are related to your overall health and wellness. Achieving a high level of health-related fitness will not only serve as protection against many diseases, but it will also contribute to a general feeling of well-being and improved self-image. You will feel better about yourself, look better and be able to perform daily activities with vigor.

The five components of health related fitness are:
• Cardiorespiratory fitness
• Muscular strength
• Muscular endurance
• Flexibility
• Body composition
These components are described below.

Cardiorespiratory fitness refers to the ability of the circulatory (heart, blood, blood vessels) and respiratory system to supply oxygen during physical activity. A good level of cardiorespiratory fitness enables you to perform vigorous large muscle exercise over a long period of time. For example, jogging and swimming are activities which depend on an adequate level of cardiorespiratory fitness.

Muscular strength is the ability of the muscle to generate the maximum amount of force for a single contraction. Lifting a heavy object is an example of using muscular strength.

Muscular endurance is the ability of the muscle to perform repetitive contractions over a prolonged period of time. The number of push-ups you are able to do indicates your muscular endurance.

Flexibility is the ability to move a joint through the full range of motion without discomfort or pain. Good flexibility is needed for performing daily activities and various sports activities.

Body composition is the relative amount of body weight that is fat weight and lean body weight (tissue, bone and muscle). Having a low percentage of body fat is important to how you look and to good health.

Evaluating Your Health-Related Fitness

How would you rate your overall fitness level? Are you in good overall health? Can you perform daily activities without tiring easily? Do you have an acceptable level of body weight and body fat? How physically fit are you? Do you know your level of fitness in each of the health-related areas of fitness?

Why Evaluate Your Health-Related Fitness?

- To learn your physical condition on important components of fitness based on your age and sex
- To gain information to help you in setting goals and developing an exercise program.
- To collect beginning data and follow up data to evaluate your progress.
- To become motivated to establish achievable fitness goals.

Analyzing Your Fitness

The steps to determining your level of fitness follow.

- Learn at least one test you can do for measuring each of the health-related areas of fitness—cardiorespiratory fitness, flexibility, muscular endurance, muscular strength and body composition. Once you know how to perform the test, you can periodically retest yourself to check your progress.
- Know how to measure the results of the test. For example, record the time it takes to walk/run a mile, number of curl-ups performed, etc.
- Determine how your score compares by referring to a chart of health fitness standards.

For **Y**our **I**nformation

There are many technology aids, such as electronic measuring devices and computer software programs, to assist you in assessing your fitness. Find out what is available at your school.

- Learn to interpret the results and determine how you stand in regard to achieving an optimal level of health fitness.
- Set goals for yourself.

Self-testing

Try retesting yourself on a regular basis—especially after you complete this course. Use the tests described here to monitor your progress and to reevaluate your goals. Fitness is your responsibility now and in the future. Take responsibility to determine your needs and set goals to improve.

Retest your health fitness on a regular basis.

Students with Special Needs

Achieving your physical best in the health-related areas of fitness is important for all students. Students with special needs should discuss with their teachers which tests they can take, which tests need to be modified, alternative tests, and ways of interpreting the results. Specific standards and guidelines for students with special needs (disabled or handicapped students) are available from a variety of sources.

Understanding the Results of Your Tests

The results of your health fitness tests are evaluated by comparing them to **criterion-referenced** health fitness standards. Simply stated, this means that first, a specific standard is selected—in this case, a standard that will help prevent health problems now and later in life. Next, a study is conducted based on public health research to determine the fitness range needed for each fitness component to maintain that level of health.

Achieving these health fitness standards is more important than comparing your test scores with other students' scores. The goal is for you to achieve a healthy fitness zone and your optimal level of health fitness – your physical best.

Reach the Healthy Fitness Zone by maintaining an active lifestyle.

The charts at the end of the chapter indicate the scores needed to reach the healthy fitness zone. High levels of physical fitness are not necessary to achieve an acceptable level of health. You should focus on comparing your own scores over time and to reaching the Healthy Fitness Zone. If you fall below the recommended health fitness standards for any of the health fitness tests, later chapters in this book will assist you in setting goals for improvement.

To check your results, refer to the charts on pages 83 and 84 or your teacher may have you use the FITNESSGRAM®, software program to enter your scores and receive an individualized report of your results.

Personal Profile Information

Height/Weight

Measure your height in inches and your weight to the nearest pound and record the results on your Health Fitness Test Evaluation form found on the *Personal Fitness for You* Student CD.

Resting Heart Rate

One measure of your physical condition is your **resting heart rate**. The best way to measure your resting heart rate is to take your pulse when you wake up in the morning and are still in bed. A **pulse** is the regular throbbing in the arteries caused by the contraction of the heart. Another good time to determine your resting heart rate is to take your pulse at a time when you have not done any physical activity for at least thirty minutes, have not eaten for several hours and feel relaxed. A lower resting heart rate is the most desirable, because it indicates that the heart is working more efficiently in meeting the body's demand for blood. It also means more blood is pumped by the heart with each beat allowing the heart more time for rest between beats.

STRESS Stopper

At least once this week, find time to enjoy nature. Study or read outside. Go to a park or to the zoo. Find a quiet spot near a scenic place (river, forest, mountain, lake). Use this time to get your thoughts together.

Studies show that people who develop high levels of cardiorespiratory fitness often have resting heart rates below 50 beats per minute. The American Heart Association identifies the normal range for resting heart rates as between 60 and 80 beats per minute, with the average around 70. Resting heart rate will decrease gradually in response to a program of regular endurance activities. By keeping a record of your resting heart rate, you can chart the progress you are making in your training program.

Counting Your Pulse

The pulse can be counted most accurately by applying light pressure to an artery which is close to the surface of the skin. One such artery—the **radial artery**—is on the inside of your wrist. Place the tips of the first two fingers on the wrist just below the base of the thumb and press lightly. When you feel the pulse (a throbbing), count the number of beats for the appropriate time. Resting heart rate should be counted for 60 seconds to ensure an accurate measurement.

During or after exercise when the heart rate is faster you can use a shorter time period for the count—10 or 15 seconds. Then calculate the pulse for one minute (for a 10 second count multiply by 6 or for a 15 second count multiply by 4).

Another spot for finding the pulse is the artery in the neck—the **carotid artery**. Place two fingers lightly under the jawbone to the side of the neck. Be careful not to apply too much pressure since this will cause the count to be inaccurate.

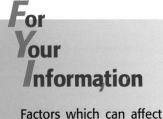

WEBSITE

To test your knowledge about health, visit the following web site:
www.afaa.com

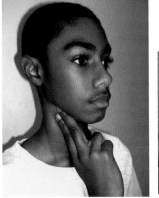

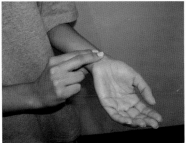

You can count your pulse using the carotid artery (in the neck) or radial artery (in the wrist).

Evaluating Your Cardiorespiratory Fitness

Cardiorespiratory fitness is the ability of the heart, lungs, blood and blood vessels to supply oxygen necessary for long-term work or activity. By achieving your optimal level of cardiorespiratory fitness, you will have a higher energy level and the ability to remain active for longer periods of time.

Another important reason to seek a high level of cardiorespiratory fitness is to reduce your risk of cardiovascular disease—a leading cause of death in the United States.

Cardiorespiratory fitness is also referred to as cardiovascular fitness, **aerobic capacity** and cardiorespiratory endurance. The best measure of cardiorespiratory fitness is a laboratory test of one's **maximal oxygen uptake** or VO_2 max. This test requires special equipment to assess cardiac output and oxygen uptake. However, the PACER test, the one-mile run test and the walk test provide excellent estimates of VO_2 max and provide an accurate measure of your cardiorespiratory fitness.

Don't try to compete against others in the class.

The PACER Test
(Progressive Aerobic Cardiovascular Endurance Run)

Purpose: Measure cardiorespiratory endurance.

Objective: To run as long as possible back and forth across a 20-meter space at a designated pace that gets faster each minute.

Equipment/Facilities: A flat, non-slippery surface that is at least 20 meters long; CD player, measuring tape, marker cones, pencil and scoresheet.

Test Directions:
- Warm-up with walking and easy jogging. Run in place and stretch.
- Select a partner to count laps completed.
- On the signal to start, run across the 20-meter distance and touch the line with your foot by the time the beep sounds. At the sound of the beep, turn around and run back to the other end.
- If you get to the line before the beep, wait for the beep before running to the other end.
- Continue until you fail to reach the line before the beep for the second time.
- At the end of each minute, a triple beep will sound to indicate that the pace will get faster.

Scoring: A lap is one 20-meter distance (from one end to the other). The partner records the number of laps completed.

One Mile Run

Purpose: Measure cardiorespiratory endurance.

Objective: To run a mile at the fastest pace possible. If you cannot run the total distance, walking is permitted.

Equipment/Facilities: A flat running course, stopwatch, pencil and scoresheet.

Test Directions:
- Warm-up with walking or easy jogging. Run in place and stretch.
- Select a partner to record time for the run.
- On the signal to start, begin running. Try to maintain a steady pace.
- If you get tired, walk until you can once again run.

Scoring: The test is scored in minutes and seconds. If you cannot complete the test, a score of 99 minutes and 99 seconds is recorded.

Walk Test

Purpose: Measure cardiorespiratory endurance.

Objective: To walk one mile as quickly as possible.

Equipment/Facilities: A flat measured running course, stopwatches, pencil and scoresheet. The use of heart rate monitors, if they are available, makes testing easier.

Test Directions:
- Warm-up with walking or easy jogging. Run in place and stretch.
- Select a partner to record time and assist with heart rate counting.
- On the signal to start, begin walking the mile as quickly as possible. Try to maintain a steady pace.

Scoring: As you cross the finish line, your elapsed time will be recorded. Take a 15-second heart rate count. If you are using a heart rate monitor, start the watch at the beginning of the walk and stop it at the end of the walk. The last heart rate recorded during the walk should be used as the walking heart rate. Your heart rate to walk a mile at a specific speed is used to determine your fitness level. If your class is not using the FITNESSGRAM® program to record results, refer to the Student CD for a Walking Test calculator to convert your score (heart rate and time) to the VO$_2$ max value.

The Walk Test is a fitness test you can easily do on your own.

SAFETY TIP When walking in the evening, always wear light-colored clothing or add reflective strips of tape to your clothes.

Evaluating Your Flexibility Fitness

A **joint** is a place where two bones meet in the skeleton of the body. Joints may be immovable (such as those in the skull) or moveable (such as those in the elbow, hip, shoulder and neck).

Flexibility is the ability to move the muscles and body joints through a maximum range of motion—to use a joint to its fullest. Loss of flexibility can limit your movements, ability to perform daily tasks and recreational activities.

Remember This ✓

Being a Team Player:

When participating in class activities such as fitness testing, team sports, weight training or stretching, it is important to recognize your role as the leader, supportive follower or passive follower. No one can be the leader all the time. For example, during fitness testing, some students will be timers, some will keep score and others will lead classmates through the tests. Success depends on each person fulfilling his or her role to benefit the entire group.

Flexibility is the ability to move the muscles and body joints through a maximum range of motion.

The back saver sit and reach test measures the flexibility of the muscles in the back of the legs.

SAFETY TIP It is very important to warm-up before doing these tests. Do slow, steady stretches. Do not bounce or jerk during the test.

In addition, weak and/or tense muscles contribute to low back disorders. Lack of physical activity contributes to a loss of flexibility—especially in the low back muscles, hip flexors and hamstring muscles (in the back of the legs). If you sit for long periods of time and are sedentary (get little physical activity), you will also lose flexibility.

No single test can measure flexibility since it is specific to each joint and muscle group. The following tests provide an indication of flexibility for various parts of the body.

Back-Saver Sit and Reach

Purpose: Measure flexibility of the hamstring muscles.

Objective: To be able to reach the specified distance (for the Healthy Fitness Zone) on the right and left sides of the body.

Equipment/Facilities: A sturdy box approximately 12 inches high. A ruler is placed on top of the box with the 9 inch mark parallel to the face of the box. The zero end of the ruler should be nearer the student.

Test Directions:
- Warm-up and do easy stretches.
- Select a partner to record distance stretched.
- Remove your shoes and sit down at the box.
- Fully extend one leg with the foot flat against the face of the box.
- The other knee is bent with the sole of the foot flat on the floor. The instep is placed in line with, and 2 to 3 inches to the side of, the straight knee.
- Extend the arms forward over the measuring scale with the hands placed one on top of the other with the palms down.
- Reach forward, keeping the back straight and the head up, with both hands along the scale four times and hold the position of the fourth reach for at least one second.
- Switch the position of the legs and measure the other side.
- The bent knee may move to the side as the body moves forward, but the sole of the foot must remain on the floor.

Scoring: Record the number of inches on each side to the nearest 1/2 inch reached, to a maximum score of 12 inches.

Shoulder Stretch

Purpose: Measure flexibility of upper arm and shoulder girdle.

Objective: To be able to touch the fingertips together behind the back by reaching over the shoulder and under the elbow.

Equipment/Facilities: None

Test Directions:
- Warm-up and easy stretching.
- Reach the right hand over the right shoulder and down the back as if trying to scratch between the shoulder blades. At the same time place the left hand behind the back and reach up, trying to touch the fingers of the right hand. Repeat for the other side.

Scoring: If you are able to touch your fingers with the opposite hand, a "Y" is recorded, if not, a "N" is recorded. To achieve the Healthy Fitness Zone, you must be able to successfully touch on both sides.

The shoulder stretch test measures the flexibility of the upper body.

Evaluating Your Muscular Strength and Endurance

Muscular strength is the amount of force that can be exerted by a single contraction of the muscle. Muscular endurance is the ability of a muscle to perform repeated contractions over an extended period of time. Since muscular endurance depends to a large extent on the strength of your muscle, these components are generally measured together.

For instance, an excellent test to determine the muscular strength and endurance of the abdominal muscles is the curl-up, and a reliable test for the upper body is the pull-up.

A good level of muscular strength and endurance is important for participating in recreational activities.

A minimal level of muscular strength and endurance is the key to:

- avoiding health problems such as low back problems
- performing daily activities without injury or fatigue
- participating in recreational activities
- preventing posture problems related to muscular weakness

The curl-up test measures the level of muscular strength and endurance of the abdominal muscles.

Curl-Up

Purpose: Measure abdominal strength and endurance.

Objective: To complete as many curl-ups as possible up to a maximum of 75 at a specified pace.

Equipment/Facilities: A gym mat and measuring strip.

Test Directions:
- Warm-up with easy stretching.
- Select a partner to count and record your score.
- Lie on your back with knees bent at an angle of approximately 140 degrees, feet flat on the floor, legs slightly apart, arms straight and parallel to the trunk with palms of hands resting on the mat.
- The fingers are stretched out and the head is in contact with the mat.
- The feet should be as far from the buttocks as possible while still keeping the feet flat on the floor.
- The partner now places a measuring strip on the mat under the partner's legs so that the fingertips are just resting on the nearest edge of the strip.
- The partner then kneels at the head in a position to count curl ups and watch for form breaks. They place a piece of paper under the partner's head to assist in judging if the head touches down on each repetition. The paper should crinkle each time the partner touches it with his or her head.
- Keeping heels in contact with the mat, curl up slowly, sliding fingertips across the measuring strip until fingertips reach the other side of the strip. Then curl back down until your head touches the piece of paper on the mat.
- Movement should be slow and gauged to the specified cadence of about 20 curl-ups per minute (1 curl every 3 seconds).
- Continue without pausing until you can no longer continue or you have completed 75 curl-ups.
- When a second form correction is made, you must stop. The following are form corrections:
  - Heels not remaining in contact with the mat.
  - Head must return to the mat on each repetition.
  - Pauses and rest periods are not allowed. The movement must be continuous.
  - Fingertips must touch the far side of the measuring strip.

Scoring: The score is the number of curl-ups performed. The curl-up is counted when the head returns to the mat.

90° Push-Up

Purpose: Measure upper body strength and endurance.

Objective: To complete as many 90° push-ups as possible at a rhythmic pace.

Equipment/Facilities: An audio tape with the recorded cadence.

Test Directions:
- Warm-up with easy stretching.
- Select a partner to count and record your score.
- Assume a prone position with hands placed under or slightly wider than the shoulders, fingers stretched out, legs straight and slightly apart, and toes tucked under.
- Push up off the mat with the arms until arms are straight, keeping the legs and back straight. The back should be kept in a straight line from head to toes throughout the test.
- Lower the body using the arms until the elbows bend at a 90° angle and the upper arms are parallel to the floor.
- The rhythm should be approximately 20 push-ups per minute or 1 push-up every 3 seconds.
- When a second form correction is made, you must stop. The following are form corrections:
  - Not achieving a 90° angle with the elbow on each repetition.
  - Not maintaining correct body position with a straight back.
  - Not extending arms fully.

Scoring: The score is the number of push-ups performed.

SAFETY TIP   Warm-up and do some arm and shoulder stretches before trying this test.

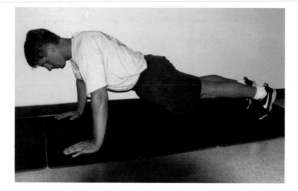 

The 90° push-up test measures upper body strength and endurance.

Trunk Lift

Purpose: Measure trunk extensor strength and flexibility.

Objective: To lift the upper body off the floor using the muscles of the back and hold the position to allow for the measurement.

Equipment/Facilities: Gym mats and a measuring device are needed. A yardstick or 15 inch ruler is preferred.

Test Directions:
- Warm-up with easy stretching.
- Select a partner to measure and record your score.
- Lie on the mat in a prone position (facedown).
- Toes are pointed and hands are placed under the thighs.
- A coin or other marker is placed on the floor in line with the student's eyes.
- During the lift, the student should focus on the coin or marker.
- Lift the upper body off the floor in a very slow and controlled manner to a maximum height of 12 inches.
- The head should be maintained in a neutral (straight) alignment with the spine.
- Hold the position long enough to allow the tester to place the ruler on the floor in front and determine the distance from the floor to your chin.
- Return to the starting position in a controlled manner. Two trials are allowed.
- Record the highest score.

Scoring: The score is recorded in inches. Distances above 12 inches should be recorded as 12 inches.

SAFETY TIP Slowly lift your head and chest off the floor. Be certain the ruler is not placed under the chin.

The trunk lift test measures the strength and flexibility of the muscles in the upper back and trunk.

Pull-Up

Purpose: Measure upper body strength and endurance.

Objective: To correctly complete as many pull-ups as possible

Equipment/Facilities: A horizontal bar at a height that allows the student to hang with arms fully extended and feet clear of the floor.

Test Directions:
- Warm-up with easy stretching.
- Select a partner to count and record your score.
- Assume a position hanging on the bar with the overhand grip (palms facing away from the body). Shorter students may be lifted to the starting position.
- Use the arms to pull the body up until the chin is above the bar.
- Then lower the body again into the full hanging position.
- Repeat as many times as possible. There is no time limit.
- When a second form correction is made, you must stop. The following are form corrections:
  - The body should not swing during the movement. A partner may hold an arm in front to prevent swinging.
  - The pull-up must be performed smoothly without kicking or jerking.
  - Forceful bending of the knees or bending at the waist is not permitted.
  - To be counted, the student must lift the chin over the bar and return to the full hanging position with elbows fully extended.

Scoring: The score is the number of pull-ups performed.

SAFETY TIP — Warm-up and do some arm and shoulder stretches before trying this test.

The pull-up test measures the level of muscular strength and endurance of the arm and shoulder muscles.

Modified Pull-Up

Purpose: Measure upper body strength and endurance.

Objective: To successfully complete as many modified pull-ups as possible

Equipment/Facilities: A modified pull up stand is needed. A mat or other soft surface is recommended.

Test Directions:
- Warm-up with easy stretching.
- Select a partner to count and record your score.
- Assume position with shoulders directly under a bar that has been set 1 to 2 inches above the shoulder's reach.
- Grasp the bar with an overhand grip (palms away from the body).
- Arms and legs should be straight, buttocks off the floor, and only the heels touching the floor.
- Pull up until the chin is above the elastic band (positioned 7 to 8 inches below the bar).
- Lower the body to the down position.
- When a second form correction is made, you must stop. The following are form corrections:
  - Stopping to rest or not maintaining a rhythmic pace.
  - Not lifting the chin above the elastic band.
  - Not maintaining a straight body position with only heels in contact with the floor.
  - Not fully extending arms in the down position.

Scoring: The score is the number of pull-ups performed.

SAFETY TIP — Warm-up and do some arm and shoulder stretches before trying this test.

The modified pull-up test measures the strength of the arm and shoulder muscles.

Flexed Arm Hang

Purpose: Measure upper body strength and endurance.

Objective: To hang with the chin above the bar as long as possible.

Equipment/Facilities: A horizontal bar, chair or stool and a stopwatch.

Test Directions:
- Warm-up with easy stretching.
- Select a partner to time your hang time and a spotter if needed.
- Grasp the bar with an overhand grip (palms facing away).
- With the assistance of one or more spotters, raise the body off the floor so that the chin is above the bar, elbows flexed and the chest close to the bar.
- A stopwatch is started as soon as you assume the starting position.
- Hold the position as long as possible.
- Timing stops when one of the following occurs:
  - Your chin touches the bar.
  - You tilt your head back to keep the chin above the bar.
  - Your chin falls below the bar.

Scoring: The score is the number of seconds you were able to maintain the correct hanging position.

Warm-up and do some arm and shoulder stretches before trying this test.

The flexed arm hang test measures the muscular strength and endurance of the arm and shoulder muscles.

Evaluating Your Body Composition

Body composition refers to the amount of your body weight which is fat compared to that which is lean body weight (tissue, bone and muscle). Maintaining a low level of body fat is a key to lowering your risk of heart disease, stroke and diabetes as well as to successful participation in daily activities. Studies show that individuals who have excess amounts of fat generally have lower levels of physical fitness. However, the standard height/weight tables can be misleading, since they do not distinguish between fat weight and lean body weight. Therefore, a complete analysis of your body composition should include height, lean body weight and fat weight evaluation.

However, all body composition tests are estimations since they are indirect measurements of body fatness. Use the values you get to measure your individual changes over time rather than becoming overly concerned about a specific body fat percentage. The accuracy of your measurements will depend on the method you use, the experience of the test administrator and the appropriateness of that test for you. To get more consistent results, make certain you use the same method by the same person.

Maintaining a low level of body fat lowers your risk of disease.

Body Fat Evaluation

The purpose of body fat evaluation tests is to determine an estimate of your percentage of body fat. There are several methods which can be used to determine the amount of body fat you possess.

Currently the method considered the most accurate is **hydrostatic weighing** - also known as **underwater weighing**. However, this method requires expensive equipment and is difficult to administer because the individual must remain fully underwater for ten seconds.

There are many types of body fat analyzers.

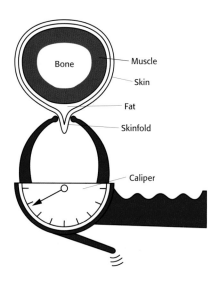

A caliper is one way to measure body fat.

Newer techniques have been developed which are easy and inexpensive to use. One such measure is **bioelectrical impedance analysis**. This uses an electrical current to measure the resistance encountered in the body. Lean tissue has less electrical resistance. Fat tissue has more electrical resistance. Many authorities believe, however, that these tests are not always accurate because factors such as sweat, dehydration, and food and beverage consumption may conflict with the electrical resistance in the body.

To increase the accuracy of the bioelectrical impedance test, the American College of Sports Medicine recommends following these guidelines:

- Do not eat or drink within four hours before the test.
- Avoid moderate or vigorous physical activity within twelve hours of the test.
- Empty the bladder and bowels before the test.
- Do not drink alcoholic beverages within 48 hours of the test.
- Unless they are prescribed by a doctor, do not use diuretic agents (a drug that promotes the removal of water from the body through the urine) prior to the test.

The newer bioelectrical impedance analyzers can provide similar classification accuracy and body composition estimates as measurements performed with skinfold calipers.

A simpler method of determining body fat is to measure the thickness of selected body **skinfolds**. Approximately one-third of the total fat is located between the skin and the muscles and can be measured using an instrument called a **caliper**. By measuring the thickness of fat under folds of the skin at various body sites, you can obtain an estimate of overall body fat.

Skinfold Measurements

Purpose: Assess body fat percentage

Objective: To measure the triceps and calf skinfold thicknesses for calculating body fat.

Equipment/Facilities: A skinfold caliper.

Test Directions:
- The tester should be trained or be monitored until the correct technique is learned.
- Take measurements on the right side.
- Relax the arm or leg being measured.
- Take measurements prior to exercising.
- Firmly grasp the skinfold between the thumb and forefinger and lift it away from the body tissue.
- Place the caliper one half inch below the pinch site.
- Three measurements are taken but it is recommended to alternate between the two sites rather than measuring three in a row at one site.
- **Triceps** Skinfold Measurement – the site is halfway between the elbow and top of the shoulder over the tricep muscle. The pinch is best done slightly above the midpoint so that the measurement is at the midpoint. The skinfold should be vertical.
- **Calf** Skinfold Measurement – the site is on the inside of the right lower leg at the largest part of the calf. The right foot should be placed on an elevated surface so that the knee is bent at a 90° angle. The pinch is done slightly above the midpoint so that the measurement is at the midpoint.
- Measurements should be taken by the same tester when future testing is done.

Scoring: The skinfold measure is recorded from the caliper in millimeters. Scores are recorded to the nearest .5 millimeters. Three measurements for each site are taken and the middle score is recorded. The charts on the following pages can be used to determine your body fat percentage based on the total of your skinfold measurements.

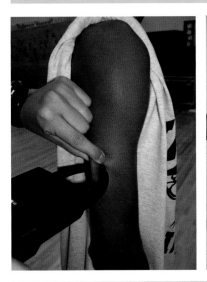 

The triceps and calf are good places to take a skinfold measurement.

Body Fat Percentages: Boys

Use this chart to determine percentage of body fat for all boys ages 5-16+. Total MM is the total of the triceps skinfold measurement and the calf skinfold measurement.

Total MM	% FAT	Total MM	% FAT	Total MM	% FAT	Total MM	% FAT	Total MM	% FAT
1.0	1.7	16.0	12.8	31.0	23.8	46.0	34.8	61.0	45.8
1.5	2.1	16.5	13.1	31.5	24.2	46.5	35.2	61.5	46.2
2.0	2.5	17.0	13.5	32.0	24.5	47.0	35.5	62.0	46.6
2.5	2.8	17.5	13.9	32.5	24.9	47.5	35.9	62.5	46.9
3.0	3.2	18.0	14.2	33.0	25.3	48.0	36.3	63.0	47.3
3.5	3.6	18.5	14.6	33.5	25.6	48.5	36.6	63.5	47.7
4.0	3.9	19.0	15.0	34.0	26.0	49.0	37.0	64.0	48.0
4.5	4.3	19.5	15.3	34.5	26.4	49.5	37.4	64.5	48.4
5.0	4.7	20.0	15.7	35.0	26.7	50.0	37.8	65.0	48.8
5.5	5.0	20.5	16.1	35.5	27.1	50.5	38.1	65.5	49.1
6.0	5.4	21.0	16.4	36.0	27.5	51.0	38.5	66.0	49.5
6.5	5.8	21.5	16.8	36.5	27.8	51.5	38.9	66.5	49.9
7.0	6.1	22.0	17.2	37.0	28.2	52.0	39.2	67.0	50.2
7.5	6.5	22.5	17.5	37.5	28.6	52.5	39.6	67.5	50.6
8.0	6.9	23.0	17.9	38.0	28.9	53.0	40.0	68.0	51.0
8.5	7.2	23.5	18.3	38.5	29.3	53.5	40.3	68.5	51.3
9.0	7.6	24.0	18.6	39.0	29.7	54.0	40.7	69.0	51.7
9.5	8.0	24.5	19.0	39.5	30.0	54.5	41.1	69.5	52.1
10.0	8.4	25.0	19.4	40.0	30.4	55.0	41.4	70.0	52.5
10.5	8.7	25.5	19.7	40.5	30.8	55.5	41.8	70.5	52.8
11.0	9.1	26.0	20.1	41.0	31.1	56.0	42.2	71.0	53.2
11.5	9.5	26.5	20.5	41.5	31.5	56.5	42.6	71.5	53.6
12.0	9.8	27.0	20.8	42.0	31.9	57.0	42.9	72.0	53.9
12.5	10.2	27.5	21.2	42.5	32.2	57.5	43.3	72.5	54.3
13.0	10.6	28.0	21.6	43.0	32.6	58.0	43.6	73.0	54.7
13.5	10.9	28.5	21.9	43.5	33.0	58.5	44.0	73.5	55.0
14.0	11.3	29.0	22.3	44.0	33.3	59.0	44.4	74.0	55.4
14.5	11.7	29.5	22.7	44.5	33.7	59.5	44.7	74.5	55.8
15.0	12.0	30.0	23.1	45.0	34.1	60.0	45.1	75.0	56.1
15.5	12.4	30.5	23.4	45.5	34.4	60.5	45.5	75.5	56.5

Reprinted from the FITNESSGRAM®, / ACTIVITYGRAM® , Test Administration Manual, Third Edition, 2005, with permission of The Cooper Institute, Dallas, Texas. FITNESSGRAM®, is a federally registered trademark of The Cooper Institute.

Body Fat Percentages: Girls

Use this chart to determine percentage of body fat for all girls ages 5-16+. Total MM is the total of the triceps skinfold measurement and the calf skinfold measurement.

Total MM	% FAT	Total MM	% FAT	Total MM	% FAT	Total MM	% FAT	Total MM	% FAT
1.0	5.7	16.0	14.9	31.0	24.0	46.0	33.2	61.0	42.3
1.5	6.0	16.5	15.2	31.5	24.3	46.5	33.5	61.5	42.6
2.0	6.3	17.0	15.5	32.0	24.6	47.0	33.8	62.0	42.9
2.5	6.6	17.5	15.8	32.5	24.9	47.5	34.1	62.5	43.2
3.0	6.9	18.0	16.1	33.0	25.2	48.0	34.4	63.0	43.5
3.5	7.2	18.5	16.4	33.5	25.5	48.5	34.7	63.5	43.8
4.0	7.5	19.0	16.7	34.0	25.8	49.0	35.0	64.0	44.1
4.5	7.8	19.5	17.0	34.5	26.1	49.5	35.3	64.5	44.4
5.0	8.2	20.0	17.3	35.0	26.5	50.0	35.6	65.0	44.8
5.5	8.5	20.5	17.6	35.5	26.8	50.5	35.9	65.5	45.1
6.0	8.8	21.0	17.9	36.0	27.1	51.0	36.2	66.0	45.4
6.5	9.1	21.5	18.2	36.5	27.4	51.5	36.5	66.5	45.7
7.0	9.4	22.0	18.5	37.0	27.7	52.0	36.8	67.0	46.0
7.5	9.7	22.5	18.8	37.5	28.0	52.5	37.1	67.5	46.3
8.0	10.0	23.0	19.1	38.0	28.3	53.0	37.4	68.0	46.6
8.5	10.3	23.5	19.4	38.5	28.6	53.5	37.7	68.5	46.9
9.0	10.6	24.0	19.7	39.0	28.9	54.0	38.0	69.0	47.2
9.5	10.9	24.5	20.0	39.5	29.2	54.5	38.3	69.5	47.5
10.0	11.2	25.0	20.4	40.0	29.5	55.0	38.7	70.0	47.8
10.5	11.5	25.5	20.7	40.5	29.8	55.5	39.0	70.5	48.1
11.0	11.8	26.0	21.0	41.0	30.1	56.0	39.3	71.0	48.4
11.5	12.1	26.5	21.3	41.5	30.4	56.5	39.6	71.5	48.7
12.0	12.4	27.0	21.6	42.0	30.7	57.0	39.9	72.0	49.0
12.5	12.7	27.5	21.9	42.5	31.0	57.5	40.2	72.5	49.3
13.0	13.0	28.0	22.2	43.0	31.3	58.0	40.5	73.0	49.6
13.5	13.3	28.5	22.5	43.5	31.6	58.5	40.8	73.5	49.9
14.0	13.6	29.0	22.8	44.0	31.9	59.0	41.1	74.0	50.2
14.5	13.9	29.5	23.1	44.5	32.2	59.5	41.4	74.5	50.5
15.0	14.3	30.0	23.4	45.0	32.6	60.0	41.7	75.0	50.9
15.5	14.6	30.5	23.7	45.5	32.9	60.5	42.0	75.5	51.2

Reprinted from the FITNESSGRAM®, / ACTIVITYGRAM® , Test Administration Manual, Third Edition, 2005, with permission of The Cooper Institute, Dallas, Texas. FITNESSGRAM®, is a federally registered trademark of The Cooper Institute.

Body Mass Index (BMI)

Another, although less accurate, measurement of your body composition is your **Body Mass Index (BMI)**. Body Mass Index uses height and weight values to calculate a score for body composition.

BMI is determined by dividing the body weight measured in kilograms by the height measured to the nearest millimeter squared.

$$\frac{\text{Weight (kg)}}{\text{Height (m)2}}$$

Remember This ☑

Body Mass Index (BMI) may incorrectly identify a very muscular person as being fat or a light-weight person without good muscular development and a high fat percentage as being acceptable.

Body Mass Index (BMI)

Purpose: Measure body composition

Objective: To calculate your Body Mass Index (BMI)

Equipment/Facilities: A scale, measuring tape, and calculator

Test Directions:
- Measure your body weight on a scale. Wear lightweight clothes and do not wear shoes. Obtain two readings and record them to the nearest .5 kilogram or nearest pound and average the two.
- Measure your height standing fully erect without shoes. Obtain two readings and record them to the nearest millimeter or to the nearest one-half inch and average the two.
- If you do not have the results measured in kilograms and meters, calculate your weight in kilograms and height in millimeters as follows:.
  - To calculate your weight in kilograms, divide your weight in pounds by 2.2.
  - To calculate your height in meters, multiply your height in inches by 2.54 and divide by 100.

> **For example:**
> If your weight in pounds = 130
> your weight in kilograms is 130÷2.2 = **59**
> If your height in inches = 66 (5'6")
> your height in meters is 66 x 2.54÷100 = **1.67**
> Next square your height in meters:
> 1.67 x 1.67 = 2.8
>
> Complete the math calculations as follows:
> **BMI = 59÷2.8 = 21**

Scoring: Check the chart at the end of the chapter for your score and record it on the Health Fitness Test Score Card.

Find Your BMI at a Glance

You can also determine your BMI by using the chart below. Find your height on the left side of the chart and look to the right to find the closest number to your weight. Then look at the top of the weight column to find your BMI.

Body Mass Index Table

	Normal						Overweight					Obese		Extreme Obesity		
BMI	19	20	21	22	23	24	25	26	27	28	29	30	35	40	45	50
4'10"	91	96	100	105	110	115	119	124	129	134	138	143	167	191	215	239
4'11"	94	99	104	109	114	119	124	128	133	138	143	148	173	198	222	247
5'	97	102	107	112	118	123	128	133	138	143	148	153	179	204	230	255
5'1"	100	106	111	116	122	127	132	137	143	148	153	158	185	211	238	264
5'2"	104	109	115	120	126	131	136	142	147	153	158	164	191	218	246	273
5'3"	107	113	118	124	130	135	141	146	152	158	163	169	197	225	254	282
5'4"	110	116	122	128	134	140	145	151	157	163	169	174	204	232	262	291
5'5"	114	120	126	132	138	144	150	156	162	168	174	280	210	240	270	300
5'6"	118	124	130	136	142	148	155	161	167	173	179	286	216	247	278	309
5'7"	121	127	134	140	146	153	159	166	172	178	185	191	223	255	287	319
5'8"	125	131	138	144	151	158	164	171	177	184	190	197	230	262	295	328
5'9"	128	135	142	149	155	162	169	176	182	189	296	203	236	270	304	338
5'10"	132	139	146	153	160	167	174	181	188	195	202	207	243	278	313	348
5'11"	136	143	150	157	165	172	179	186	193	200	208	215	250	286	322	358
6'	140	147	154	162	169	177	184	191	199	206	213	221	258	294	331	368
6'1"	144	152	159	166	174	182	189	297	204	212	219	227	265	302	340	378
6'2"	148	155	163	172	179	186	194	202	210	218	225	233	272	311	350	389
6'3"	152	160	168	176	184	192	200	208	216	224	232	240	279	319	359	399
6'4"	156	164	172	180	189	197	205	213	221	230	238	246	287	328	369	410

Height (in feet and inches)

Weight (in pounds)

Source: Adapted from Clinical Guidelines on the Identification, Evaluation, and Treatment of Overweight and Obesity in Adults: The Evidence Report.

Waist Circumference

Waist circumference is another indirect way to measure your body composition. Waist circumference is the distance around your natural waist (just above your navel). Your goal for waist circumference is less than or equal to 40 inches for males and less than or equal to 35 inches for females.

Healthy People 2010 Goals

◆ Improve health, fitness and quality of life through daily physical activity.

◆ Increase the proportion of adolescents who engage in moderate physical activity for at least 30 minutes on 5 or more of the previous 7 days.

◆ Increase the proportion of adolescents who engage in vigorous physical activity that promotes cardiorespiratory fitness 3 or more days per week for 20 or more minutes per occasion.

◆ Increase the proportion of adolescents who participate in daily school physical education.

◆ Increase the proportion of adolescents who spend at least 50 percent of school physical education class time being physically active.

◆ Increase the proportion of children and adolescents who view television 2 or fewer hours per day.

◆ Increase proportion of people who perform physical activity that enhances and maintains muscular strength, muscular endurance and flexibility.

Health Fitness Standards

Boys

The Scores Below represent the Health Fitness Standards established by the FITNESSGRAM® program. The number on the left is the lower end of the HEALTHY FITNESS ZONE and the number on the right is the upper end of the HEALTHY FITNESS ZONE.

Age	13	14	15	16	17	17+
VO$_2$max (ml • kg^{-1} • min^{-1})	42-52	42-52	42-52	42-52	42-52	42-52
Pacer (number of laps)	41-83	41-83	51-94	61-94	61-106	71-106
One Mile Run (min:sec)	10:00-7:30	9:30-7:00	9:00-7:00	8:30-7:00	8:30-7:00	8:30-7:00
Walk Test (VO$_2$max)	42-52	42-52	42-52	42-52	42-52	42-52
Percent Fat	25-7	25-7	25-7	25-7	25-7	25-7
Body Mass Index	23-15.1	24.5-15.6	25-13.2	26.5-16.6	27-17.3	27.8-17.8
Curl-Up (no. completed)	21-40	24-45	24-47	24-47	24-47	24-47
Trunk lift (inches)	9-12	9-12	9-12	9-12	9-12	9-12
90° push-up (no. completed)	12-25	14-30	16-35	18-35	18-35	18-35
Modified pull-up (no. completed)	8-22	9-25	10-27	12-30	14-30	14-30
Pull-up (no. completed)	1-4	2-5	3-7	5-8	5-8	5-8
Flexed arm hang (seconds)	12-17	15-20	15-20	15-20	15-20	15-20
Back-saver sit and reach*	8 inches	8 inches	8 inches	8 inches	8 inches	8 inches
Shoulder Stretch	*Healthy Fitness Zone = touching fingertips together behind the back on both the right and left sides*					

Test Scored Pass/Fail; must reach this distance to pass.

Reprinted from the FITNESSGRAM®, / ACTIVITYGRAM® , Test Administration Manual, Third Edition, 2005, with permission of The Cooper Institute, Dallas, Texas. FITNESSGRAM®, is a federally registered trademark of The Cooper Institute.

Health Fitness Standards

Girls

The Scores Below represent the Health Fitness Standards established by the FITNESSGRAM® program. The number on the left is the lower end of the HEALTHY FITNESS ZONE and the number on the right is the upper end of the HEALTHY FITNESS ZONE.

Age	13	14	15	16	17	17+
VO$_2$max (ml • kg^{-1} • min^{-1})	36-44	35-43	35-43	35-43	35-43	35-43
Pacer (number of laps)	23-51	23-51	32-51	32-61	41-61	41-72
One Mile Run (min:sec)	11:30-9:00	11:00-8:30	10:30-8:00	10:00-8:00	10:00-8:00	10:00-8:00
Walk Test (VO$_2$max)	36-44	35-43	35-43	35-43	35-43	35-43
Percent Fat	32-13	32-13	32-13	32-13	32-13	32-13
Body Mass Index	24.5-14.9	25-15.4	25-16.0	25-16.4	26-16.8	27.3-17.2
Curl-Up (no. completed)	18-32	18-32	18-35	18-35	18-35	18-35
Trunk lift (inches)	9-12	9-12	9-12	9-12	9-12	9-12
90° push-up (no. completed)	7-15	7-15	7-15	7-15	7-15	7-15
Modified pull-up (no. completed)	4-13	4-13	4-13	4-13	4-13	4-13
Pull-up (no. completed)	1-2	1-2	1-2	1-2	1-2	1-2
Flexed arm hang (seconds)	8-12	8-12	8-12	8-12	8-12	8-12
Back-saver sit and reach*	10 inches	10 inches	12 inches	12 inches	12 inches	12 inches
Shoulder Stretch	*Healthy Fitness Zone = touching fingertips together behind the back on both the right and left sides*					

Test Scored Pass/Fail; must reach this distance to pass.

Reprinted from the FITNESSGRAM®, / ACTIVITYGRAM® , Test Administration Manual, Third Edition, 2005, with permission of The Cooper Institute, Dallas, Texas. FITNESSGRAM®, is a federally registered trademark of The Cooper Institute.

Setting Realistic Goals

Once you have completed the tests described in this chapter, you are ready to establish realistic goals for improvement. Your goals should indicate how much change you can expect to accomplish at certain intervals (such as one month, two months or by the end of the semester). Your goals can help you attain your personal best! Follow these steps to begin designing your personal fitness activity plan.

- Identify your areas of strength and weakness. Which health related fitness components were below the recommended Healthy Fitness Zone?
- Set specific goals for each component. Establish smaller, short term goals that you can attain.
- Make a commitment to build activity in your daily routine. Make physical activity a priority.
- Select a variety of different activities that you enjoy. Find whatever it is that gets you motivated to be active.
- Plan how you will overcome barriers and obstacles to achieve your goals.
- Refer to the appropriate chapters for each health related component to learn goal setting methods for each component.
- Periodically reassess your performance on the health related tests to check your progress.

Family Activity

Discuss the test evaluation with members of your family. For as many tests as possible, test others in your family.

Everyone can be a winner by achieving the Healthy Fitness Zone.

What can you do to improve your personal fitness starting today?

Summary

A number of tests are available to help you measure your level of fitness. A set of criterion-referenced health standards can be used to evaluate your test results. Reaching these standards is important, since they represent a minimum level necessary to prevent health problems in each fitness area.

In establishing a plan for improvement, seek your personal best rather than trying to compete with others. Strive to reach your optimal level of personal fitness. By understanding these tests and how to interpret the results, you can use them to retest yourself from time to time. Using these methods of evaluating your fitness, establish a goal of optimal personal fitness for you.

Chapter 4 Review

Lesson Checklist

- Can you name the five components of health-related fitness?
- Can you name at least one test which measures each health-related fitness component?
- Were you able to interpret your test results and determine your level of health-related fitness?

Chapter Projects

Write a response to each of the following:

1. List two tests for measuring each of the following fitness areas: cardiorespiratory fitness, muscular strength and endurance, flexibility, body composition.
2. Explain the importance of having a low resting heart rate.
3. Describe each of the health-related fitness components: flexibility, muscular strength, muscular endurance, cardiorespiratory fitness, body composition.
4. Explain the importance of distinguishing between body fat and lean body weight.
5. Explain why you should participate in a fitness evaluation.
6. Why is it important to achieve the health fitness standards which are established for each of the health-related fitness components?

Behavior Change Evaluation

Review the following items to see if you have gained an understanding of fitness and wellness. On a piece of paper briefly state how you will make these changes.

- I will use the fitness tests described and performed in class to periodically evaluate my health-related fitness.
- I will continue to monitor my level of health-related fitness as I participate in a fitness program.

Critical Thinking

What do the results of your fitness testing indicate about your level of fitness? Are you surprised by the results? If so, why?

Chapter 4 Review

Test Your Knowledge

Read the questions below and select the best possible answer for each.

1. Which term refers to the distribution of fat, tissue, bone, and muscle in the body?
   a. Body fat
   b. Body composition
   c. BMR
   d. Healthy composition

2. Which is not an accurate way to measure your body fat?
   a. Scale
   b. Underwater weighing
   c. Bioelectrical impedance machine
   d. Skinfold caliper

3. Body mass index is calculated using
   a. Weight and fat percentage
   b. Height, weight, and gender
   c. Weight and height
   d. Age, gender, height and weight

4. The ability of a muscle to generate the maximum amount of force with a single contraction is known as
   a. Muscular power
   b. Muscular strength
   c. Muscular endurance
   d. Muscular force

5. The ability of a muscle to perform repetitive contractions over time is called
   a. Muscular power
   b. Muscular strength
   c. Muscular endurance
   d. Muscular force

6. The ability of the circulatory and respiratory system to supply oxygen during physical activity is called
   a. Muscular fitness
   b. Muscular endurance
   c. Cardiorespiratory strength
   d. Cardiorespiratory fitness

7. Which statement about resting heart rate is NOT true?
   a. Resting heart rate is a good measure of your physical condition.
   b. Resting heart rate will decrease gradually in response to regular endurance exercise.
   c. The average resting heart rate is around 70 beats per minute.
   d. A high resting heart rate indicates that the heart is working efficiently.

8. Which is the best for assessing muscular endurance?
   a. Curl ups
   b. Jumping jacks
   c. One mile walk
   d. Sit and reach test

9. Which statement is NOT true about flexibility
   a. Flexibility is the ability to move the muscles and joints through their full range of motion.
   b. It is not necessary to warm-up before stretching and performing flexibility tests
   c. Lack of physical activity contributes to loss of flexibility
   d. Weak and/or tense muscles contribute to low back disorders

10. If your BMI is 25 or greater, then your waist circumference in inches should be
    a. 30 or less for males, 25 or less for females
    b. 50 or less for males, 40 or less for females
    c. 40 or less for females, 30 or less for males
    d. 40 or less for males, 35 or less for females

Evaluating Your Skill-Related Fitness

5

Chapter Topics

- Why Skill-Related Fitness Is Important
- Understanding the Skill-Related Components of Fitness
- Factors Determining Your Skill-Related Fitness
- Evaluating Your Skill-Related Fitness
- Setting Realistic Goals

Chapter Objectives

After completing this chapter, you will:

- Know why you need to achieve an acceptable level of skill-related fitness.
- Be able to define the skill-related components of fitness.
- Know the factors which determine your level of skill-related fitness.
- Be able to evaluate your skill-related fitness using a variety of tests.

Key Words

agility   reaction time
balance   skill-related fitness
coordination   speed
power

Healthy People 2010 Goals

◆ Improve health, fitness and quality of life through daily physical activity.
◆ Increase the proportion of adolescents who engage in moderate physical activity for at least 30 minutes on 5 or more of the previous 7 days.
◆ Increase the proportion of adolescents who participate in daily school physical education.
◆ Increase the proportion of children and adolescents who view television 2 or fewer hours per day.

Suggested Physical Activities

In preparation for taking the skill-related tests described in this chapter, try doing some of the following activities:
◆ 20-yard sprint, walk back, sprint again
◆ Using the lines marking the basketball free throw line (or a distance of 10-22 feet), run from one line to touch the other, turn and run back to the first line and touch it. Repeat three times.
◆ Stand next to a wall. Using a knee bend, jump to touch the highest point on the wall you can reach.

Use the *Personal Fitness for You* Student CD for:

◆ Lab 5-1: Cultural Awareness
◆ Lab 5-2: Your Skill-Related Fitness
◆ Chapter Practice Test
◆ Chapter Study Guide
◆ Chapter Crossword Puzzle
◆ Vocabulary Flash Cards
◆ Chapter Power Point Review
◆ Skill Related Fitness Score Sheet

Skill-related components of physical fitness are those which help a person perform motor tasks (that is, tasks involving motion), such as sports, games, recreational and everyday activities at home, school or work. The skill-related components are:

- agility
- balance
- coordination
- power
- reaction time
- speed

Why Skill-Related Fitness Is Important

Achieving good levels of the skill-related fitness components can help your performance in a variety of sports and other activities. The ability to successfully participate in a variety of activities makes it easier for you to perform at least 30 to 60 minutes of moderate intense physical activity on most days of the week. Learning a skill you enjoy enables you to maintain an active lifestyle.

Each sport requires different combinations of fitness components and levels. Training to improve these components is very specific-you must first identify the skill-related component and then focus on activities which will lead to improvement in that particular component.

There is very little crossover among these components, so you must work to achieve competence for the specific skills of each sport or activity. Unless you are a highly trained athlete, it is not likely that you will achieve a high level in all skill-related fitness components. In addition, reaction time and speed are closely linked to genetic background, so improvements in these areas may be limited.

Knowing the level of your skill-related fitness can help you select a sport or lifetime activity best suited to your skills.

Achieving a good level of skill-related fitness can help you perform in a variety of sports.

In many cases, the results of the tests reflect the type of things you already do. With the right training you can further develop these skills.

Each sport or activity has a set of skills necessary for success-for example, baseball involves throwing, catching and running. Having a good level of skill-related fitness in the specific areas related to a sport (such as, power for jumping and throwing in baseball) can lead to greater success and enjoyment in that sport.

Remember This ☑

You can achieve a high level of physical fitness without being highly successful in skill-related fitness.

Understanding the Skill-Related Components of Physical Fitness

It is important to learn about each skill-related component of fitness.

To learn more about disability and sports, visit the following web site:
teach.virginia.edu/go/apens

Agility is the ability to start, stop and move the body quickly and in different directions. This is an important fitness quality for an athlete to possess. Sports such as soccer, racquetball, basketball and tennis require the ability to change direction while maintaining body control.

Balance is a kind of coordination which allows you to maintain control of your body while stationary or moving. Activities such as skiing, gymnastics, skating, and surfing require a high level of balance.

Coordination is the ability to do a task integrating movements of the body and different parts of the body. There are many sports activities which require a high level of coordination - golf, tennis, basketball, baseball, volleyball and racquetball are good examples.

Power is the ability to combine strength and speed in a movement. High levels of power are needed to perform well in the following activities: volleyball, football, high jumping, throwing an object (softball, discus, shot put) and vertical jumping.

Reaction time is the time required to start a movement after being alerted to the need to move. The ability to react quickly is extremely important in such activities as track, swimming, baseball and karate.

Speed is the ability to move your total body quickly from one point to another. A high level of speed is required for activities such as running the bases in baseball or softball, sprinting in track, or running for a touchdown.

Factors Determining Your Skill-Related Fitness

Heredity

The skill-related fitness components are influenced by heredity. Speed and reaction time, in particular, are often limited by heredity. Maybe you have heard people referred to as "natural athletes"—those who seem to be good without working at it. These individuals have benefited from inherited characteristics which make a high level of skill-related fitness possible. However, there are also many people who, through determination, desire, and "heart," seem to find a way to achieve in spite of limited natural ability.

Practice

Learning a skill takes practice. Those willing to devote more time and effort to learning will not only improve faster but will be more likely to reach their full potential in that activity. Even if your level of skill-related fitness is already high, practice will lead to greater success.

Learning a skill takes practice.

The key to effective practice sessions is to work on specific skills.

Specific Training

The key to effective practice sessions is to work on specific skills and skill-related components. Although several of the components (for example, speed and power) may be interrelated, it is important to identify the specific skill-related components which will contribute to successful performance of the sport or activity and then train to improve these components. In addition to performing the skill itself, your practice should include drills specific to the skill. For example, to improve agility, reaction time and speed to play tennis, practice footwork drills without hitting a ball.

Specific Training

Heredity

Practice

Family Activity

Select a sport your entire family can play together such as bowling, miniature golf or tennis. Rate your family on their skill-related fitness.

Evaluating Agility

Zigzag Run

Objective: To maneuver as quickly as possible through a figure 8 course.

Test Directions:

Stand behind the starting line and on the signal "go" follow the pattern drawn below:

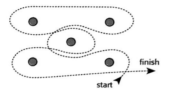

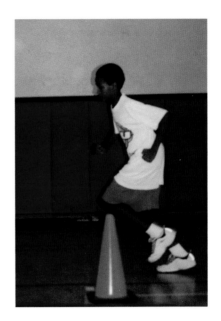

Score: Time is recorded to the nearest tenth of a second.

Acceptable Score: **Girls:** 12.0 seconds
(Ages 14-18)   **Boys:** 8.0 seconds

Evaluating Balance

One Foot Stand

Objective: To maintain balance on one foot for as long as possible without moving the foot.

Test Directions:

1. Remove shoes and socks and stand on a flat, smooth floor.
2. Place one foot on the inside of the opposite knee and the hands on the sides of the hip.
3. On the signal to start, raise your heel off the floor and maintain your balance as long as possible.
4. The test will be stopped if:
   - The supporting foot moves from the starting position.
   - The raised heel is lowered to the floor.
   - The hands do not remain on the hips.
5. The maximum test time is 60 seconds.

Score: Time is recorded to the nearest tenth of a second.
Acceptable score: **Girls:** 10 seconds
(Ages 14-18) **Boys:** 10 seconds

Evaluating Coordination

Alternate Hand Wall Toss

Objective: To toss a tennis ball against a wall and catch it as many times as possible, using first the right hand and then the left hand.

Test Directions:

1. Stand behind a six-foot restraining line facing the wall with a tennis ball in the right hand.
2. At the signal to start, toss the ball to the wall with an underhand motion, catch it with the left hand and then throw it to the wall again.
3. Continue throwing and catching the ball alternating hands.
4. Do not cross the line. Do not catch the ball against the body.
5. Two extra balls should be placed in a container next to your right foot.

Score: The number of successful catches in 30 seconds.
Acceptable Score: **Girls:** 19
(Ages 14-18) **Boys:** 28

Achieving an acceptable level of skill-related fitness will help your sports performance in activities such as tennis.

Special Students and Sports Activities

Participating in sports activities is an important lifelong activity for everyone. There are many organizations dedicated to assisting individuals with physical limitations. See these websites:

www.aw/outdoors.com
www.aquaskier.com
www.nscd.org
www.specialolympics.org

Evaluating Power

Standing Long Jump

Objective: To measure the distance one is able to leap forward on both feet.

Test Directions:
1. Stand behind the starting line with feet parallel and even with the line.
2. Swing the arms downward and backward while bending forward at the waist.
3. Swing the arms forward and upward as you spring forward and upward simultaneously off both feet.
4. Land on both feet with the weight shifted forward.
5. Three trials may be taken.

Score: Measure the distance from the takeoff line to the nearest point (foot, hand or buttocks) in the landing area. Score to the nearest inch.

Acceptable Score: **Girls:** jumping your height
(Ages 14-18)   **Boys:** jumping your height
                                     plus one foot

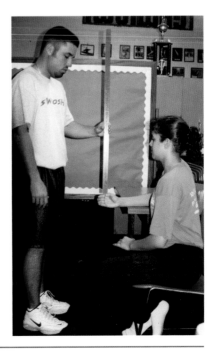

SAFETY TIP Warm-up by walking and slowly jogging. Then stretch all leg and back muscles.

Evaluating Reaction Time

Yardstick Test

Objective: To react as quickly as possible to catch a yardstick when it is dropped by a partner.

Test Directions:
1. Sit in a chair with an arm rest or next to a table.
2. A partner holds a yardstick above your hand so that the bottom edge of the yardstick is even with the upper edge of your thumb and index finger.
3. Concentrate on the yardstick-not the partner.
4. When the partner drops the yardstick, try to catch the stick as quickly as possible.
5. Several trials may be taken.

Score: Record the measurement on the yardstick to the nearest 1/2 inch (measure just above the upper edge of the thumb).

Acceptable Score: **Girls:** 5 inches
(Ages 14-18)   **Boys:** 5 inches

Evaluating Speed

50 yard Dash

Objective: To run as quickly as possible from the starting line to the finish line 50 yards away.

Test Directions:

1. Stand behind the starting line in a ready position.
2. On the signal "go," run to the finish line.

Score: Time is recorded to the nearest tenth of a second.

Acceptable Score: **Girls:** 8.4 seconds
(Ages 14-18) **Boys:** 6.8 seconds

(Source for acceptable scores: Robert Hockey, Physical Fitness: The Pathway to Healthful Living. CV Mosby, 1977)

Setting Realistic Goals

One of the keys to enjoying greater success in lifetime activities such as golf, tennis and racquetball is to achieve an acceptable level of skill-related fitness. The skill related components are also important in helping you cope with emergency situations in daily life. For example, good reaction time, balance, coordination and agility can help you avoid a fall or other accident. When establishing your personal fitness activity plan include goals for improving your skill related fitness components.

My Activity Plan (MAP)

My goal is to do the following activities to improve my Skill Related Fitness:

Skill Related Component	Activity (specific drills or exercises and sports)	Times per Week
Agility	Footwork drills	2
Balance	Balancing on one foot	4
Coordination	Playing tennis	2
Power	Jumping drills	1
Reaction Time	Ball toss close to the wall	1
Speed	Sprints or Softball	1

Refer to the student *Personal Fitness for You* CD for the *My Activity Plan* form.

Summary

In order to successfully participate in sports, recreational activities and everyday activities, it is important to achieve an acceptable level of skill-related fitness. Identifying your areas of strength and weakness will enable you to establish a plan for improvement, and you will have more success and enjoyment in your sports activities. In addition, these skills will help you enjoy being active and reaching the goal of 30 to 60 minutes of moderate to intense activity on a daily basis.

Portfolio Idea

Skill-Related Assessment

After completing the evaluation of your skill related fitness, answer the following questions. Record the answers in your personal portfolio or follow instructions from your teacher.

- In which sports and activities do you perform well?
- What skill-related fitness components are needed to perform well in these sports?
- In which skills identified above did you perform well?
- Which skills identified above still need more work?
- Are there sports you would like to participate in but feel you do not have the needed skills? If so, which ones and which skills do you need to improve?
- How do you think you could go about learning these skills?

Chapter 5 Review

Lesson Checklist

- Can you state why it is important to achieve an acceptable level of skill-related fitness?
- Can you define the skill-related fitness components?
- Do you know the factors which determine your level of skill-related fitness?
- Do you know tests you can use to evaluate your skill-related fitness level?

Chapter Projects

Write a response to each of the following:

1. What are the benefits of achieving acceptable levels of skill-related fitness?
2. Write a paper comparing and contrasting the skill-related and health-related components of fitness.
3. Explain the role of your heredity in achieving a high level of skill-related fitness.

Behavior Change Evaluation

Review the following item to see if you have gained an understanding of fitness and wellness. On a piece of paper briefly state how you will make these changes.

- I will use the skill-related fitness tests described and performed in class to periodically evaluate my skill-related fitness.

Critical Thinking

How did your overall level of skill-related fitness compare to your health-related fitness scores? Were you surprised with the results? Do you believe highly skilled athletes are therefore highly fit persons? Why or why not?

Test Your Knowledge

Read the questions below and select the best possible answer for each.

1. Which is the ability to start, stop and move the body quickly and in different directions?
   a. Coordination
   b. Body control
   c. Agility
   d. Reaction time

2. Which is the ability to do a task integrating movements of the body and different parts of the body?
   a. Coordination
   b. Agility
   c. Reaction time
   d. Power

3. Which is the ability to combine strength and speed in a movement?
   a. Reaction time
   b. Power
   c. Coordination
   d. Agility

4. Which statement is true of skill-related fitness?
   a. The skill related components help you cope with emergency situations in daily life.
   b. Attaining an acceptable level of skill related fitness will help you enjoy greater success in lifetime activities such as golf, tennis and racquetball.
   c. Skill related fitness activities will help you reach your goal of 30 minutes of moderate physical activity on at least 5 out of 7 days.
   d. All of the above are true.

5. The standing long jump measures
   a. Coordination
   b. Power
   c. Reaction time
   d. Speed

6. The zig zag run evaluates
   a. Power
   b. Speed
   c. Agility
   d. Reaction time

7. Speed is evaluated by the
   a. Long jump
   b. 50 yard dash
   c. Zig zag run
   d. Mile run

8. Which is not a skill related component?
   a. Reaction time
   b. Speed
   c. Agility
   d. Flexibility

9. Which two skill related components are often limited by heredity?
   a. Speed and power
   b. Speed and reaction time
   c. Reaction time and balance
   d. Agility and speed

10. Which of the following is the ability to maintain control of your body while stationary or moving?
    a. Speed
    b. Balance
    c. Agility
    d. Coordination

Training for Fitness

6

Chapter Topics

- Principles of Training
- Training Program Guidelines
- Applying the Principles of Training
- The Warm-Up
- The Cool Down
- Other Training Factors
- Common Exercise Training Myths

Chapter Objectives

After completing this chapter, you will:

- Understand the training principles of overload, progression, specificity, regularity and individuality.
- Understand how to apply the principles of training by using frequency, intensity, time and type (FITT).
- Know the importance of warm-up and cool down.
- Understand common exercise training myths

Key Words

cool down
cross-training
frequency
individuality
intensity
overload

overtraining
plateau
·progression
·regularity
specificity
time (duration)

training
training adaptations
type
warm-up

Suggested Physical Activities

Apply the principle of time (see page 108) by selecting an exercise such as walking and doing three workouts: one for 10 minutes, one for 15 minutes and one for 25 minutes. How did you feel after each workout?

Healthy People 2010 Goals

◆ Increase the proportion of adolescents who engage in moderate physical activity for at least 30 minutes on 5 or more of the previous 7 days.
◆ Increase the proportion of adolescents who engage in vigorous physical activity that promotes cardiorespiratory fitness 3 or more days per week for 20 or more minutes per occasion
◆ Increase proportion of people who perform physical activity that enhances and maintains muscular strength, muscular endurance and flexibility.

Use the *Personal Fitness for You* Student CD for:

◆ Lab 6-1: Applying the Principles of Training
◆ Lab 6-2: Interest Clubs
◆ Chapter Practice Test
◆ Chapter Study Guide
◆ Chapter Crossword Puzzle
◆ Vocabulary Flash Cards
◆ Chapter Power Point Review

Understanding and applying the principles of training is essential to developing an exercise program.

Principles of Training

Now that you have evaluated your health fitness level, you are ready to develop a sound exercise program. A sound exercise program is one that is based on the proven principles of training.

As you learned in Chapter 2, you can improve your health by becoming moderately active on a regular basis. However, greater health benefits can be achieved by participating in a more vigorous program. In addition, adolescents should participate in some continuous and regular activity.

The first things you need to determine are your specific goals. Some are ready to focus on a training program that will enable them to reach a higher level of fitness. Others will need to focus on getting moderate to vigorous physical activity that will enable them to reach the Healthy Fitness Zone for the key health related components. Their main goal may be one of weight loss, improved cardiorespiratory health, increased flexibility or better muscle fitness.

An effective **training** program includes an exercise prescription that specifies how the principles of training will be applied to bring about the desired outcomes.

Whether your goal is to improve sports performance, achieve a high level of fitness or improve your overall conditioning; it is important to follow certain basic principles of training. Understanding and applying these principles is essential to developing an exercise program which produces improvement. In addition, following these principles will enable you to engage safely in a progressive training program. The basic principles of training are:

• Overload
• Progression
• Specificity
• Regularity
• Individuality

These principles determine how the body responds to physical activity. The changes which occur during a training program are called **training adaptations**. Each person needs to develop an individualized training program to meet his or her needs and should realize that training adaptations will vary with each individual.

Unfortunately, many people with good intentions become frustrated and fall short of their goal because they do not observe these important principles. You can achieve maximum results from your training by carefully following these principles. After gaining an understanding of these principles, you will learn how to apply them to each of the fitness components in the chapters that follow.

Principle of Overload

Overload occurs when increased demands are made upon the body. This increased stress causes the body to adapt or adjust thus improving physical condition.

Overload occurs when increased demands are made upon the body.

Principle of Progression

Progression refers to the gradual increase in exercise or activity over a period of time. This increase could be in terms of frequency (number of days per week), intensity (reaching a higher heart rate), or time (exercising for a longer duration). As you push your body to work harder, it will adjust to the extra workload and improve. The amount of work must be increased again in order to continue to improve.

For example, if you begin an exercise program that involves running one mile a day in nine minutes, you might find the workout somewhat stressful. If you continue to run at the nine-minute pace, you would improve your cardiorespiratory fitness for the next several weeks. But if you continued to perform at that level (run the same distance in the same time), your cardiorespiratory

SAFETY TIP It is important to gradually increase your exercise or activity.

improvement would eventually stop, because your body has adjusted to the work. To continue improving, you will have to increase the stress on your cardiorespiratory system by either increasing the distance you run or running faster. In a few weeks or months, additional overload would have to be added again. Of course, once you reach your goal, you can perform a maintenance program at a certain level.

Principle of Specificity

The **specificity** principle refers to the fact that improvements in the various fitness areas require specific kinds of activity. Each area of fitness requires specific demands. Training for one area does not necessarily improve another. If particular muscles are used in an exercise, those are the muscles that will adapt according to the way they are used.

The mode or type of activity you do is very important in determining the fitness results you achieve. For example, use activities that are aerobic, such as swimming, jogging and cycling, to improve cardiorespiratory fitness. Use stretching exercises to improve flexibility. Use weight training activities to improve strength.

Select the exercise program which is appropriate for the specific fitness component you are seeking to improve.

Principle of Regularity

This principle is based on the concept that if you don't "use it," you "lose it." It is important to perform physical activity on a regular basis.

Principle of Individuality

The principle of individuality states that a training program must be based on an individual's goals and objectives for physical activity and fitness.

Weight training activities will help you improve your muscular strength and endurance.

Perform physical activity on a regular basis.

In addition, each person starts at a different level and has different potential for change. Each person has a different rate of response to his or her particular training program. Some people seem to get into shape or become conditioned more quickly than others.

Possible reasons for this include the individual's current condition, heredity, age, body type, nutrition, weight, lack of disease, motivation, injury proneness and athletic ability. Don't become discouraged if someone seems to be making faster progress than you.

Applying the Principles of Training

As you design your physical activity plan, you need to use these principles as a guide. The process of designing a routine of physical activity in a systematic and individualized manner is called your exercise prescription.

The five principles of training can be safely and effectively applied to your activities by using the FITT guidelines – frequency, intensity, time and type.

1. Frequency

Frequency refers to increasing how often you exercise. The number of times per day or week that an activity is performed can be increased. Exercise must be performed on a regular basis to be effective. For instance, cardiorespiratory fitness benefits can be achieved with at least three workouts per week. The workouts should be spaced throughout the week rather than on consecutive days. A frequency of four or five times per week produces a great enough calorie expenditure to help control weight. More frequent exercise can also contribute to improvement in other fitness areas such as flexibility.

Family Activity

Explain the principles of training to your family members. Remind them to incorporate these principles into their own fitness program.

To learn more about wellness, health and fitness, visit the following web site:
www.acefitness.org/ fitfacts/fitbits_list.aspx

SAFETY TIP Follow the principles of training when you exercise.

2. Intensity

Intensity refers to increasing the difficulty of an exercise. You can increase the speed of a run, amount of weight lifted or distance a muscle is stretched. Exercise must be strenuous enough to require the body to work harder than it usually does. As the body adjusts to the workload, an increased demand can be placed upon it. The intensity needed to produce improvement varies depending on your current physical condition. In a poorly conditioned person, walking may be strenuous enough to produce a training effect.

3. Time

Time (or duration) refers to increasing the length of each training session. In order to be effective, exercise must be maintained for a specified length of time. A thirty-minute workout allows for sufficient warm-up and cool down with at least twenty minutes for the fitness session. Exercise duration and intensity are directly related. An activity performed at a higher intensity can be done for a shorter duration. To achieve the same benefits, a lower intensity activity, such as walking, must be performed for a longer duration.

4. Type

Type refers to the kind of activity a person chooses for each area of his or her training program. There are a variety of activities that can be used in your exercise plan so choose those that you enjoy and will do on a regular basis. However, be certain you select those that will benefit the specific fitness component. For instance, walking and swimming are excellent for cardiorespiratory fitness, stretching improves flexibility and weight training improves muscular fitness.

An easy way to remember the training guidelines is to think of the first letter of each word—they form the letters "FITT" which reminds us to keep FIT!

For some people, walking is an excellent way to begin a cardiorespiratory exercise program. Start at a level right for you.

Weight training helps improve your muscular fitness.

*F*requency

*I*ntensity

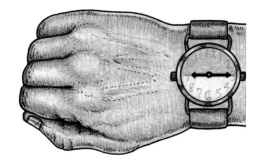

*T*ime

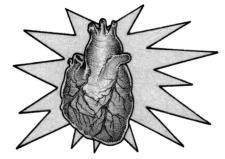

*T*ype

Training Program Guidelines

The following chart describes how the training guidelines can be applied to exercise programs for each of the health-related fitness components.

Cardiorespiratory Fitness

Frequency	3–5 days per week
Intensity	60-85% maximum heart rate (see Chapter 12)
Time (Duration)	20–60 minutes of continuous activity
Type	Large muscle movement (walking, cycling, jogging, swimming, aerobic exercise to music) that can be maintained at the appropriate intensity

Flexibility

Frequency	At least 2-3 times per week, 5-7 is optimal
Intensity	Slow stretch until mild tension is felt
Time (Duration)	Hold each stretch 15–30 seconds. 2-4 repetitions.
Type	Stretching should be slow and steady—no bouncing

Muscular Strength

Frequency	Every other day (2–4 times per week)
Intensity	High resistance (heavier weights)
Time (Duration)	8–12 repetitions
Type	Resistance-type activity (weights and weight machines)

Muscular Endurance

Frequency	Every other day (3 days per week)
Intensity	Low resistance (light weights)
Time (Duration)	12–20 repetitions
Type	Resistance-type activity (weights and weight machines)

Body Composition

Frequency	3–5 days per week, daily is best
Intensity	Continuous activity that is sufficient to cause sweating
Time (Duration)	30 minutes at least
Type	Large muscle movement (walking, cycling, jogging, swimming, aerobic exercise to music) that can be maintained at the appropriate intensity.

The Warm-Up

Properly warming up your body prepares it for exercise and decreases your chance of injury. The **warm-up** increases your heart rate and respiration rate thus supplying more blood and oxygen to the working muscles. This also increases heat in the muscles and joint tissues and helps prevent strains.Walking, light jogging, calisthenics, riding a stationary bicycle and stretching are good ways to warm-up prior to physical activity.

Most people take about five to ten minutes to warm-up, starting with bicycling, slow jogging or other large muscle activities. The body is then ready for stretching, holding each stretch for fifteen to thirty seconds, which increases the flexibility of specific joints.

Slowly copying the motions of the sport you are about to perform is another good way to warm-up. Swinging the golf club, tennis racquet or baseball bat are examples of this type of warm-up. Warming up is beneficial for all activities, not just aerobic exercise. Warming up can also help you get used to new conditions, such as a different court, field or floor.

Make warming up a regular part of your exercise routine. For more information on specific techniques, see Chapters 12, 14 and 15.

Why Warm-Up?

The benefits of warm-up are:

- increases active muscle blood flow
- increase blood flow to the heart
- raises body temperature and may reduce the risk of muscle injury and muscle soreness
- facilitates temperature regulation by causing earlier sweating

Walking and stretching are good ways to warm-up before exercising.

The Cool Down

Following the conditioning phase of your training, you should devote about the same amount of time for the cool down period as you did for the warm-up. The **cool down** enables the body to adjust slowly to reduced activity. Cooling down properly helps prevent muscle cramps and muscle soreness. It also helps prevent pooling of the blood in the legs, which may occur if you stop exercising suddenly. When that happens, it is possible that not enough blood will be returned to the heart and less oxygen will be supplied to the brain. Fainting may occur.

To cool down, slow to a jog or walk after running.

After you finish exercising, you should continue your activity at a slow pace. For example, after running, jog slowly or walk. After walking rapidly, walk slower. After bicycling, cycle slower or walk. After swimming, walk through the water. You should continue this part of the cool down until your heart rate is 100 beats per minute or less.

Stretching exercises should be performed during the second part of the cool down period. This will help prevent muscle soreness and loosen tight muscles. You may be more flexible than you were during the warm-up period.

This is a good time to work on increasing flexibility in specific areas of the body. It is also a good time to work on muscle toning exercises such as crunches for the abdomen. See Chapter 14 for more information.

Stretch out to help your body cool down after exercising.

Plateau

Sometimes when you are on a training program, you may find that you reach a **plateau** in performance. This means that your performance shows no improvement for a period of time. You may even decrease in performance. Then for no apparent reason, you may surge ahead again, breaking all your previous records. The reason for this is unknown. Some speculate that the body may be making an adjustment to meet the demands of the overload.

Overtraining

Overtraining occurs when a person participates in any physical activity at very high intensity levels or for unusually long periods of time or without adequate recovery time. In other words, exercising too much! It can be harmful to a person's physical well-being.

Some people think if some exercise is good, more must be better. They exceed the exercise guidelines described in the principles of training. Some push themselves to improve faster. Since their bodies are not accustomed to the extra demands that training requires, overtraining occurs. Others may become exercise addicts. These people fail to realize the importance of giving the body time to recover between workouts. They worry about losing their fitness if they miss a day of exercise.

For Your Information

Signs of Overtraining

Psychological:
- Lower motivation to work out
- Difficulty sleeping
- Increased irritability—feelings of stress and anxiety

Physical:
- Overuse injuries—muscular or skeletal
- Lower performance
- Slower recovery time
- Chronic fatigue
- Decreased appetite
- Loss of weight
- Increased muscular tension
- Higher resting heart rate

Symptoms of overtraining are:

- fatigue
- difficulty sleeping
- lack of enjoyment of exercise
- anxiety
- overuse injuries
- impaired physical performance
- increased resting heart rate

Be certain you mix lighter workouts with heavier ones and build in periodic rest days.

Cross-training

No single exercise can yield all the benefits needed for fitness. **Cross-training** involves combining two or more types of exercise in one workout or using different exercises alternately in successive workouts. Cross-training helps you develop your entire body. Many exercisers use this approach to maintain variety and prevent boredom. Cross-training also allows you to keep training even when you are injured. If you have an ankle injury, try activities such as rowing, water aerobics and cycling.

Your cross-training program can be planned to include activities for just one fitness component such as cardiorespiratory fitness—jogging, brisk walking, aerobic exercise, cycling. Or you can include exercise for each of the fitness components—cardiorespiratory, muscular and flexibility.

SUNDAY	MONDAY	TUESDAY	WEDNESDAY	THURSDAY	FRIDAY	SATURDAY
	1 Cycling	2	3 WALKING	4	5 ROWING	6
7	8 Hiking	9	10 RUNNING	11	12 WALKING	13
14	15	16	17	18	19	20

Many exercisers use cross-training to maintain variety and prevent boredom.

Losing Your Training

Many people wonder how long it takes to lose fitness if they become inactive. Some lose fitness rapidly, others at a slower rate. Generally, a person with good cardiorespiratory fitness will lose about 10-15% of his or her ability to process oxygen two weeks after stopping exercising. Muscular fitness takes longer to decline. Without continued training, a person could lose up to 35% of his or her muscular strength and endurance in five weeks.

Factors to Consider Before You Start

There are several other factors that you should consider before you begin your exercise or training program. Each may change your starting point and the activities you select. These factors are:
- Previous involvement in physical activities— Have you been active or inactive?
- Present fitness level—How did you do on the Health Fitness Tests?
- Present health—Are you in reasonably good health? How are your blood pressure and resting heart rate? Have you had a recent illness or disease?
- Medical history—What medical problems or illnesses have you had?

Consult a physician if your present health history suggests potential problems or limitations.

SAFETY TIP Before beginning your program, answer these questions (left).

Follow the safety guidelines and principles of training to achieve maximum benefits.

Did You Know?

A well-designed exercise program using the principles of training will provide many benefits. Get active!

Common Exercise Training Myths

No pain, no gain.

Remember, pain is a signal to you that something is wrong. If you feel pain during a workout, you should slow down and possibly stop your workout. Pushing yourself to achieve overload causes you to experience a slight level of discomfort but not pain. Highly trained athletes may be able to train hard and overcome a certain level of pain, but this takes years of training.

I can get fit by participating in a sport.

Actually this statement is backwards. You should get in shape first, so you can safely enjoy participating in a sport. People who participate in sports only on the weekend are especially vulnerable to injury. It is important to exercise everyday.

Pain is a signal that something is wrong.

Get in shape before participating in a sport.

A little exercise doesn't help.

Any activity is better than doing nothing. Moderate exercise for as little as ten minutes can contribute to your health. There may be days you don't have time to complete your usual program, but doing some activity everyday is important. Consistency makes the difference!

Cardiorespiratory exercise is the most important.

A balanced exercise program should include flexibility activities, muscular fitness training and cardiorespiratory activities.

A little exercise is better than none.

Summary

By following the basic principles of training you can develop a program that will lead to improved health and fitness. These principles are overload, progression, specificity, regularity and individuality. It is important to understand these principles as you develop your exercise program.

You can vary the overload placed on the body during exercise by changing the frequency, intensity, time and/or type of the workout based on the fitness component you are working to improve.

Once the body adjusts or adapts to this increased overload, it becomes necessary to increase the workload again. This is the principle of progression.

Improvements that occur as a result of your training should also follow the principle of specificity—they will be based on the particular fitness area that you train. The type of exercises selected also affects the results you achieve.

To avoid injuries and make certain your workout will have the benefits you are seeking, follow the principles of training, warm-up before exercise, cool down after exercise, avoid overtraining and consider a cross-training program.

Chapter 6 Review

Lesson Checklist

- Do you know how to apply the principles of overload, progression and specificity?
- Can you apply the training program guidelines for the health-related fitness components?
- Do you know how to warm-up before a workout and cool down after it?
- Do you understand the concepts of overtraining, cross-training and losing your training?

Chapter Projects

Write a response to each of the following:
1. Why is it important to follow a well-designed training program?
2. Describe the principle of overload.
3. Give one example of using overload in a cycling program.
4. Describe the principle of progression.
5. Describe the principle of specificity.
6. List three factors to consider in developing an individualized exercise program.
7. Describe a warm-up program you can follow before beginning a jogging workout.
8. Describe a cross-training program that includes activities you would be likely to follow.
9. Describe several signs that indicate you might be overtraining.

Behavior Change Evaluation

Review the following items to see if you have gained an understanding of fitness and wellness. On a piece of paper briefly state how you will make these changes.
- I will monitor my fitness program to make certain it follows the training principles.
- I will warm-up before my exercise session and use cool down techniques after the workout.

Critical Thinking

Based on what you have learned about training for fitness, describe an exercise program that would be appropriate for you. Make certain it applies the training principles.

Chapter 6 Review

Test Your Knowledge

Read the questions below and select the best possible answer for each.

1. Increased demands made upon the body that cause the body to adapt or adjust is known as
   a. Overload
   b. Specificity
   c. Regularity
   d. Individuality

2. Which principle is based on the concept that if you don't "use it," you "lose it?"
   a. Overload
   b. Specificity
   c. Regularity
   d. Individuality

3. Which principle states that a training program must be based on a person's goals and objectives for physical activity and fitness?
   a. Regularity
   b. Specificity
   c. Individuality
   d. Progression

4. Which principle refers to the fact that improvements in the various fitness areas require specific kinds of activity?
   a. Progression
   b. Individuality
   c. Overload
   d. Specificity

5. Increasing the pace of your workout is an example of increasing the
   a. Frequency
   b. Time
   c. Duration
   d. Intensity

6. What is the recommended time for cardiorespiratory fitness activities?
   a. 10 minutes
   b. 20 to 60 minutes
   c. 2 hours
   d. 5 to 30 minutes

7. What are the benefits of the warm-up?
   a. Increased active muscle blood flow
   b. Raises body temperature
   c. Increases blood flow to the heart
   d. All of the above

8. Which is NOT true about the cool down?
   a. Helps the body adjust slowly to reduced activity
   b. Prevents pooling of the blood in the extremities
   c. Helps prevent muscle cramps and soreness
   d. Should last at least an hour

9. What is the minimum number of vigorous workouts per week to improve cardiorespiratory fitness?
   a. 2
   b. 3
   c. 5
   d. 7

10. When your performance shows no improvement over a period of time, it is known as a
   a. Plateau
   b. Progression
   c. Resistance
   d. Underload

Nutrition and Your Fitness

7

Chapter Topics

- Nutrition Basics
- What Is Nutrition?
- Why Is Nutrition Important?
- Nutrition and Physical Activity
- What Is a Calorie?
- How Can You Obtain the Nutrients You Need?
- The Basic Nutrients
- Nutrition Terminology

Chapter Objectives

After completing this chapter, you will be able to:

- Understand the relationship of good nutrition to achieving a high level of physical fitness.
- Identify the six basic nutrients and understand why the body needs them.
- Understand some common dietary problem areas: cholesterol, saturated fat, trans fat, fiber intake, sugar intake.
- List foods that are good sources of the essential nutrients.
- Understand when mineral and vitamin supplements may be needed.
- Understand information related to the recommended dietary intake of vitamins and minerals.

Key Words

adequate intake (AI)
antioxidant
amino acid
beta carotene
calorie
carbohydrate
cholesterol
complete protein
complex carbohydrate
dietary reference
 intake (DRI)
glycemic index
enriched
essential amino acids

estimated average
 requirement (EAR)
fat
fat-soluble vitamin
fatty acid
fiber
free radical
glycemic index
HDL
LDL
lipoprotein
minerals
monounsaturated fat
nutrients

nutrition
Omega-3 fatty acid
oxidation
polyunsaturated fat
protein
recommended dietary
 allowance (RDA)
saturated fat
tolerable upper level (UL)
trans fatty acids
vitamins
water-soluble vitamin

Suggested Physical Activities

This week focus on increasing your muscular fitness: use weight resistance devices, use dumbbells (or substitute cans of food), try elastic bands, increase curl-ups and push-ups. (See Chapter 14 for specific exercises.)

Use the *Personal Fitness for You* Student CD for:

◆ Lab 7-1: How Good is Your Diet?
◆ Lab 7-2: Inventory of Eating Habits
◆ Chapter Practice Test
◆ Chapter Study Guide
◆ Chapter Crossword Puzzle
◆ Vocabulary Flash Cards
◆ Chapter Power Point Review
◆ Food Selection Charts
◆ Vitamin and Mineral Charts

Knowledge of the basics of nutrition will help you to make wise food choices.

Now is the time for you to take charge of your health, and it begins with taking control of your eating habits. As a teenager you are going through a lot of changes, and you are learning to become more independent. You are starting to make more choices about all areas of your life. One very important area is that of the foods you eat. As a child, your parents selected your foods and guided you in your meal choices. Now as you begin to eat more meals away from home and fix your own meals at home, you are responsible for your nutrition. Begin by looking at your eating habits – what you eat, where you eat and why you eat are important to your health. As a teen, you need to eat a variety of nutritious foods that your growing body needs. Eating better is a key to helping you feel better, look better and think more clearly.

Eating is clearly one of our favorite activities. Americans spend billions each year at fast food restaurants alone. Most of us are thinking about our next meal as we finish our current one!

And it is no wonder. The advertising media constantly bombard us with information about wonderful, delicious selections. Supermarket flyers display pictures of meals and include tasty recipes to stimulate our interest in buying certain foods. At the same time, we hear more and more about the dangers of eating certain foods and the problems of overeating. Some advertisements urge us to take vitamin and mineral supplements, while others say they are a waste of money.

If you are confused by conflicting nutrition reports, you need the knowledge of the basics of nutrition to guide you in your decision-making and food choices.

What Is Nutrition?

Nutrition is the process by which the body uses food for maintenance of life, growth, normal functioning of every organ and tissue, and the production of energy.

Food is that material of plant or animal origin which nourishes and sustains the human body and enables the body to function and grow. Food is composed of nutrients. **Nutrients** are chemicals or chemical compounds found in food that not only nourish the body but also are necessary to life and good health. Essential nutrients are those necessary for proper functioning of the body. Six groups of essential nutrients are found in food:

Eating a variety of foods is important to good nutrition.

Carbohydrates   Minerals
Protein   Vitamins
Fats   Water

These nutrients will be discussed in detail in this chapter.

Why Is Nutrition Important?

Whether your goal is to achieve a high level of personal fitness in order to compete as an athlete, to achieve a level of personal fitness which will enable you to enjoy each day to its fullest or to simply feel good about the way you look; following good eating habits and observing sound nutritional guidelines are important.

Sound nutrition provides the energy for physical activity.

Did You Know?

Calories Per Gram from Foods

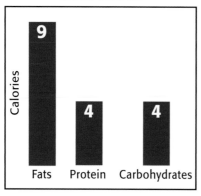

Nutrition and Physical Activity

Exercising and training develop your fitness but, neglecting the rules of good nutrition automatically limits your potential for improvement.

The foods you eat form the foundation of your health and fitness. Food provides:

- the fuel (energy) in the form of calories for your physical activity.
- the stamina and vigor needed to enjoy daily activities.
- the basis for sound, healthy skin, teeth, hair, muscles and bones.

What Is a Calorie?

Each of the foods you eat contains **calories**. The number of calories depends on the specific nutrients and the amount of each in the food. The calorie is the common unit of measurement used to express the potential energy of food. Calories are actually by-products of the chemical changes which your body produces from the food you eat.

When you eat food, the body produces energy from the food. For instance, there are nine calories produced per gram of fat, four calories per gram of carbohydrate and four calories per gram of protein.

How Can You Obtain the Nutrients You Need?

The nutrients you need can be obtained from the foods you eat, if you include a variety of foods and eat a balanced diet. If you make wise eating choices you will not need dietary supplements of vitamins and minerals. It is important to include a variety of foods in your diet, because no single food or class of foods provides all the nutrients you need in the proper amounts you need. The foods you need to secure these nutrients are readily available in all parts of the country year-round.

STRESS Stopper

Each day this week try to get up a few minutes earlier. Avoid having to rush through your daily routine. Take a few minutes to plan and organize your day. Get off to a good start.

Each of the nutrients is described in detail on the following pages. It is especially important to note the suggested food sources for each.

Guidelines for Good Nutrition

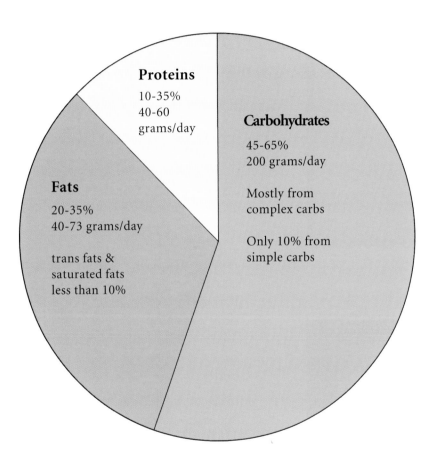

Proteins
10-35%
40-60 grams/day

Carbohydrates
45-65%
200 grams/day

Mostly from complex carbs

Only 10% from simple carbs

Fats
20-35%
40-73 grams/day

trans fats & saturated fats less than 10%

The specific recommended amounts for each person depend on the total number of calories you take in during the day.

Fiber Facts

- Water-soluble fiber helps lower cholesterol levels. It is found in citrus fruits and apples.
- Insoluble fiber protects against colon cancer. It is found in whole grain products, especially bran.
- Recommended intake of fiber is 21-38 grams per day.

Grains are an excellent source of complex carbohydrates.

Carbohydrates

(Starches and Sugars)

Function: Major source of energy; supplies fiber (or roughage)

Suggested Food Sources: Fruits, vegetables, grains, cereal

Recommended Percentage in Diet: 45-65% mostly from complex carbohydrates rather than simple carbohydrates.

Special Notes: Limit your intake of refined carbohydrates such as table sugar, sweets, pastries and soft drinks. Increase your intake of **complex carbohydrates** such as grains, cereals and vegetables.

Sources of complex carbohydrates include:

- Starches – flour, bread, rice, corn, oats, barley, potatoes, legumes, fruits and vegetables
- Fiber – insoluble: whole-wheat breads and cereals, wheat bran, cabbage, beets, carrots, Brussel sprouts, turnips, cauliflower and apple skin
- Fiber – Soluble: oat bran, oats, legumes, citrus fruits, strawberries, apple pulp, rice bran and barley

Sources of simple carbohydrates include:

- Sucrose – table sugar, brown sugar, confectioners sugar, raw sugar
- Glucose – dextrose, corn syrup and glucose syrup
- Fructose – fruits, vegetables and honey
- High fructose corn syrup – liquid sweetener that contains 42-90 percent fructose
- Honey – made up of glucose, fructose and water
- Sugar alcohols – sorbitol, mannitol, xybitol
- Lactose – milk and milk products
- Maltose, dextrose – cereals and some baked goods

Fiber sources include many vegetables and beans.

Understanding the Glycemic Index

The **Glycemic Index (GI)** was developed as a means of comparing foods based on how quickly the foods are digested into glucose and absorbed; and therefore how much they cause the blood glucose to rise. The GI is determined by comparing the rate of a given food's digestion to that of a food known to be rapidly digested. The reference food (usually pure glucose or white bread) is assigned a GI of 100 and the tested food is measured against this standard. Foods with high GI – 70 and above – break down quickly and cause a spike in blood sugar levels. Foods with a low GI – 55 and below – break down more slowly and steadily. They provide a sustained supply of energy. One limitation to using the GI is that it only considers single foods eaten by themselves. When foods such as potatoes are eaten as part of a meal, they will have much less effect on blood sugar. Therefore, according to the University of California Berkeley Wellness Letter, "The glycemic index has little practical use...."

Carbohydrates supply the fiber (roughage or bulk) needed by the body. **Fiber** is the structural part of plants which is neither digested nor absorbed by the body. The most important role of fiber is to serve as an intestinal "house cleaner." It provides added bulk which makes the intestines contract and speed food through the digestive system. A high-fiber diet has been linked to a lower risk of colon cancer and lower blood cholesterol.

Eating honey, sugar, soft drinks, candy bars or any sweets does not provide quick energy. This sugar rapidly gets into the bloodstream which may provide a short feeling of quick energy; however, the blood sugar level (glucose level) quickly falls lower than normal, which may cause weakness, light-headedness and even dizziness. To avoid this roller-coaster energy effect, maintain a consistent energy level by eating a diet high in **complex carbohydrates.**

The best sources of fiber are fruits, vegetables, grains and cereals. Fiber is not found in animal foods.

*F*or
*Y*our
*I*nformation

When selecting grain products the best choices are those that say "whole wheat or whole wheat flour." Whole grains are low in fat and have a higher fiber content. Don't be fooled by the words "wheat bread" or "wheat flour" - look for the word "whole."

Dairy products are good sources of protein.

Carbohydrates and Exercise

A high carbohydrate diet before, during and after exercise is important for maintaining and replacing the muscular glycogen used during exercise. Carbohydrates are stored in the body as glycogen and they are the primary energy source for muscle building exercise. The harder and longer you workout, the more glycogen your muscles need. Source: The Physician and Sportsmedicine, 1998.

Proteins

Function: Important for growth, maintenance, repair of tissue

Suggested Food Sources: Chicken, fish, meat, low-fat dairy products (milk, cheese), eggs, dried peas, beans

Recommended Percentage in Diet: 10-35%

Facts you should know about **proteins**:

- Proteins are made up of substances called **amino acids**.
- The body can manufacture some amino acids, but not all. Those which must be supplied by the foods we eat each day are known as **essential amino acids**.
- If a protein food has all the essential amino acids needed by the body it is called a **complete protein**.
- Generally, animal sources of protein are complete while plant sources are incomplete.
- A combination of plant sources can be included in the diet to form complete proteins. For example, you can combine beans and rice or dairy products with a vegetable protein to form a complete protein.

Where's the Protein?

You don't have to eat beef or poultry to get your daily supply of protein (approximately 40-60 grams). Use the list below to identify other foods to help you meet your protein requirement.

- 1/2 cup 1% fat cottage cheese = 12 grams of protein
- 8 oz. low-fat yogurt = 9-12 grams of protein
- 3 Tbsp. wheat germ = 9 grams of protein
- 1/2 cup cooked legumes, including black beans, kidney beans, lentils and split peas = 7-9 grams of protein
- 1 cup skim milk = 8 grams of protein
- 2 Tbsp. peanut butter = 8 grams of protein
- 1 oz. cheddar cheese = 7 grams of protein
- 1 oz. peanuts = 7 grams of protein
- 1 large egg = 6 grams of protein
- 1 cup cooked enriched white or brown rice = 6 grams of protein

Fats

Function: Source of stored energy; provide and carry the fat-soluble vitamins (A, D, E, K)

Food Sources:
- **Monounsaturated fat:** olive oil, canola oil, peanut oil
- **Polyunsaturated fat:** safflower oil, corn oil, liquid margarines
- **Saturated fat:** meat, butter, milk, solid shortenings
- **Trans Fat:** cookies, crackers, french fries, donuts, stick margarine

Recommended Percentage in Diet: 20-35% (Trans fats and saturated fats combined should be less than 10% of the total)

Special Note: Most people eat too much fat.

Limit your calories from saturated fat from foods such as meat to less than ten percent of your diet.

Fatty acids are the basic building blocks of fats.

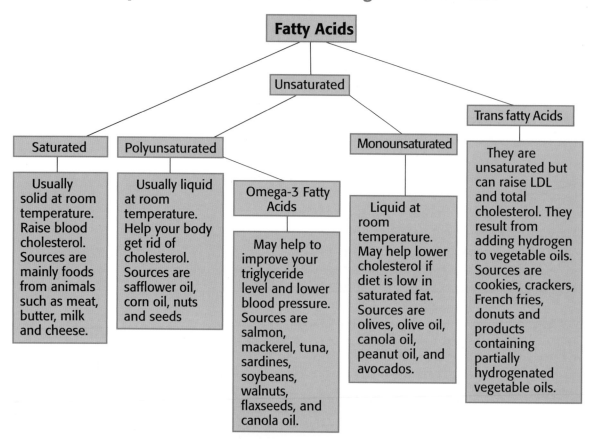

Fatty Acids

Unsaturated

Trans fatty Acids

Saturated

Polyunsaturated

Monounsaturated

Saturated: Usually solid at room temperature. Raise blood cholesterol. Sources are mainly foods from animals such as meat, butter, milk and cheese.

Polyunsaturated: Usually liquid at room temperature. Help your body get rid of cholesterol. Sources are safflower oil, corn oil, nuts and seeds

Omega-3 Fatty Acids: May help to improve your triglyceride level and lower blood pressure. Sources are salmon, mackerel, tuna, sardines, soybeans, walnuts, flaxseeds, and canola oil.

Monounsaturated: Liquid at room temperature. May help lower cholesterol if diet is low in saturated fat. Sources are olives, olive oil, canola oil, peanut oil, and avocados.

Trans fatty Acids: They are unsaturated but can raise LDL and total cholesterol. They result from adding hydrogen to vegetable oils. Sources are cookies, crackers, French fries, donuts and products containing partially hydrogenated vegetable oils.

Butter or Margarine?

The American Heart Association recommends using a margarine labeled "trans fat free". Look for a margarine that contains no more than 2 grams of saturated fat per tablespoon and that lists liquid vegetable oil as it first ingredient. Butter is considered high in saturated fats even though it does not have trans fat. Look at the fat in one tablespoon of each of the following:

	Calories	Trans Fat (g)	Saturated Fat (g)	Total Fat (g)
Butter	100	0	8	8
Stick Margarine	100	2	2.5	4.5
Tub Margarine	100	1.7	2	3.7

The best choice is tub margarine. The American Heart Association recommends using soft margarine from a tub or a squeeze bottle. There are also new products on the market that contain added plant stanols or sterols which help block the absorption of cholesterol.

Estimating Your Daily Target Fat Intake

Daily Calorie Level	Fat Calories Per Day	Total Fat (Maximum grams allowed)	Saturated Fats (Maximum grams allowed)
1,200	360	40	9
1,800	540	60	14
2,400	720	80	18
3,000	900	100	23

Cholesterol

Cholesterol is a waxy, fat-like material manufactured in the body and used by the body in many chemical processes. Cholesterol is also found in many foods of animal origin.

When the level of cholesterol in the blood is more than needed by the body, the excess is deposited on the lining of the arteries. These deposits may narrow the arteries in the heart and cause reduction of blood flow to the heart muscle. This can lead to cardiovascular problems, including a heart attack.

There are two types of cholesterol:

High Density Lipoprotein (HDL), which is considered the good cholesterol because it picks up the extra cholesterol and eliminates it from the body rather than allowing it to collect in the artery walls.

Low Density Lipoprotein (LDL), which is considered the bad cholesterol because it contributes to the clogging of the arteries by depositing the extra cholesterol on the lining of the arteries.

A **Lipoprotein** is a protein wrapped molecule which transports cholesterol and fats through the bloodstream.

For Your Information

Avoiding trans fats in your diet is important to your health. Many food companies are replacing trans fat with an equal amount of saturated fat (mostly from palm oil) which is also unhealthy. The total amount of saturated fat and trans fat in a food should not add up to more than 3 grams and preferably should be 1 gram or less. A word of caution when eating a food that says it has "0 grams of trans fat" - that can actually mean it contains less than 0.5 grams of trans fat per serving. Therefore, if you eat more than one serving you are getting more than 1 gram of trans fat. Try to keep trans fat consumption to zero or close to zero by checking the label for the words "partially hydrogenated" or "vegetable shortening" which mean they contain small amounts of trans fat.

HDL
45 mg/dl
and above

LDL
Below
100 mg/dl

Recommended Cholesterol Levels
For Individuals Between 2 and 19 Years Old

Total Cholesterol
Normal . . . . Below 170
Moderately High . . 170-199
High . . . . Above 200

LDL Cholesterol
Normal . . . . Below 110
Moderately High . . 110-129
High . . . . Above 130

Source: American Heart Association, 2003

Another very important measure of risk for heart disease is related to the ratio of HDL to total cholesterol in the blood. You can determine this ratio by dividing the HDL cholesterol level into the total cholesterol level. This number should be under 4.0 for males and under 3.8 for females. For example, if your total cholesterol is 178 and your HDL level is 52, your ratio is 178 divided by 52 = 3.4.

Lowering Your Cholesterol

- Reduce saturated fat—it raises the level of harmful LDL cholesterol in your blood.
- Avoid meats high in fat (hamburger, sausage, bacon).
- Avoid products that contain large amounts of hydrogenated vegetable oils, cocoa butter, coconut and palm oils, beef, fat, lard.
- Remove the skin from poultry; trim fat around meat; eat lean beef, pork, or veal.
- Drink fat-free or reduced fat milk and avoid cream substitutes which are made with high fat oils.
- Eat low-fat cheese (for example, part skim mozzarella).
- Snack on pretzels, air-popped popcorn and fruit instead of candy, nuts and chips.
- Cut back on foods high in cholesterol—eggs, meat, butter, whole milk.
- Eat unsaturated fats:

Polyunsaturated fats lower your total blood cholesterol level (corn oil, sunflower seed oil, safflower oil).

Monounsaturated fats lower LDL levels but leave beneficial HDL alone (olive oil, canola oil).

Your blood cholesterol level can be checked by having a blood test. This test also indicates levels of HDL and LDL cholesterol.

Some individuals may be lucky enough to maintain a low blood cholesterol level regardless of their diet, but most people are advised to limit the intake of foods containing cholesterol—eggs, red meat, liver—and foods high in saturated fats and trans fat.

Minerals

Function: Important in activating numerous reactions within the body—two general body functions are building and regulating. For example, potassium regulates the balance of fluids; iron assists in red blood cell formation; calcium maintains strong bones and teeth; iodine helps the thyroid gland function; sodium helps maintain a proper fluid balance in our blood and tissues.

Suggested Food Sources: Vary with the specific mineral. A variety of foods in the diet is necessary to supply the different minerals at the recommended levels.

Recommended Percentage in Diet: Adequate intake is indicated by the **Recommended Dietary Allowance (RDA)**. The RDA varies with the specific mineral. Quantities are extremely small—some are the size of a pea and others the size of a grain of sand.

Special Notes: The balance between minerals is important. If you take too much of one mineral you may offset the functioning of another.

Facts you should know about **minerals**:
- Minerals are found in food and water.
- Some minerals are needed in larger quantities (100 milligrams or more per day) and are called microminerals. These include sodium, potassium, chloride, calcium, phosphorus and magnesium.

Fruits and vegetables contain many essential minerals.

- There are fourteen other minerals called trace minerals. These are needed in amounts—as small as a few micrograms.
- Salt is an essential mineral composed of sodium and chloride. Salt is needed to maintain a proper fluid balance in our blood and tissues. An excessive intake of salt, however, forces the kidneys to work overtime and contributes to bloating. In addition, the relationship of salt to the development of high blood pressure is well-documented. A safe and adequate range of sodium intake a day is about 3/4 to 1-1/2 teaspoons of salt.

Don't Overdo It....

Taking too many mineral supplements can lead to a mineral imbalance or toxicity. Too much of one mineral may keep your body from absorbing another mineral. The best way to get the minerals you need is from the foods you eat. Listed below are good food sources for several important minerals.

These foods are excellent sources of calcium.

Calcium Rich Foods   Goal = 1300 mg./day

Calcium is the key to the metabolism of nearly every cell in the body. It is important in the development and maintenance of strong bones and teeth. You need to make sure that your bones retain as much calcium as possible throughout life by maintaining your level of calcium intake.

- Plain yogurt (nonfat - 8 oz.)   400 mg.
- Collards (1 cup frozen)   357 mg.
- Calcium-fortified fruit juice (8 oz.) 350 mg.
- Fat-free milk (1 cup)   302 mg.
- Swiss cheese (1 oz.)   272 mg.

Potassium Rich Foods   Goal = 1300 mg./day

Potassium is needed (with sodium) to regulate the balance and volume of body fluids. It also affects the ability of the muscles to contract.

• Baked potato with skin (1)	844 mg.
• Florida avocado (1/2)	742 mg.
• Dried figs (5)	666 mg.
• Raisins (1/4 cup)	563 mg.
• Cantaloupe (1 cup)	494 mg.
• Orange Juice (1 cup)	474 mg.
• Banana (1)	451 mg.
• Spinach (1/2 cup cooked)	419 mg.

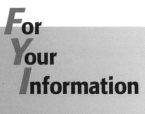

Zinc Rich Foods   Goal = 15 mg./day

Zinc strengthens hair and nails, contributes to healthy skin, and fights colds and flu.

• Oysters (6-8)	7 mg.
• Beef (4 oz.)	4 mg.
• Corn (1/3-2/3 cup)	2.5 mg.
• Cheese (3-4 oz.)	2.4 mg.
• Eggs (2)	1.5 mg.

Vitamins

Function: Aid in absorbing and using the nutrients. Each vitamin helps one or more specific functions in the body. For example: vitamin B1 Thiamin—nervous system; vitamin C—cells and tissues; vitamin K—blood clotting.

Suggested Food Sources: Vary with the specific vitamin. A variety of foods in the diet is necessary to supply the different vitamins at the recommended levels.

Recommended Percentage in Diet: Adequate intake is indicated by the Recommended Dietary Allowance (RDA). The RDA can serve as a guideline for how much you should consume of each vitamin.

Fruits contain many water soluble vitamins.

Broccoli is high in vitamin C.

Facts you should know about **vitamins**:
- Vitamins are organic substances (from a living thing) which are essential for the body to perform its complex chemical reactions.
- Vitamins cannot be produced by the body, but they are important in aiding the body to utilize and absorb nutrients.

Vitamins can be divided into two groups:

Fat-soluble—Vitamins A, D, E, K

These vitamins are found in foods associated with fats and tend to be stored in body fat deposits.

Water-soluble—Vitamins B and C

These vitamins dissolve in water and are not stored in the body. You must make certain you include them in your diet every day. These vitamins may also be affected by cooking methods and can be lost by discarding the water in which food was cooked or soaked. To preserve vitamins, the best methods for cooking vegetables are steaming and microwaving.

- If you eat a 1200-1500 calorie diet with a variety of wholesome foods, you probably get an adequate supply of vitamins. Extra vitamins will not enhance athletic performance, increase strength or endurance, increase energy or build muscles. If you develop a vitamin deficiency, you should consult a doctor for advice on correcting the problem.

The following groups of people should consider taking a vitamin supplement:
- Dieters who take in less than 1,200 calories per day.
- People who are lactose intolerant—unable to digest milk sugar found in dairy foods.
- People with food allergies who cannot eat certain foods.
- Vegetarians who do not eat animal foods.
- Heavy smokers who smoke 1 1/2 packs a day or more.
- Heavy drinkers.

Remember: Taking vitamin supplements cannot compensate for a diet that is deficient in nutrients. Vitamins do not supply energy. Some vitamins help the body use energy, but these are easily supplied by your normal diet.

Did You Know?

Beta carotene is a plant product which is converted to vitamin A in the body.

Vitamin and Mineral Super Foods

The following list of foods are considered vitamin and mineral super foods because they give you only the best! See if you can find ways to add these foods to your daily eating pattern.

- **Garlic:** one clove may contain more than 15 antioxidants
- **Onions:** contain phosphorous and potassium; may help control high cholesterol
- **Spinach:** contains vitamin C, vitamin E, folic acid, protein, calcium and beta carotene
- **Strawberries:** high in vitamin C, potassium and dietary fiber
- **Carrots:** full of beta carotene and fiber
- **Fat-free milk:** loaded with calcium, protein and riboflavin
- **Beans:** contain protein, folic acid and fiber
- **Broccoli:** high in fiber, calcium, folic acid and vitamin C
- **Sweet potatoes:** rich in vitamin C, vitamin E, beta carotene, fiber, potassium and iron
- **Citrus fruits:** loaded with vitamin C
- **Soy:** contains iron, calcium, magnesium and fiber
- **Tomatoes:** contain fiber and vitamin C
- **Cantaloupe:** one cup provides 125% of the Daily Value for vitamin C and more than 50% for vitamin A
- **Oatmeal:** full of fiber, iron, copper, folic acid, vitamin E and zinc
- **Brown rice:** one cup contains more than 20% of the Daily Value for magnesium and selenium, plus fiber

Carrots are excellent sources of beta carotene and fiber.

Vitamin C As An Antioxidant

Free radicals cause irreversible damage or oxidation to the cells. vitamins C and E have been found to reduce free radical production and oxidation.

Family Activity

Discuss the importance of good nutrition with your family. Try to eat more meals together as a family.

Nutrition As We Age: Free Radicals and Antioxidants

Free Radicals and Antioxidants

What is a free radical? A **free radical** is a chemical that causes damage to the cells. It's a molecule or atom that has an extra free-floating electron (one without a matched pair—therefore it is free). Free radicals can cause cell damage (**oxidation**) that may be partly responsible for the effects of aging and certain diseases. Cigarette smoke, exhaust fumes, radiation, excessive sunlight, certain drugs and stress can all increase the number of free radicals.

Antioxidants help prevent and possibly repair damage done to the body by the free radicals. Antioxidants are your body's natural defense mechanism against free radicals. However, as we get older and are subjected to more and more free radicals, our natural defenses may be overwhelmed. Antioxidants prevent the free radicals from causing the LDL cholesterol to damage the lining of the arteries and from allowing the buildup of plaque in the walls of the arteries.

Foods rich in antioxidants have been found to include those that are orange or green in color, such as:

Mangoes	Green leafy vegetables
Cantaloupes	Spinach
Tangerines	Broccoli
Carrots	Green Peppers
Squash	Sweet Potatoes

Taking Vitamin Supplements for Antioxidants

There is evidence to indicate that the real protection against free radicals comes from the combination of the foods and its antioxidants rather than just the specific antioxidants themselves. In other words, eating foods high in vitamin C, vitamin E and beta carotene has greater benefits than simply taking vitamin supplements.

Source: The Physician and Sportsmedicine. August 1996

Water

Function: Provides a medium within the cells in which the chemical reaction of the cells takes place; water also helps regulate body temperature, digest food, excretion, glandular secretion and the formation of blood plasma.

Suggested Food Sources: Beverages and liquids in foods.

Recommended Percentage in Diet: Two to three quarts daily

Special Notes: It is important to drink more than just to satisfy thirst. Those involved in strenuous exercise programs must drink enough water to replace what is lost through perspiration. Drink water before, during and after exercise.

Facts you should know about **water:**

- Water is considered an essential nutrient even though it provides no energy.
- Water plays an essential role in the regulation of body temperature. When the body sweats, the water evaporates from the skin's surface, thus cooling the body. It is important for exercisers to replace the body water lost through perspiration. Failure to do so can lead to heat exhaustion or heatstroke which can cause death.

Drink 2 to 3 quarts of water a day.

Remember This ☑

Your food choices affect your energy level and even your appearance.

To learn more about nutrition, visit the following web sites:

www.nutrition.gov
www.eatright.org
www.navigator.tufts.edu
kidshealth.org/teen/food

Remember This ☑

Eating a poor diet will prevent you from achieving your optimal level of fitness and wellness. Good health starts with good nutritional habits!

Recent research has helped scientists and nutritionists gain a greater understanding of the relationship between nutrition and chronic diseases. Guidelines referred to as **Dietary Reference Intake (DRI)** place an emphasis on optimizing health by recommending intakes that will help people to not only avoid disease but also achieve good health. These recommendations also set maximum limits to reduce the risk of adverse health effects from consuming too much of a nutrient.

The DRI is actually four separate recommendations, each of which addresses a different nutritional issue. These include:

Use the Dietary Reference Intake to select healthy foods.

What you eat can contribute to higher or lower levels of tension, anxiety and stress. This week try eating a healthy breakfast (no extra sugar), drinking less coffee or caffeine drinks, and drinking more water, herbal teas and decaffeinated drinks.

- **Recommended Dietary Allowance (RDA)**— The RDA is a recommendation for the amount of a nutrient that is necessary to meet the nutritional needs of almost every healthy person in a specific age and gender group (for example, 14-18 year old girls). It is designed to not only prevent a nutrient deficiency but also reduce the risk for disease.
- **Adequate Intake (AI)**—This is actually an interim RDA which is used when scientific data isn't strong enough to recommend an RDA, but there is enough evidence to give a general guideline. This number is used to help set dietary goals. There is an AI for calcium, Vitamin D and fluoride.
- **Estimated Average Requirement (EAR)**—This is the amount of a nutrient needed by specific groups of people (such as pregnant women under 18) and is not used for individual diet planning.
- **Tolerable Upper Level Intake (UL)**—This refers to the maximum amount of a nutrient including intake from food, fortified foods and nutritional supplements that a person can take without risking "adverse health effects." Exceeding these amounts could result in toxic reactions. In other words, these are the safe upper limits for nutrients.

Summary

The first step to eating right is gaining an understanding of nutrition—especially the six food nutrients. It is important to know the relationship of these nutrients to your daily health and energy levels and to know which food sources contain each nutrient.

Being aware of common dietary problems associated with cholesterol, saturated fats, trans fats, sugar intake and low fiber intake can help you make better food choices.

Once you have gained an understanding of nutrition basics, you will be able to develop a nutrition plan that will contribute to your lifelong fitness and wellness. The next chapter will guide you through this planning process.

Healthy People 2010 Goals

◆ Promote health and reduce chronic disease associated with diet and weight.

◆ Reduce the proportion of children and adolescents who are overweight or obese.

◆ Increase the proportion of persons aged 2 years and older who consume at least two daily servings of fruit.

◆ Increase the proportion of persons aged 2 years and older who consume at least three daily servings of vegetables with at least one-third being dark green or deep yellow vegetables.

◆ Increase the proportion of persons aged 2 years and older who consume at least six daily servings of grain products with at least three being whole grains.

◆ Increase the proportion of persons aged 2 years and older who consume less than 10 percent of calories from saturated fat.

◆ Increase the proportion of persons aged 2 years and older who consume no more than 30 percent of calories from fat.

◆ Increase the proportion of persons aged 2 years and older who consume 2,400 mg or less of sodium daily.

◆ Increase the proportion of persons aged 2 years and older who meet dietary recommendations for calcium.

◆ Reduce iron deficiency among young children and females of childbearing age.

◆ Increase the proportion of children and adolescents aged 6 to 19 years whose intake of meals and snacks at schools contributes proportionally to good overall dietary quality.

◆ Reduce coronary heart disease deaths.

Chapter 7 Review

Lesson Checklist

- Do you know the importance of good nutrition in achieving an optimal fitness level?
- Do you have a good understanding of the six basic nutrients—their function, suggested food sources and recommended dietary percentage?
- Can you make an informed decision regarding the use of vitamin and mineral supplements?

Chapter Projects

Write a response to each of the following:

1. Why is nutrition important in achieving total fitness?
2. List one suggested food source for the following nutrients: carbohydrates, protein, fats.
3. Why are vitamins considered an essential nutrient?
4. What function do minerals have in our body?
5. Describe the importance of drinking 2-3 quarts of water a day.
6. Why should most people limit the amount of cholesterol in their diet?
7. How does fiber contribute to health?

Behavior Change Evaluation

Review the following items to see if you have gained an understanding of fitness and wellness. On a piece of paper briefly state how you will make these changes.

- I will increase my intake of the complex carbohydrates by eating more grains and pastas.
- I will try to cut back on my intake of saturated fat by substituting items with monounsaturated or polyunsaturated fat.
- I will not be mislead by false claims in regard to vitamin and mineral supplements.
- I will drink more water each day.

Critical Thinking

Based on what you have learned about the foods which have the best supply of nutrients, make a list of fifteen foods that you like that will provide you with a high nutrient intake. Make certain they are foods you will eat on a regular basis.

Chapter 7 Review

Test Your Knowledge

Read the questions below and select the best possible answer for each.

1. Chemical compounds that are found in food which nourish the body and are necessary to life and good health are called
   a. calories
   b. nutrients
   c. metabolism
   d. dietary factors

2. Sources of sucrose include
   a. fruits, vegetables, and honey
   b. milk and milk products
   c. Dextrose, corn syrup and glucose syrup
   d. Table sugar, brown sugar, raw sugar

3. Maintaining and replacing muscle glycogen used during exercise is best achieved by eating
   a. a high carbohydrate diet before, during, and after exercise
   b. A high protein diet before, during, and after exercise
   c. a high fat diet before, during, and after exercise
   d. vitamins

4. Which is a good source of complex carbohydrates?
   a. whole wheat pasta
   b. candy bar
   c. energy drink
   d. glazed donut

5. Which is an example of a monounsaturated fat?
   a. olive oil
   b. peanut oil
   c. canola oil
   d. all of the above

6. Unsaturated fats that result from adding hydrogen to vegetable oils are called
   a. Monounsaturated fatty acids
   b. Polyunsaturated fatty acids
   c. Omega 3 fatty acids
   d. Trans fatty acids

7. Cold water fish such as salmon, mackerel, tuna, and sardines are good sources of
   a. Monounsaturated fat
   b. Saturated fat
   c. Omega 3 fat
   d. Trans fat

8. The type of cholesterol which contributes to the clogging of the arteries is called
   a. High density lipoproteins (HDL)
   b. Low density lipoproteins (LDL)
   c. Triglycerides
   d. Very low density lipoproteins (VLDL)

9. The recommended total cholesterol level for teenagers is
   a. above 200
   b. below 200
   c. below 170
   d. above 170

10. Proteins contain ___ calories per gram
    a. 4
    b. 7
    c. 9
    d. 10

Planning a Diet for Fitness and Wellness

8

Chapter Topics

- Forming a Nutrition Plan
- Dietary Guidelines for Americans, 2005
- The MyPyramid Food Guide
- Ethnic Foods and MyPyramid
- The Nutrition Facts Label
- Comparing Your Diet
- Facts and Fallacies about Food and Fitness

Chapter Objectives

After completing this chapter, you will be able to:

- Describe how you can achieve a balanced, healthy diet.
- Understand the recommendations of the Dietary Guidelines for Americans, 2005.
- Describe the MyPyramid Food Guide including the food groups which are in each area of the pyramid.
- Comprehend the nutrition information on the Nutrition Facts Label and apply it to make better food choices.
- Describe facts and fallacies related to nutrition and physical activity.

Key Words

daily values
dietary guidelines
fallacy

MyPyramid
myth
nutrition facts label

percent daily value

Suggested Physical Activities

At the beginning of the week write in blocks of time on your calendar for exercise. On really busy days, try doing two things at once. For example, do activities such as curl-ups, push-ups, running in place, jumping rope, stretching, elastic band resistance exercises, etc. while watching television.

Use the *Personal Fitness for You* Student CD for:

◆ Lab 8-1: MyPyramid Food Guide
◆ Lab 8-2: Nutrition Log
◆ Lab 8-3: Understanding Food Labels
◆ Lab 8-4: Food Labeling
◆ Lab 8-5: Nutrition and Diet Analysis
◆ Lab 8-6: Diet Comparison
◆ Lab 8-7: Menu Planning
◆ Lab 8-8: Improving Your Diet
◆ Chapter Practice Test
◆ Chapter Study Guide
◆ Chapter Crossword Puzzle
◆ Vocabulary Flash Cards
◆ Chapter Power Point Review
◆ Dietary Guidelines for Americans, 2005
◆ MyPyramid Charts
◆ Nutrition Facts Label Guides
◆ Fast Food Nutrition Charts

Forming a Nutrition Plan

Obviously we are creatures of what we eat, but we are also creatures of what we fail to eat. To maintain optimal health and achieve our optimal fitness level, we must supply our body with the right foods in sufficient amounts. Whether at school, at work, in sports or in leisure activities, we can perform only as well as our physical well being allows. Now that you have a basic understanding of nutrition, you are ready to develop a nutrition plan that works for you. The key to planning a diet for fitness and wellness is to follow the sound nutritional information provided by the following keys.

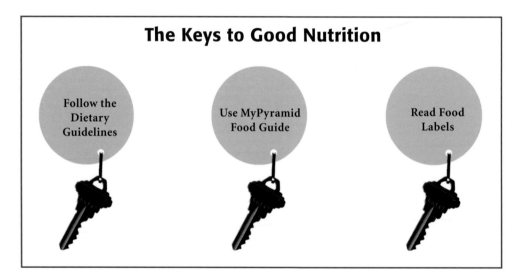

The Keys to Good Nutrition

Follow the Dietary Guidelines

Use MyPyramid Food Guide

Read Food Labels

Dietary Guidelines for Americans, 2005

Refer to the student CD for a description of the Dietary Guidelines in Spanish.

The **Dietary Guidelines** are based on what experts have determined to be the best scientific knowledge about what we should eat and how much physical activity we need. These guidelines are designed to help Americans choose diets that will meet nutrient requirements, promote health, support active lives, and reduce risks of chronic disease. The chart on page 147 summarizes the key recommendations of the Dietary Guidelines. Refer to the *Personal Fitness for You Student CD* for a description of all the recommendations.

Key Recommendations of the Dietary Guidelines for Americans, 2005

Adequate Nutrients Within Calorie Needs
- Consume a variety of nutrient dense foods and beverages within and among the basic food groups while choosing foods that limit the intake of saturated and trans fats, cholesterol, added sugars, salt and alcohol.
- Meet recommended intakes within energy needs by adopting a balanced eating pattern.

Weight Management
- To maintain body weight in a healthy range, balance calories from foods and beverages with calories expended.
- To prevent gradual weight gain over time, make small decreases in food and beverage calories and increase physical activity.

Physical Activity
- Engage in regular physical activity and reduce sedentary activities to promote health, psychological well-being, and a healthy body weight.
- Achieve physical fitness by including cardiovascular conditioning, stretching exercises for flexibility, and resistance exercises or calisthenics for muscle strength and endurance.

Food Groups to Encourage
- Consume a sufficient amount of fruits and vegetables while staying within energy needs.
- Choose a variety of fruits and vegetables every day. In particular, select from all five vegetable subgroups (dark green, orange, legumes, starchy vegetables, and other vegetables) several times a week.
- Consume 3 or more ounce-equivalents of whole-grain products per day, with the rest of the recommended grains coming from enriched or whole-grain products. In general, at least half the grains should come from whole grains.
- Consume 3 cups per day of fat-free or low-fat milk or equivalent milk products.

Fats
- Consume less than 10 percent of calories from saturated fatty acids and less than 300 mg/day of cholesterol and keep trans fatty acid consumption as low as possible.
- Keep total fat intake between 20 to 35 percent of calories, with most fats coming from sources of polyunsaturated and monounsaturated fatty acids, such as fish, nuts, and vegetable oils.
- When selecting and preparing meat, poultry, dry beans, and milk or milk products, make choices that are lean, low-fat, or fat free.
- Limit intake of fats and oils high in saturated and/or trans fatty acids, and choose products low in such fats and oils.

Carbohydrates
- Choose fiber-rich fruits, vegetables, and whole grains often.
- Choose and prepare foods and beverages with little added sugars or caloric sweeteners.

Sodium and Potassium
- Consume less than 2,300 mg (approximately 1 teaspoon of salt) of sodium per day.
- Choose and prepare foods with little salt. Consume potassium-rich foods, such as fruits and vegetables.

Alcoholic Beverages
- Those who choose to drink alcoholic beverages should do so sensibly and in moderation—defined as the consumption of up to one drink per day for women and up to two drinks per day for men.

Food Safety
- Avoid microbial foodborne illness by following the suggestions for handling food.

MyPyramid Food Guide

MyPyramid
STEPS TO A HEALTHIER YOU
MyPyramid.gov

GRAINS	VEGETABLES	FRUITS	MILK	MEAT & BEANS

GRAINS Make half your grains whole	VEGETABLES Vary your veggies	FRUITS Focus on fruits	MILK Get your calcium-rich foods	MEAT & BEANS Go lean with protein
Eat at least 3 oz. of whole-grain cereals, breads, crackers, rice, or pasta every day 1 oz. is about 1 slice of bread, about 1 cup of breakfast cereal, or 1/2 cup of cooked rice, cereal, or pasta	Eat more dark-green veggies like broccoli, spinach, and other dark leafy greens Eat more orange vegetables like carrots and sweetpotatoes Eat more dry beans and peas like pinto beans, kidney beans, and lentils	Eat a variety of fruit Choose fresh, frozen, canned, or dried fruit Go easy on fruit juices	Go low-fat or fat-free when you choose milk, yogurt, and other milk products If you don't or can't consume milk, choose lactose-free products or other calcium sources such as fortified foods and beverages	Choose low-fat or lean meats and poultry Bake it, broil it, or grill it Vary your protein routine — choose more fish, beans, peas, nuts, and seeds

For a 2,000-calorie diet, you need the amounts below from each food group. To find the amounts that are right for you, go to MyPyramid.gov.

Eat 6 oz. every day	Eat 2 1/2 cups every day	Eat 2 cups every day	Get 3 cups every day; for kids aged 2 to 8, it's 2	Eat 5 1/2 oz. every day

Find your balance between food and physical activity
- Be sure to stay within your daily calorie needs.
- Be physically active for at least 30 minutes most days of the week.
- About 60 minutes a day of physical activity may be needed to prevent weight gain.
- For sustaining weight loss, at least 60 to 90 minutes a day of physical activity may be required.
- Children and teenagers should be physically active for 60 minutes every day, or most days.

Know the limits on fats, sugars, and salt (sodium)
- Make most of your fat sources from fish, nuts, and vegetable oils.
- Limit solid fats like butter, stick margarine, shortening, and lard, as well as foods that contain these.
- Check the Nutrition Facts label to keep saturated fats, *trans* fats, and sodium low.
- Choose food and beverages low in added sugars. Added sugars contribute calories with few, if any, nutrients.

The **MyPyramid** Plan can help you choose the foods and amounts that are right for you. The new MyPyramid developed by the U.S. Department of Agriculture symbolizes a personalized approach to healthy eating and physical activity.

The MyPyramid also provides other guidelines to help you plan your food intake.

MyPyramid Food Intake Pattern Calorie Levels

This chart identifies the calorie levels for males and females by age and activity level.

	MALES				FEMALES		
Activity Level	Sedentary	Moderately Active	Active	Activity Level	Sedentary	Moderately Active	Active
AGE				**AGE**			
14	2000	2400	2800	14	1800	2000	2400
15	2200	2600	3000	15	1800	2000	2400
16	2400	2800	3200	16	1800	2000	2400
17	2400	2800	3200	17	1800	2000	2400
18	2400	2800	3200	18	1800	2000	2400

Sedentary = less than 30 minutes a day of moderate physical activity in addition to daily activities.
Moderately Active = at least 30 minutes up to 60 minutes a day of moderate physical activity in addition to daily activities.
Active = 60 or more minutes a day of moderate physical activity in addition to daily activities.

MyPyramid Food Intake Pattern Calorie Levels

The suggested amounts of food to consume from the basic food groups, subgroups, and oils to meet recommended nutrient intakes at 12 different calorie levels is listed below. The table also shows the discretionary calorie allowance that can be accommodated within each calorie level. The discretionary calorie allowance is the remaining amount of calories in a food intake pattern after accounting for the calories needed for all food groups – using forms of foods that are fat-free or low-fat and with no added sugars.

DAILY AMOUNT OF FOOD FROM EACH GROUP

Calorie Level	1,000	1,200	1,400	1,600	1,800	2,000	2,200	2,400	2,600	2,800	3,000	3,200
Fruits	1 cup	1 cup	1.5 cups	1.5 cups	1.5 cups	2 cups	2 cups	2 cups	2 cups	2.5 cups	2.5 cups	2.5 cups
Vegetables	1 cup	1.5 cups	1.5 cups	2 cups	2.5 cups	2.5 cups	3 cups	3 cups	3.5 cups	3.5 cups	4 cups	4 cups
Grains	3oz-eq	4oz-eq	5oz-eq	5oz-eq	6oz-eq	6oz-eq	7oz-eq	8oz-eq	9oz-eq	10oz-eq	10oz-eq	10oz-eq
Meat and Beans	2oz-eq	3oz-eq	4oz-eq	5oz-eq	5oz-eq	5.5oz-eq	6oz-eq	6.5oz-eq	6.5oz-eq	7oz-eq	7oz-eq	7oz-eq
Milk	2 cups	2 cups	2 cups	3 cups	3 cups	3 cups	3 cups	3 cups	3 cups	3 cups	3 cups	3 cups
Oils	3 tsp	4 tsp	4 tsp	5 tsp	5 tsp	6 tsp	6 tsp	7 tsp	8 tsp	8 tsp	10 tsp	11 tsp
Discretionary calorie allowance	165	171	171	132	195	267	290	362	410	426	512	648

To learn more about the MyPyramid go to:

www.mypyramid.gov

For Your Information

The *Personal Fitness for You Student CD* has the personalized plans based on your age, sex and activity level. It also contains Spanish and English information about the new pyramid.

Fruits and vegetables are an important part of a healthy diet.

A key feature of the MyPyramid Plan is the website which includes numerous tools to help you plan your diet. These features are:

- Tour MyPyramid – an animated tour of the new pyramid
- Inside the Pyramid – learn about the food groups and the amount of activity you should be getting
- Tips and Resources
- MyPyramid Plan – a personalized food plan based on your age, sex and activity level
- MyPyramid Tracker – an in-depth assessment of your diet quality and physical activity status

Ethnic Foods and the MyPyramid Plan

Your diet is influenced by your cultural background. Different cultures tend to eat foods that may not be common to others and therefore may not be represented in the MyPyramid Plan. We usually make food choices from familiar foods that have been served in our home. Not only can these food choices be modified to follow the MyPyramid Plan, but many recipes can also be altered to meet the guidelines for healthy food choices.

The ethnic food pyramids assist you in including ethnic foods in the MyPyramid Plan. The colors of each section match the colors of the MyPyramid Food Guide. Remember it is still important to eat the recommended number of servings. If you know of other ethnic foods which are not included in these pyramids, try creating your own pyramid by following these models.

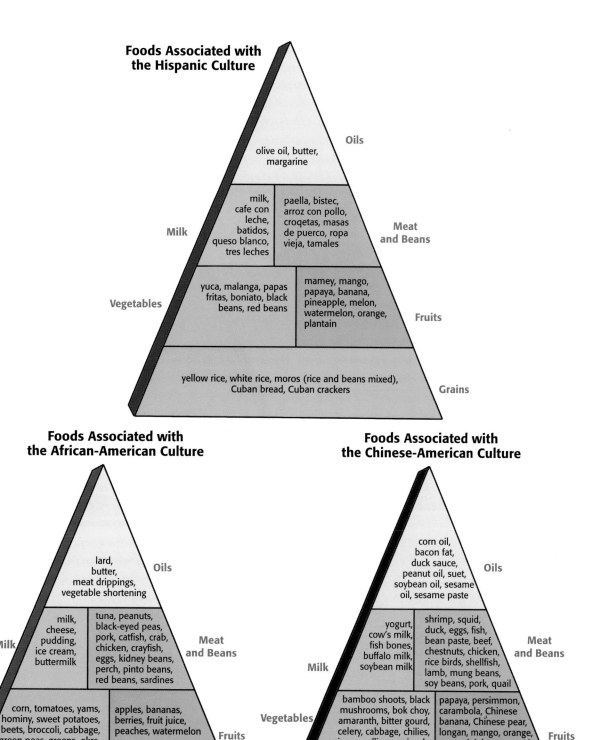

Foods Associated with the Hispanic Culture

Oils: olive oil, butter, margarine

Milk: milk, cafe con leche, batidos, queso blanco, tres leches

Meat and Beans: paella, bistec, arroz con pollo, croqetas, masas de puerco, ropa vieja, tamales

Vegetables: yuca, malanga, papas fritas, boniato, black beans, red beans

Fruits: mamey, mango, papaya, banana, pineapple, melon, watermelon, orange, plantain

Grains: yellow rice, white rice, moros (rice and beans mixed), Cuban bread, Cuban crackers

Foods Associated with the African-American Culture

Oils: lard, butter, meat drippings, vegetable shortening

Milk: milk, cheese, pudding, ice cream, buttermilk

Meat and Beans: tuna, peanuts, black-eyed peas, pork, catfish, crab, chicken, crayfish, eggs, kidney beans, perch, pinto beans, red beans, sardines

Vegetables: corn, tomatoes, yams, hominy, sweet potatoes, beets, broccoli, cabbage, green peas, greens, okra, potatoes, spinach, squash

Fruits: apples, bananas, berries, fruit juice, peaches, watermelon

Grains: biscuits, cookies, cornbread, grits, pasta, rice

Foods Associated with the Chinese-American Culture

Oils: corn oil, bacon fat, duck sauce, peanut oil, suet, soybean oil, sesame oil, sesame paste

Milk: yogurt, cow's milk, fish bones, buffalo milk, soybean milk

Meat and Beans: shrimp, squid, duck, eggs, fish, bean paste, beef, chestnuts, chicken, rice birds, shellfish, lamb, mung beans, soy beans, pork, quail

Vegetables: bamboo shoots, black mushrooms, bok choy, amaranth, bitter gourd, celery, cabbage, chilies, onions, scallions, spinach, peas, choy sum, lotus root, sprouts, taro, water chestnuts

Fruits: papaya, persimmon, carambola, Chinese banana, Chinese pear, longan, mango, orange, guava, jujube, pummelo, kumquats, watermelon, litchi

Grains: barley, bing, dumplings, fried rice, rice vermicelli, rice congee, rice flour, nin goh, cellophane noodles, rice sticks, glutinous rice, hau juan, mianbao, mantou, steamed rice, sorghum, wonton wrappers, zong-zi

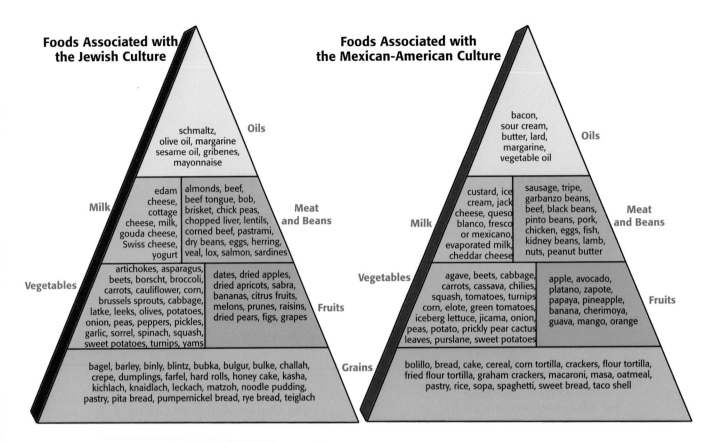

Foods Associated with the Jewish Culture

Oils
schmaltz, olive oil, margarine sesame oil, gribenes, mayonnaise

Milk
edam cheese, cottage cheese, milk, gouda cheese, Swiss cheese, yogurt

Meat and Beans
almonds, beef, beef tongue, bob, brisket, chick peas, chopped liver, lentils, corned beef, pastrami, dry beans, eggs, herring, veal, lox, salmon, sardines

Vegetables
artichokes, asparagus, beets, borscht, broccoli, carrots, cauliflower, corn, brussels sprouts, cabbage, latke, leeks, olives, potatoes, onion, peas, peppers, pickles, garlic, sorrel, spinach, squash, sweet potatoes, turnips, yams

Fruits
dates, dried apples, dried apricots, sabra, bananas, citrus fruits, melons, prunes, raisins, dried pears, figs, grapes

Grains
bagel, barley, binly, blintz, bubka, bulgur, bulke, challah, crepe, dumplings, farfel, hard rolls, honey cake, kasha, kichlach, knaidlach, leckach, matzoh, noodle pudding, pastry, pita bread, pumpernickel bread, rye bread, teiglach

Foods Associated with the Mexican-American Culture

Oils
bacon, sour cream, butter, lard, margarine, vegetable oil

Milk
custard, ice cream, jack cheese, queso blanco, fresco or mexicano, evaporated milk, cheddar cheese

Meat and Beans
sausage, tripe, garbanzo beans, beef, black beans, pinto beans, pork, chicken, eggs, fish, kidney beans, lamb, nuts, peanut butter

Vegetables
agave, beets, cabbage, carrots, cassava, chilies, squash, tomatoes, turnips, corn, elote, green tomatoes, iceberg lettuce, jicama, onion, peas, potato, prickly pear cactus leaves, purslane, sweet potatoes

Fruits
apple, avocado, platano, zapote, papaya, pineapple, banana, cherimoya, guava, mango, orange

Grains
bolillo, bread, cake, cereal, corn tortilla, crackers, flour tortilla, fried flour tortilla, graham crackers, macaroni, masa, oatmeal, pastry, rice, sopa, spaghetti, sweet bread, taco shell

Take time to read food labels.

The Nutrition Facts Label

An important skill that can help you make a good selection of foods for snacking or meals is the ability to read and understand a food label. The labels on foods can provide you with a great deal of information about the nutritional quality of the food before you purchase it.

The following information will help you use the information on a food label more effectively and easily.

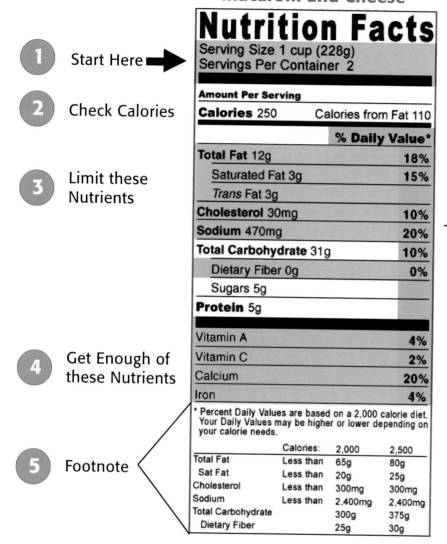

Sample Label for Macaroni and Cheese

Nutrition Facts	
Serving Size 1 cup (228g)	
Servings Per Container 2	

Amount Per Serving	
Calories 250	Calories from Fat 110

	% Daily Value*
Total Fat 12g	**18%**
Saturated Fat 3g	**15%**
Trans Fat 3g	
Cholesterol 30mg	**10%**
Sodium 470mg	**20%**
Total Carbohydrate 31g	**10%**
Dietary Fiber 0g	**0%**
Sugars 5g	
Protein 5g	

Vitamin A	**4%**
Vitamin C	**2%**
Calcium	**20%**
Iron	**4%**

* Percent Daily Values are based on a 2,000 calorie diet. Your Daily Values may be higher or lower depending on your calorie needs.

	Calories:	2,000	2,500
Total Fat	Less than	65g	80g
Sat Fat	Less than	20g	25g
Cholesterol	Less than	300mg	300mg
Sodium	Less than	2,400mg	2,400mg
Total Carbohydrate		300g	375g
Dietary Fiber		25g	30g

1 Start Here ➡

2 Check Calories

3 Limit these Nutrients

4 Get Enough of these Nutrients

5 Footnote

6 Quick Guide to % DV

5% or less is low, 20% or more is high

The Nutrition Facts Label – An Overview:

The information in the main or top section (see #1-4 and #6 on the label above) can vary with each food product. It contains product-specific information (serving size, calories and nutrient information). The bottom part (see #5 above) contains a footnote with Daily Values (DVs) for 2,000 and 2,500 calorie diets. This footnote provides recommended dietary information for important nutrients, including fats, sodium and fiber. The footnote is found only on larger packages and does not change from product to product.

1 – The Serving Size

Serving sizes are standardized to make it easier to compare similar foods; they are provided in familiar units such as cups, pieces, followed by the metric amount, e.g., the number of grams. Pay attention to the serving size, especially how many servings there are in a food package. Then ask yourself, "How many servings am I consuming"? Eating more than one serving changes the calories and other nutrient numbers you are consuming.

2 – Calories (and Calories from Fat)

The number of servings you consume determines the number of calories you actually eat (your portion amount). The General Guide to Calories provides a general reference for calories when you look at a Nutrition Facts Label. This guide is based on a 2,000 calorie diet

General Guide to Calories

- 40 Calories is low
- 100 Calories is moderate
- 400 Calories or more is high

3, 4 – The Nutrients: How Much?

The nutrients listed first (#3) are the ones Americans generally eat in adequate amounts, or even too much. On this sample label, they are in yellow and listed as Limit These Nutrients.

In section #4, blue area on this label, are the nutrients listed Get Enough of these Nutrients. Most Americans don't get enough dietary fiber, vitamin A, vitamin C, calcium, and iron in their diets.

#5 – Understanding the Footnote on the Bottom of the Nutrition Facts Label

Note the * used after the heading "% Daily Value" on the label. It refers to the Footnote in the lower part of the nutrition label which tells you "% DVs are based on a 2,000 calorie diet". This statement must be on all food labels.

#6 – The Percent Daily Value (%DV)

The % **Daily Values** (% DVs) are based on the Daily Value recommendations for key nutrients but only for a 2,000 calorie daily diet – not 2,500 calories. You can use the % DV as a frame of reference whether or not you consume more or less than 2,000 calories. The % DV helps you determine if a serving of food is high or low in a nutrient.
A Quick Guide to % DV tells you that **5% DV or less is low** for all nutrients, those you want to limit (e.g., fat, trans fat, cholesterol, sodium), or for those that you want to consume in greater amounts (fiber, calcium, etc.). As the Quick Guide shows, **20% DV or more is high** for all nutrients.

Food Label Ingredient List

A list of ingredients is required on all foods that have more than one ingredient. This is especially important so that people who may be allergic to certain additives can avoid them. In addition, by looking at the ingredient list you can select the most nutritious foods for the calories you are consuming. You should also look for hidden dangers such as added sugars, trans fatty acids, and partially hydrogenated oils. While the ingredient list does not tell you how much of an ingredient it contains, the items must be listed in descending order by weight. This gives you an idea of the proportion of an ingredient in a food.

INGREDIENTS: ENRICHED FLOUR (WHEATFLOUR, NIACIN, REDUCED IRON, THIAMINE MONONITRATE, RIBOFLAVIN, FOLIC ACID), VEGETABLE SHORTENING (PARTIALLY HYDROGENATED SOYBEAN AND/OR COTTONSEED OIL), SUGAR, CRUSHED WHEAT, TOASTED DEFATED WHEAT GERM, OATMEAL, STONE GROUND WHOLE WHEAT FLOUR, CONTAINS TWO PERCENT OR LESS OF SALT, HIGH FRUCTOSE CORN SYRUP, MALTED BARLEY FLOUR, ANNATTO EXTRACT COLOR, TUMERIC OLEORESIN.

CONTAINS WHEAT INGREDIENTS. PROCESSED ON EQUIPMENT WHICH ALSO PROCESSES MILK.

The Food Label Health Claim Definitions	
Label Claim	Definition
Calorie Free	Less than 5 calories
Low Calorie	40 calories or less
Light or Lite	1/3 fewer calories or 50% less fat; if more than half the calories are from fat, fat content must be reduced by 50% or more
Light in Sodium	50% less sodium
Fat Free	Less than 1/2 gram fat
Low Fat	3 grams or less fat
Cholesterol Free	Less than 2 milligrams cholesterol and 2 grams or less saturated fat
Low Cholesterol	20 milligrams or less cholesterol and 2 grams or less saturated fat
Sodium Free	Less than 5 milligrams sodium
Very Low Sodium	35 milligrams or less sodium
Low Sodium	140 milligrams or less sodium
High Fiber	5 grams or more fiber
Good Source of Fiber	2.5 grams to 4.9 grams of fiber per serving
Sugar Free	Less than 0.5 grams of sugar per serving
Reduced Sugar	At least 15% less sugar per serving than reference food

Making wise food choices is the key to eating healthier.

Salads can be a good choice at fast food restaurants.

Comparing Your Diet

Think about the foods you typically eat. Do you usually have a balanced diet? Unfortunately, the favorite foods of many Americans—especially teenagers—are those that consist primarily of:

- Fatty foods—hamburgers, French fries
- Sugars—sweets, milkshakes, soft drinks
- Sodium-loaded snacks—potato chips

All these foods contribute little to your nutritional needs and can even have harmful effects. You may find yourself eating certain foods because your:

- lifestyle is too busy to fix or wait for a healthier meal so you stop at a vending machine.
- family likes the convenience of foods that can be prepared in a hurry.
- peers enjoy eating at fast food places.

Fast Food

There are three primary problems with eating most fast foods: too much salt, too much fat and too many calories. These foods also contain large amounts of sugar and little fiber or vitamins. It is possible, though, to select foods of good nutritional quality at fast food restaurants. Use the following guidelines:

- Select the salad bar and use a low-calorie dressing.
- Eat a baked potato (without butter and sour cream).
- Skip the French fries!
- Substitute water, fruit juice or milk for a milkshake or soft drink.

See the fast food charts on the *Personal Fitness Student CD* to learn the poor nutritional values associated with most fast foods.

"Junk" Food

Most nutritionists agree that no foods are actually "junk" foods, because almost all foods have some nutritional value. However, there are foods which have so few (if any) nutrients and are so high in calories, sugar and fat that they should be avoided. Foods in this group include sweets, soft drinks and many snacks. If these foods dominate your diet, it is likely you are excluding other foods with more nutritional value.

Snacking

Not all snacking is bad. Some people prefer to eat small amounts of food spread out through the day. Others find it necessary to eat items such as fruits, vegetables and nuts between meals in order to maintain a consistent level of blood sugar. There are, however, two potential problems with snacking:
- Snacks may add extra calories to the diet and therefore contribute to overweight and obesity.
- Snacks may be non-nutritious foods (such as sweets, chips, candy, etc.) that end up taking the place of healthier foods in your diet.

Healthy Snacks

Here are ten excellent choices for snacks:
1. Fruits and vegetables
2. Dried apricots (rich in vitamin A, but high in calories. Many other dried fruits are also a good choice.)
3. Banana chips (good salt-free substitute for potato chips)
4. Bran muffin (high in fiber, vitamin B and zinc)
5. Whole grain bread (high in nutrition and fiber)
6. Pretzels (another good substitute for chips)
7. Cheese (choose those made with low-fat or skim milk)

Remember This ✓

Soft Drink Dangers

Limit your intake of soft drinks—especially diet drinks because they may contain phosphorous, dietary sodium and caffeine which can increase the loss of calcium from the bones.

Did You Know?

The best source of energy before a workout...
An energy bar is convenient but packed with calories. You can get the same energy from healthy snacks.

These are all excellent snack choices.

Family Activity

Discuss the MyPyramid Guide with your family members. Does your family make food choices based on the Pyramid?

8. Popcorn (cook with no oil, avoid butter and salt)
9. Yogurt (choose low-fat and add your own fruit)
10. Raisins (high in vitamins A and C, iron and fiber)

Many of us are looking for ways to improve our physical performance or increase our energy level. Unfortunately, some people look for the easiest way and not the safest way to accomplish this and are willing to try almost anything. It is important to be able to recognize misleading and false claims, so you will be able to avoid them.

Facts

- Good nutrition practices contribute to greater energy potential for physical activity.
- You should make certain your intake of water is sufficient. Water is the main component of sweat and must be replaced after exercise. When exercising in hot, humid weather it is especially important to drink lots of liquids before, during and after the activity.
- Eating a high carbohydrate meal is the best source of energy before participating in a strenuous workout. Eating a meal with complex carbohydrates—grains, pastas, potatoes and other vegetables is recommended. These carbohydrates are slowly broken down by the body and provide energy for a longer period of time.
- Even though there are a variety of food pyramids (e.g. Mediterranean, Asian, Vegetarian), the advice in all is to eat a greater proportion of calories that are carbohydrate-rich grains, vegetables, fruits, and a smaller proportion from high-protein meat and dairy.

Make certain you know the facts about good nutrition.

Fallacies or Myths

A **fallacy** is a deceptive or false idea A **myth** is a theory backed by too little evidence or an outdated idea that has been disproved by research.

You do not need supplements to achieve health or fitness.

- **Consuming extra protein will lead to greater or faster strength development.** Excess protein in the diet is stored in the form of fat just as other excess nutrients are, and does not contribute to strength gains.
- **Taking vitamin supplements will give you more energy.** Vitamins do assist the body in using nutrients which provide you with energy, but increasing your intake of vitamins beyond the recommended level does not mean you will have more energy or improve your endurance.
- **It is necessary to take salt tablets if you perspire a lot during exercise.** Not only do you get enough salt in your normal diet, but the body learns to conserve salt so you do not lose as much in your sweat. Salt tablets may also irritate the stomach lining, causing vomiting and nausea.
- **Drinking a sports drink is necessary after exercise.** Only very small amounts of minerals are lost in your sweat. The minerals which are lost can be replaced by foods eaten after exercise. Sweat is primarily plain water. Most of the sports drinks contain too much sugar which slows their absorption into the bloodstream. Therefore, if you do use these drinks, it is suggested you dilute them with water by at least 50% and use them after exercise.
- **Drinking caffeine improves athletic performance.** This claim has not been proven. Caffeine does stimulate the central nervous system and tends to increase alertness.

for food label information:
www.cfsan.fda.gov/~dms/foodlab.html

for dietary guidelines:
www.health.gov/dietaryguidelines
kidshealth.org/teen/food_fitness/
dieting/diet_supplements.html

- **Organically grown foods provide many health benefits.** The fact is that organically grown foods do not contain extra health benefits over commercially grown foods.
- **Tofu is considered a healthy food.** Tofu is soybean curds that are high in protein but also high in polyunsaturated fat. Four ounces of tofu has 5 g of fat. So while some consider tofu a health food, it is 53% fat.
- **Bottled water is safer from impurities.** While lab tests now being required indicate that bottled water is safe and doesn't pose any health hazards, it is not necessarily any purer than regular tap water.

Healthy People 2010 Goals

- Promote health and reduce chronic disease associated with diet and weight.
- Reduce the proportion of children and adolescents who are overweight or obese.
- Increase the proportion of persons aged 2 years and older who consume at least two daily servings of fruit.
- Increase the proportion of persons aged 2 years and older who consume at least 3 daily servings of vegetables with at least one-third being dark or deep yellow vegetables.
- Increase the proportion of persons aged 2 years and older who consume at least six daily servings of grain products with at least three being whole grains.
- Increase the proportion of persons aged 2 years and older who consume less than 10 percent of calories from saturated fat.
- Increase the proportion of persons aged 2 years and older who consume no more than 30 percent of calories from fat.
- Increase the proportion of persons aged 2 years and older who consume 2400 mg or less of sodium daily.
- Increase the proportion of persons aged 2 years and older who meet dietary recommendations for calcium.
- Reduce iron deficiency among young children and females of childbearing age.
- Increase the proportion of children and adolescents aged 6 to 19 years whose intake of meals and snacks at schools contributes proportionally to good overall dietary quality.
- Reduce coronary heart disease deaths.
- Reduce stroke deaths.
- Reduce the proportion of adults with high blood pressure.
- Reduce the mean of total blood cholesterol levels among adults.
- Reduce the proportion of adults with high total blood cholesterol levels.

Although many perceive bottled water to be healthier, studies show about 25% of bottled water comes from the same municipal water sources as tap water but costs 300-1,200 times more per gallon. If you like the taste of bottled water better and don't mind the added cost that's fine, but don't be mislead into thinking it is necessarily better for your health.

- **When you eat less, your stomach shrinks.** Your stomach cannot shrink even though it can expand as you eat large amounts. Dieting may cause your appetite to drop but that is not because you stomach has gotten smaller.

- **Natural herbs can melt pounds away without diet or exercise!** There is no evidence that dietary supplements can cause weight loss, and there is evidence that some supplements can cause serious damage to your health.

Bottled water is not necessarily any purer than regular tap water.

Summary

Making wise food choices is the key to good nutrition. By using the Dietary Guidelines for Americans 2005, MyPyramid Food Guide, and the Nutrition Facts Label in making your food selections, you can be assured that your diet will contain the appropriate vitamins, minerals and other nutrients. By avoiding low nutrient foods and selecting healthy choices for meals and snacks, you will be on the way to having the energy for your daily activities including exercise, fitness and playing sports.

Learning how to read and interpret a food label is important to making these wise choices. We need calories each day to maintain our normal body functions as well as to perform daily activities. There are differences, however, in the quality of those calories. Some foods we eat have very little nutritional value to go with their high caloric value. Once again, choosing a diet which contains the nutrients while not exceeding your required caloric level is the key.

It is clear that diet is related to achieving an optimal level of health and fitness. However, being able to separate facts from the fallacies about nutrition is not always easy. This chapter has provided you with the information you need to make sound nutritional choices. It is now up to you to make the necessary changes in your current eating habits. It may not be easy at first, but once you notice how much better you look and feel, you will realize healthy eating is worth the effort.

Chapter 8 Review

Lesson Checklist

- Do you understand the steps needed to achieve a balanced, healthy diet?
- Do you have a good understanding of the MyPyramid Food Guide and know how to apply the recommendations to your daily eating habits?
- Do you understand what information is provided on a food label and how it can help you make better food choices?
- Do you know how to distinguish which fast foods are good food choices?

Chapter Projects

Write a response to each of the following:
1. Why is nutrition important to achieving total fitness?
2. Draw the MyPyramid Food Guide and write in the number of daily servings recommended for each food group.
3. How can you make a wise selection of desserts and beverages?
4. Describe the recommended meal to eat before participating in an athletic event.
5. What are the major problems from eating fast foods?

Behavior Change Evaluation

Review the following items to see if you have gained an understanding of fitness and wellness. On a piece of paper briefly state how you will make these changes.
- I will work toward establishing a daily eating pattern which follows the recommendations of the MyPyramid Food Guide.
- I will read food labels to monitor my fat and calorie intake.
- I will not listen to false claims in regard to either foods or drinks.
- I will select more nutritious snacks.

Critical Thinking

After reviewing the MyPyramid Food Guide and the ethnic food guide pyramids, describe how your diet is based on family history, culture, etc.

Chapter 8 Review

Test Your Knowledge

Read the questions below and select the best possible answer for each.

1. The % Daily Values are based on a diet of
   a. 2500 calories
   b. 2000 calories
   c. 1000 calories
   d. 1500 calories

2. A food that is labeled calorie free must contain
   a. less than 5 calories
   b. 0 calories
   c. 40 calories or less
   d. less than one gram of fat

3. A food that is labeled fat free must contain
   a. Less than 1/2 gram of fat
   b. 0 grams of fat
   c. less than 2 grams of fat
   d. no cholesterol

4. Which of the following are fallacies?
   a. When you eat less, your stomach shrinks
   b. Natural herbs can melt away pounds away without diet or exercise
   c. All bottled waters are safer than tap water
   d. All are fallacies

5. You should consume less than ___ of sodium per day
   a. 1500 mg
   b. 3000 mg
   c. 2300 mg
   d. 2000 mg

6. How many cups of fat free or low fat milk or equivalent milk products should you consume per day?
   a. 5
   b. 4
   c. 3
   d. 2

7. Which is not true about a food label?
   a. It must tell the serving size
   b. It must list the servings per container
   c. It must list the calories from fat
   d. The ingredients are listed in ascending order by weight, with the heaviest ingredients listed last

8. The percent daily value:
   a. states that 5% DV or less is low
   b. states that 25% DV or more is high
   c. refers to a 2,000 calorie diet
   d. all of the above

9. The most healthful bread is made from
   a. Enriched flour
   b. Gluten free flour
   c. 100% whole wheat flour
   d. Whole wheat and enriched flour

10. Which of the following is NOT a guideline for a good nutrition plan?
    a. use salt sparingly
    b. eat a variety of foods
    c. choose a diet high in saturated fat
    d. choose a diet moderate in sugar

Managing Your Weight

9

Chapter Topics

- Body Composition Basics
- Determining Your Body Composition
- Why Worry about Excess Fat?
- Causes of Overweight and Overfat
- Balancing Your Caloric Intake and Expenditure
- Achieving a Healthy Weight
- Exercise as a Method of Weight Control
- Combining Exercise and a Diet Plan
- Why "Diets" Don't Work
- Myths about Weight Control
- Special Dangers of Dieting
- Gaining Weight Safely

Chapter Objectives

After completing this chapter, you will be able to:

- Identify health-related problems associated with an abnormal percentage of body fat.
- Calculate your ideal body weight.
- Understand the difference between overweight, overfat and obesity.
- Identify the major causes of overweight and overfat.
- Explain the use of exercise and diet as methods of weight control.
- Explain the combined use of exercise and diet as a method of weight control.
- Understand the dangers of dieting: fad diets, fasting and diet aids.
- Understand the guidelines for achieving a healthy weight.
- Identify common myths about weight control.
- Understand how to gain weight safely.

Key Words

anorexia nervosa
body fat percentage
bulimia
cellulite
creeping obesity
ectomorph
endomorph

fad diet
fasting
fat weight
ideal body weight
lean body weight
mesomorph
obese

overweight
overfat
set point
somatotype
spot reducing

Suggested Physical Activities

Include a 20-minute (or more) walk/jog session in your daily schedule. See if you notice a change in weight.

Healthy People 2010 Goals

- ◆ Reduce coronary heart disease deaths.
- ◆ Promote health and reduce chronic disease associated with diet and weight.
- ◆ Reduce the proportion of children and adolescents who are overweight or obese.
- ◆ Increase the proportion of children and adolescents aged 6 to 19 years whose intake of meals and snacks at schools contributes proportionally to good overall dietary quality.

Use the *Personal Fitness for You* Student CD for:

- ◆ Lab 9-1: Identifying Your Body Type
- ◆ Lab 9-2: Your Desirable Body Weight
- ◆ Lab 9-3: Your Eating Behavior
- ◆ Lab 9-4: Diet Readiness Test
- ◆ Lab 9-5: Weight Management
- ◆ Lab 9-6: Weight Control Contract
- ◆ Lab 9-7: Calculating Calories Burned
- ◆ Chapter Practice Test
- ◆ Chapter Study Guide
- ◆ Chapter Crossword Puzzle
- ◆ Vocabulary Flash Cards
- ◆ Chapter Power Point Review
- ◆ Analyzing Diet Plans

Eating Less but Weighing More...

Americans eat 10% less today than they did in 1970, but the average American now weighs a few pounds more. The reason is probably because the nation as a whole has become less physically active.

For Your Information

23% of U.S. Hispanics ages 6-19 are overweight compared with 15% of non-Hispanic youth.

Eating the right kind of food is important to weight control.

Do you consider yourself overweight? Do you have bulges on your thighs, a protruding abdomen or other unwanted fat deposits? Did your fitness evaluation of your body composition indicate that you had areas "out of proportion" or that your body fat percentage was too high? Extra fat is usually caused by:

- eating too much.
- eating the wrong kind of foods.
- exercising too little.

The news media bombard us with quick-fix solutions to weight control problems. Unfortunately, there is no quick way to control weight and make the change a lasting one. Instead of thinking about dieting, concentrate on eating well. Instead of focusing on the foods you shouldn't eat, think about the foods that will help you feel and look the way you want to.

This chapter will describe the problems and causes of overfat, obesity and overweight; discuss diet techniques to avoid; and suggest guidelines for permanent weight loss.

Overweight

It is estimated that one-third of the population over 20 years of age is overweight and that 21% of youth 12-19 are overweight. The percentage of overweight people varies by race/ethnic background, socioeconomic status, sex and age. For instance, minority populations, especially minority women, have a much higher percentage of those overweight. According to the U.S. Public Health Service nearly half of African-American adults are overweight.

Body Composition Basics

It is important to understand several common terms related to weight control.

Overweight means weighing more than most people your age, sex and height. This is usually determined by referring to a height/weight chart. This information is not very meaningful since someone who is very muscular (such as a trained athlete) might be overweight according to a height/weight chart, yet in actuality this person might have an excellent proportion of lean body mass to fat tissue that on a body composition test would meet acceptable health fitness standards.

Overfat means having more fat than you should as determined by your skinfold measurements (see Chapter 4). For females, being overfat is having 25-30% of total body weight as fat. For males, being overfat is having 20-25% of total body weight as fat. While a little extra fat may not be cause for concern, it is a warning signal that a weight control program is needed. Some people whose body build is tall and thin, may actually be overfat for their size. A measure of body fat may show that these people are actually beginning to accumulate fat and not build muscle mass. People who are overfat should begin a muscle toning program and monitor their intake of fatty foods.

Ectomorph Mesomorph Endomorph

Understanding Body Fat

Essential fat is the fat in the body necessary for normal body functioning for protection of the organs.

Nonessential fat is storage fat and exists primarily within fat cells just below the skin and around the major organs.

Excessive body fat is referred to as being obese.

Obese refers to having an excessively high amount of body fat. Individuals with body fat percentages greater than 30% for females and 25% for males are generally considered obese. Since obese individuals have an excessive amount of body fat, it is not likely they will be in an acceptable range on a height/weight chart. However, if they are, this can be misleading and dangerous because excessive body fat can contribute to many health problems.

Ideal Body Weight refers to the best weight for a person with body fat percentage maintained within an acceptable range. The ideal body fat percentage for males is between 11-17% and for females it is between 19-22%. It is possible to calculate your ideal or optimal weight by using the percentage of body fat (from the evaluation in Chapter 4) and your body weight. Strive to reach your ideal body weight. At this weight you not only look better, but you feel better and function more efficiently.

Determining Your Body Composition

In Chapter 4 you learned about the health-related components of physical fitness. Recall that body composition is one of the components. You also learned several ways to determine your body composition.

Your body is composed of **lean body weight** (muscle, bone, tendons, ligaments, internal organs) and **fat weight**. Generally, lean weight is referred to as lean body mass and your fat weight is referred to as **body fat percentage**.

Fat tissue is a result of excess calories that were taken in, and not burned during activity. Therefore, they have been stored by the body.

The key to good health is maintaining a body composition that has a proper ratio of lean body mass to fat weight.

Underwater weighing, bioelectrical impedance and skinfold measurement methods of measuring body fat were described in Chapter 4. In addition, using the BMI and waist circumference measurement were explained.

No doubt you are like many other young people (and even older adults) who are concerned with how they look. Most of us really don't need a skinfold measurement or a scale to tell us if we are too fat. We can look in the mirror and see it! We know when we have gained a few pounds and our clothes begin to feel a little tight. The main concern is how we deal with it—how do we shed those extra pounds or firm up those bulging areas?

Why Worry about Excess Fat?

You may be wondering why you should worry about extra fat, if you are satisfied with the way you look and feel. One reason is that every extra pound of fat forces your heart to pump blood through an extra two-thirds of a mile of blood vessels. This creates a lot of extra work for your heart and endangers your health. If you are overfat, you may not only increase your risk of developing some diseases, you may aggravate (worsen) diseases which are caused by other factors.

Overweight and excessive fat have been linked to the following problems:
- High blood pressure
- Increased level of cholesterol and fats in the blood
- Many types of bone and joint disorders
- Diabetes
- Lower back difficulties
- Respiratory ailments
- Greater chance of accidents

Remember This ☑

A scale may do more harm than good if you believe a certain body weight alone is a desirable goal. It is more important to know how much of your weight is body fat.

Family Activity

Share the information in this chapter with your family. If you are trying to lose weight, ask your family for their support.

For **Y**our **I**nformation

Obese individuals are usually inactive and may have had a poor experience with exercise in the past (got injured, became bored, etc.).

Heredity influences your distribution of body fat.

Did You Know?

Previously inactive people can lose one pound a month simply by walking 20 minutes each day—as long as they don't increase their calorie intake.

Causes of Overweight and Overfat

Do you know how obesity develops? What are the major causes of obesity: Heredity? Environment? Emotional problems? Lack of activity? Obviously, the answer may vary from individual to individual, and it is likely that more than one cause is involved.

Consuming more calories than you use during activity causes weight gain. However, not everyone who overeats is fat. There are a number of factors which interact to determine whether you are overweight.

Heredity and Environment

Your genes play a role in how your body balances calorie intake and calorie expenditure. Studies show that children of obese parents are likely to be overweight, and children whose parents are lean are usually also lean.

Even though heredity does influence the amount of body fat and the distribution of fat, it does not mean you are automatically going to be fat. Your eating and exercise pattern make a difference. This relationship may also be caused by acquired family eating habits or culturally-developed attitudes toward weight and eating.

Childhood Obesity

Eating patterns that contribute to obesity are typically established early in life. Human fat cells increase in number very rapidly during childhood and, once formed, become fixed for life. Overfeeding children, especially infants, can lead to a lifetime of weight problems. Studies show that obese children have three times the number of fat cells as normal weight children. After adolescence the number of fat cells remains almost constant throughout the rest of life. If you were overweight as a child, you may have a constant challenge to maintain a healthy weight throughout your life.

Inactivity

Although other factors play a part, studies show that inactivity is the main cause for the high incidence of obesity. Most obese individuals do not eat any more than the non-obese, and very few people have hormonal or glandular problems which cause them to be overfat.

Obese people simply do not have the level of activity to "burn up" the calories they take in each day. Therefore, the real key to controlling your weight is to be active. You must include a planned exercise program as a part of your daily life.

High Fat Diet

Not only does fat provide more than twice the calories that proteins and carbohydrates do, a person eating a high fat diet tends to store more excess calories as body fat than someone who eats a low-fat diet.

Medical Problems

Some people are eager to blame their overweight on a medical problem rather than making an effort to deal with the real cause. According to the Mayo Clinic, less than 5% of all cases of obesity can be linked to a metabolic disorder or hormonal imbalances.

Creeping Obesity

As individuals grow older, they may become less active. This reduction of activity, along with a decline in the rate at which the body burns calories to maintain daily functions (basal metabolic rate), means that eating habits must be adjusted to avoid a weight gain. If this is not done, gains in weight or increases in body fat percentages will occur. This gradual weight gain during aging is referred to as **creeping obesity**.

The key to controlling weight is to stay active.

Family Activity

Add physical activity to your family life by trying these ideas:
- Celebrate special occasions by adding a hike and picnic to the party.
- Add physical activity to your weekend plans - a hike, swim, bicycle trip.
- Each weekend plan one special physical activity event such as a walk, bicycle trip, swim, etc.

A person who eats a high fat diet tends to store more excess calories as body fat.

Balancing Your Caloric Intake and Expenditure

Balancing your caloric intake and expenditure is the key to managing your weight. You must burn up the calories you take in. If more calories are taken in than used, the body stores them as fat. If fewer calories are taken in than are needed for the day's activities, the body converts stored fat into energy.

A pound of fat equals 3500 calories. Therefore, if you want to lose weight, the goal should be to take in 500 fewer calories each day or burn up 500 more calories each day. This will cause a loss of approximately one pound per week. This is a good approach to weight loss, because it is a sure thing. Maintaining weight at an optimal level is a lifetime activity, and for most people, a lifetime of dieting cannot be successful. You must not think in terms of "going on a diet," but changing your lifestyle to increase exercise and improve eating habits. Make permanent changes in your eating and exercise habits.

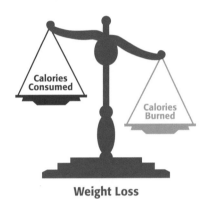

Weight Loss

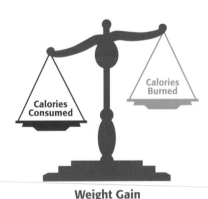

Weight Gain

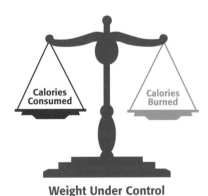

Weight Under Control

Achieving a Healthy Weight

The goal for achieving a healthy weight is to develop a habit of good eating and activity that are a part of your everyday lifestyle. Instead of dieting, you need to change the eating habits that you have learned which are counterproductive. Focus on changing your eating habits – not going on a diet. The following techniques can help you establish a plan that will work for a lifetime of healthy eating.

Getting Ready

- Evaluate your current eating and exercise habits. Keep a food and activity diary. A diary can help you identify attitudes about eating you need to change, positive things that are working and trouble spots and their possible causes.

- Record what you typically eat in a day. What are your meal patterns and eating habits?
   Do you nibble or snack during the day?
   Do you eat fast?
   Do you take big bites?
   Do you eat huge dinners?
   Do you eat while watching TV?
   Do you overeat when you are tired, stressed, nervous or bored?
   Do you frequently binge eat?
   What triggers you to eat?
   Are there activities that have become closely associated with eating?

- Determine what causes you to overindulge. Try to eat only when you are hungry and stop when you feel full.

- Examine when you eat. If you tend to eat very light during the day but overeat at night, try eating a bigger breakfast or lunch so that you will eat a lighter dinner.

- Make certain you are ready to change your eating habits – see the box on page 175 to help you get ready.

For Your Information

"Overweight children are at risk for cardiovascular diseases, diabetes, and other serious health problems. They are part of an epidemic of overweight and obesity that must be addressed so that they can lead healthier lives."

Dr. Jeffrey P. Kaplan, Former Director of the Center for Disease Control.

Remember This ☑

The key to weight control is balancing **caloric intake** (energy equivalent of the food you eat) and **caloric expenditure** (the energy related to resting metabolism, activity, intake of food, etc.)

Make a commitment to your goals and put them in writing.

Setting Goals

- Set reasonable, realistic goals. Determine what a realistic weight for you to achieve would be. Consider establishing weight goals that offer a range of possibilities such as:

  My ideal weight – the weight you would choose if you could pick any weight you wanted.

  Happy weight – the weight you would be happy with even though it is not your ideal weight.

  Acceptable weight – a weight you could accept because at least it is less than your current weight.

  Disappointed weight – a weight that would be disappointing because it is not much less than your current weight.

- Consider why you want your goal? Is it so you look better, feel better, or to please someone else? You must make a commitment to your goals and must be internally motivated to change your eating plan. Trying to do it to please someone else rarely is successful. Make sure you stay committed to the program for the time it will take.

- Complete a weight control contract (see Lab 9-6 on the *Personal Fitness for You Student CD*.

Getting Started

- Do what you can do. Something is always better than nothing. If you can only do a little exercise, do it. If you can only cut out 200 or 300 calories, do it. Any positive change is worth doing!

- Keep track of calories and fat when you are getting started. Soon you will be able to make good food choices based on the awareness you have gained. Learn the nutritional values of foods so that you make wise choices.

Did You Know?

If you walk 15 minutes a day and don't take in more calories, you could lose 10 pounds in a year!

Remember This ☑

Be patient!

You have gained weight over the years, so give yourself time to lose it slowly. A slow weight loss is a permanent one.

Losing even small amounts of weight - 10-15% of your initial body weight - can be very beneficial to your health.

Are You Ready to Lose Weight?

- **Why do you want to lose weight?**

- **Are you motivated enough to change your lifestyle habits *forever?***
Are your reasons strong enough to support a long-term commitment? Has a doctor or other health professional suggested you lose weight? Think carefully about your reasons because they can make the difference in your success or failure.

- **Is this the right time to change your diet and exercise habits?**
If you are currently experiencing added stress at home, school or work, maybe it would be better to wait until you have these situations under control. Once you begin a weight loss plan, you need to stay focused on it.

- **How much weight do you want to lose?**
Be realistic about the amount of weight you want to lose (remember too thin is not healthy) and how quickly you want to lose it. Losing more than one or two pounds per week generally leads to regaining the weight. Revise your plan if you expect to lose more weight than this.

- **Can you commit to exercising regularly?**
The biggest factor in keeping weight off is exercising more. Will you definitely schedule time for walking, swimming, aerobics or some other activity? If not, the likelihood of a long-term weight loss is less.

- **How will the people around you react to your trying a weight loss plan?**
Will family and friends support you, nag you or be bothered by your insistence on low-fat foods and recipes? Sometimes you may find it easier not to discuss it with people—other times announcing it will help you gain support. Consider your situation and act accordingly.

Use the Dietary Guidelines, the MyPyramid Plan, and the Nutrition Facts Label to assist you in making choices.

- Be certain you include exercise in your lifestyle. Studies confirm that those who exercise are more likely to lose fat and keep it off than those who try to diet only. Exercise is the only method that significantly raises the rate at which the body burns calories at rest. Even though regularly scheduled aerobic exercise is best for losing fat, any extra activity will help burn calories.

- Learn to enjoy the diet changes and healthful foods you are now eating.

WEBSITE

To learn more about weight loss tips, visit the following web sites:
//win.niddk.nih.gov
www.weight.com
//eatingdisorders.
mentalhelp.net
www.cyberdiet.com

Strategies for Weight Control

- Eat slowly. Studies show you will eat less if you give your body time to let you know you have had enough.
- Keep only low-calorie foods and snacks on hand.
- Exercise regularly.
- Take up enjoyable activities that don't involve food.
- Avoid packaged snacks, cookies and high-fat baked goods.
- Don't skip meals or go hungry—this contributes to eating too much at the next meal.

Remember This ✓

Since building muscle through exercise may increase weight, measure your fat percentage to check your progress.

Did You Know?

The more muscle you have, the more calories your body uses—even while resting. A fit person can actually eat more calories.

Learn to eat smaller portions of any food that you currently enjoy and would like to eat throughout the rest of your life.

- Learn to cope with your problem foods. Identify the foods that you like but which are not wise choices because of excessive calories and/or fat content. Instead of making them permanently "off limits" or forbidden, avoid them temporarily or eat only a small portion.

Staying on Target

- Chart your progress. Keep track of your measurements (the inches you are losing) as well as your weight. Through exercise you may gain muscle which is heavier than fat but be losing inches.

- Identify people who will either work with you in achieving a weight loss goal or who will encourage and support you along the way. It is also a good idea to avoid people who may tempt you to stray from your healthy eating plan.

- Learn to handle discouragement and setbacks. The process of losing weight will probably not follow a steady decline. Things will happen to interfere with your eating habits and exercise plan. Do not get discouraged or quit. Instead, identify the problem, consider ways of overcoming the problem, and implement a plan.

- Reward yourself for your successes along the way to achieving your goals. Feel good about any and all positive changes such as being able to exercise longer, body composition changes, or avoiding problem eating. Make certain your reward is not related to eating but instead involves something you like to do such as going to a movie, buying something special, or doing something like a favorite hobby, reading, or taking a trip.

- Think thinner! Visualize yourself at your optimal weight. Stay positive and remember that overeating will keep you from your goal.

- Consider weight management as a long term program that will require continued monitoring and adherence to behavioral changes. Remember the goal of a healthy eating plan is for weight loss that is permanent.

Think thinner!

Exercise as a Method of Weight Control

Exercise and activity cause you to burn calories. Activities that are vigorous involve the entire body and if sustained over a period of time will burn the most calories. It is possible to calculate the number of calories burned during an activity, but this can be misleading because studies show that the body may continue to burn more calories for hours after the exercise. So even if the number of calories burned during exercise seems small, over a period of time they can add up to cause a loss of fat.

Exercise plays an important role in your effort to regulate weight.

- Exercise burns calories and helps maintain muscle tone and shape.
- Exercise improves the body's ability to burn fat. Vigorous exercise enables the body to use its stores of fat more efficiently as muscle fuel.
- Exercise may help suppress appetite.

Exercise may also help regulate the size and number of fat cells and lower the body's set point for fatty tissue. Your **set point** is the weight you normally maintain, give or take a few pounds, when you are not consciously attempting to control it. It is the weight to which your body returns after dieting or overeating. Unless you change your set point, the battle against overweight is continuous and usually futile.

SAFETY TIP If you are very obese, you may be at increased risk for orthopedic injury. Try:

- non-weight bearing activities such as cycling
- rotating activities, frequent changes in frequency and duration
- beginning with low-intensity exercise and progressively longer activity sessions
- increasing the intensity as you respond positively—with a higher intensity, you can have shorter sessions or fewer sessions per week
- a walking or other low-intensity program

FITT for Body Composition

Frequency:	3-5 days per week-daily is best
Intensity:	continuous activity that is sufficient to cause sweating
Time : (duration)	30 minutes at least
Type:	large muscle movement that can be maintained to the appropriate intensity (walking, cycling, jogging, swimming, aerobic exercise)

Exercise is the most effective way to lower your set point. This is because we are designed to be active and lean. For most people inactivity and a sedentary lifestyle has raised the set point above what it should be. Dieting will not decrease the set point.

As one loses fat through increased exercise, lean muscle tissue, muscle tone and firmness are increased. Weight lost through exercise tends to stay off, while weight lost on a diet tends to come back.

The information below is an estimate of the number of calories used during vigorous exercise.

No. of Calories	Exercise
100	Walking or jogging one mile
150 - 200	40 minutes of continuous aerobic exercise
180 - 250	Swimming for 1/2 hour
210	Bicycling at 10 m.p.h. for 1/2 hour

The following factors determine how many calories you burn:
- how large you are
- how hard you work
- muscles involved
- movement efficiency
- fitness
- amount of body fat
- environmental conditions

My Activity Plan (MAP)

My goal is to do the following activities to maintain or improve my body composition:

Type of Activity	Frequency: Times Per Week	Intensity of the Workout (heart rate, perceived exertion)	Time: Number of Minutes per Day	Approximate # of Calories Burned
Walking	3	133-143 bpm	40	200 per day
Bicycling	4	133-143 bpm	30	210 per day
Swimming	2	133-143 bpm	30	230 per day

Refer to the student *Personal Fitness for You* CD for the *My Activity Plan* form.

Which Type of Exercise Will Burn the Most Calories?

The chart on page 181 lists the number of calories burned per minute at different body weights for a variety of activities. The basic rule is that the fuel you burn is based on the amount of weight you move and the distance you move it. Therefore, the exercises which develop cardiorespiratory fitness burn the most calories. Aerobic exercises which involve total body activity, are rhythmical and can be maintained for a long time are best.

Although any increased activity will burn calories, the most effective exercises for weight loss are those that also contribute to your cardiorespiratory fitness: walking, jogging, cycling, swimming and aerobic exercise to music. Studies also show that vigorous exercise curbs the appetite, while less strenuous exercises sometimes cause the appetite to increase.

Combining Exercise and a Diet Plan

The best strategy for a lifetime of successful weight control is a sound, nutritious diet combined with regular, vigorous exercise. The advantages of combining exercise with a diet plan for weight control are:

- Cutting back on fat calories and adding exercise causes the majority of the pounds you lose to be fat and not lean tissue. Losing weight without exercise causes you to lose approximately 50 percent lean tissue and 50 percent fat.
- An extra pound of muscle burns 30-50 calories per day. By increasing the muscle you have, you can eat more and maintain your weight because your metabolism is higher.

For Your Information

Prolonged low intensity workouts burn a higher percentage of calories from fat (50%), while intense workouts only burn 40% of calories from fat; however, since you burn more calories during intense exercise, you will burn more fat.

Remember This ☑

Consistently doing some type of exercise is more important than the type or amount of exercise.

Did You Know?

Aerobic activities are more efficient in calorie expenditure because they involve a sustained, high rate of energy expenditure.

- Exercise will help develop muscle as it "burns" excess body fat. Combining exercise with diet will result in a weight loss of more fatty tissue.
- Since there are 3,500 calories in a pound of stored body fat, one pound a week can be lost by eliminating 500 calories a day from the diet. This may be done by "burning" 500 more calories each day through exercise, or through a combination of eliminating 250 calories from the diet and increasing exercise by 250 calories. This may be easier than adding activities that burn 500 calories or eliminating 500 calories from your daily diet.
- Your ultimate goal is to establish permanent, healthful eating habits—those that you can and will maintain throughout your life.

Why "Diets" Don't Work

Regardless of how successful a particular "diet" plan is, most people do gain back the weight. In addition, within five years people not only regain their original weight, they add three to four extra pounds. You can lose weight on most "diets." The trick is to not only lose the weight but to keep it off.

Dieting can be risky and there are several behaviors that should be avoided:

- Fasting
- Skipping meals
- Very-low calorie diets
- Diet pills
- Laxative use
- Self-induced vomiting

These behaviors can lead to eating disorders.

Fad Diets

Fad diets are extremely popular because everyone is looking for a quick, easy way to achieve weight control.

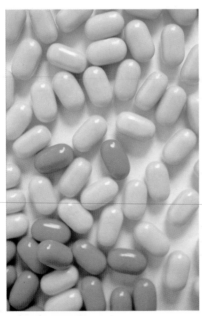

Using diet pills can be a risky behavior.

Calorie Expenditure Per Minute for Various Activities

Body Weight	90	99	108	117	125	134	143	152	161	170	178	187	196	205	222
Archery	3.1	3.4	3.7	4.0	4.5	4.6	4.9	5.2	5.5	5.8	6.1	6.4	6.7	7.0	7.6
Badminton (recreation)	3.4	3.8	4.1	4.4	4.8	5.1	5.4	5.6	6.1	6.4	6.8	7.1	7.4	7.8	8.3
Baseball (player)	2.8	3.1	3.4	3.6	3.9	4.2	4.5	4.7	5.0	5.3	5.5	5.8	6.1	6.4	6.9
Basketball (competition)	5.9	6.5	7.1	7.7	8.2	8.8	9.4	10.0	10.6	11.1	11.7	12.3	12.9	13.5	14.6
Bicycling (level) 5.5 mph	3.0	3.3	3.6	3.9	4.2	4.5	4.8	5.1	5.4	5.6	5.9	6.2	6.5	6.8	7.4
Bicycling (level) 13 mph	6.4	7.1	7.7	8.3	8.9	9.6	10.2	10.8	11.4	12.1	12.7	13.4	14.0	14.6	15.9
Bowling (nonstop)	4.0	4.4	4.8	5.2	5.6	5.9	6.3	6.7	7.1	7.5	7.9	8.3	8.7	9.1	9.8
Boxing (sparring)	3.0	3.3	3.6	3.9	4.2	4.5	4.8	5.1	5.4	5.6	5.9	6.2	6.5	6.8	7.4
Calisthenics	3.0	3.3	3.6	3.9	4.2	4.5	4.8	5.1	5.4	5.6	5.9	6.2	6.5	6.8	7.4
Canoeing, 2.5 mph	1.8	1.9	2.0	2.2	2.3	2.5	2.7	3.0	3.2	3.4	3.6	3.7	3.9	4.1	4.4
Dance, modern (vigorous)	3.4	3.7	4.1	4.4	4.7	5.1	5.4	5.7	6.1	6.4	6.7	7.1	7.4	7.7	8.4
Dance, square	4.1	4.5	4.9	5.3	5.7	6.1	6.5	6.9	7.3	7.8	8.1	8.5	8.9	9.3	10.1
Fencing (moderate)	3.0	3.3	3.6	3.9	4.2	4.5	4.8	5.1	5.4	5.6	6.0	6.2	6.5	6.8	7.4
Football (vigorous)	5.0	5.5	6.0	6.4	6.9	7.4	7.9	8.4	8.9	9.4	9.8	10.3	10.8	11.3	12.3
Golf	2.4	2.7	2.9	3.2	3.4	3.6	3.9	4.1	4.3	4.6	4.8	5.1	5.3	5.5	6.0
Handball	5.9	6.4	7.0	7.6	8.1	8.7	9.3	9.9	10.4	11.0	11.6	12.1	12.7	13.3	14.4
Hiking, 40lb. pack, 3.0 mph	4.1	4.5	4.9	5.3	5.7	6.1	6.5	6.9	7.3	7.7	8.1	8.5	8.9	9.3	10.1
Judo, Karate	7.7	8.5	9.2	10.0	10.7	11.5	12.2	13.0	13.7	14.5	15.2	16.0	16.7	17.5	19.0
Mountain Climbing	6.0	6.5	7.2	7.8	8.4	9.0	9.6	10.1	10.7	11.3	11.9	12.5	13.1	13.7	14.8
Paddleball, Racquetball	5.9	6.4	7.0	7.6	8.1	8.7	9.3	9.9	10.4	11.0	11.6	12.1	12.7	13.3	14.4
Pool, Billiards	1.1	1.2	1.3	1.4	1.5	1.6	1.7	1.8	1.9	2.0	2.1	2.2	2.4	2.5	2.7
Racquetball	6.0	6.6	7.2	7.8	8.3	8.9	9.5	10.1	11.7	11.3	11.9	12.5	13.1	13.7	14.8
Rowing (machine)	8.2	9.0	9.8	10.6	11.4	12.2	13.0	13.8	14.6	15.4	16.2	17.0	17.8	18.6	20.2
Running, 11 min., 5.5 mph	6.4	7.1	7.7	8.3	9.0	9.6	10.2	10.8	11.5	12.1	12.7	13.4	14.0	14.6	15.9
Running, 8.5 min., 7 mph	8.4	9.2	10.0	10.8	11.7	12.5	13.3	14.1	14.9	15.7	16.6	17.4	18.2	19.0	20.7
Sailing	1.8	2.0	2.1	2.3	2.4	2.7	2.8	3.0	3.2	3.4	3.6	3.8	3.9	4.1	4.4
Sprinting	13.8	15.2	16.6	17.9	19.2	20.5	21.9	23.3	24.7	26.1	27.3	28.7	30.0	31.4	34.0
Skating (vigorous)	6.2	6.8	7.4	8.0	8.6	9.2	9.8	9.9	11.0	11.6	12.2	12.8	13.4	14.0	15.2
Skiing (downhill)	5.8	6.4	6.9	7.5	8.1	8.6	9.2	9.8	10.3	10.9	11.4	12.0	12.6	13.1	14.4
Skiing (level, 5 mph)	7.0	7.7	8.4	9.1	9.8	10.5	11.1	11.8	12.5	13.2	13.9	14.6	15.2	15.9	17.3
Skiing (racing downhill)	9.9	10.9	11.9	12.9	13.7	14.7	15.7	16.7	17.7	18.7	19.6	20.6	21.6	22.6	24.4
Snowshoeing (2.3 mph)	3.7	4.1	4.5	4.8	5.2	5.5	5.9	6.3	6.7	7.0	7.4	7.8	8.1	8.5	9.2
Soccer	5.4	5.9	6.4	6.9	7.5	8.0	8.5	9.0	9.6	10.1	10.6	11.1	11.6	12.2	13.2
Squash	6.2	6.8	7.5	8.1	8.7	9.3	9.9	10.5	11.1	11.7	12.3	12.9	13.5	14.2	15.4
Stationary running 140 counts/min.	14.6	16.1	17.5	18.9	20.4	21.8	23.2	24.6	26.1	27.5	28.9	30.4	31.8	33.2	36.1
Swimming, pleasure 25 yds./min.	3.6	4.0	4.3	4.7	5.0	5.4	5.7	6.1	6.4	6.8	7.1	7.5	7.8	8.2	8.9
Swimming, breast 20 yds./min.	2.9	3.2	3.4	3.8	4.0	4.3	4.6	4.9	5.1	5.4	5.7	6.0	6.3	6.5	7.1
Swimming, butterfly 50 yds./min.	7.0	7.7	8.4	9.1	9.8	10.5	11.1	11.9	12.5	13.2	13.9	14.6	15.2	15.9	17.3
Swimming, crawl 20 yds./min.	2.9	3.2	3.4	3.8	4.0	4.3	4.6	4.9	5.1	5.4	5.7	5.8	6.3	6.5	7.1
Table Tennis	2.3	2.6	2.8	3.0	3.2	3.5	3.7	3.9	4.1	4.2	4.6	4.8	5.0	5.3	5.7
Tennis (recreation)	4.2	4.6	5.0	5.4	5.8	6.2	6.6	7.0	7.4	7.8	8.2	8.6	9.0	9.4	10.2
Volleyball (moderate)	3.4	3.8	4.0	4.4	4.8	5.1	5.4	5.8	6.1	6.4	6.8	7.1	7.4	7.8	8.3
Walking (4.5 mph)	4.0	4.4	4.7	5.1	5.5	5.9	6.3	6.7	7.1	.7.5	7.8	8.2	8.6	9.0	9.8
Water-skiing	4.7	5.1	5.6	6.1	6.5	7.0	7.4	7.9	8.3	8.8	9.3	9.7	10.2	10.6	11.5
Weight Training	4.7	5.1	5.7	6.2	6.7	7.0	7.5	7.9	8.4	8.9	9.4	9.9	10.3	10.8	11.7
Wrestling	7.7	8.5	9.2	10.0	10.7	11.5	12.2	13.0	13.7	14.5	15.2	16.0	16.7	17.5	19.0

Saving Calories

Try cutting 100 calories from your daily diet by:
- eating smaller portions
- eat a little less
- substituting healthier food such as:

Instead of . . .	(cal.)	Substitute these . . .	(cal.)	Save
milkshakes	260	yogurt shake with fruit	140	120
brownie with nuts, 2 in.	300	angel food cake, 1 slice	125	175
fruit pie, 1 slice	300	apple, baked	95	205
doughnut, glazed	235	muffin (corn, bran, berry)	135	100
fish, breaded and fried, 3 oz.	175	fish, broiled, 3 oz.	80	95
ice cream, 1/2 cup	175	ice milk, 1/2 cup	90	85

A Portion vs. A Serving

Food portions have become larger. The portion is the amount of a specific food you choose to eat. A serving is a unit of measure used to describe the amount of food recommended from a food group.

Remember This ☑

Forget the Guilt . . .

If you get off your diet or exercise plan occasionally, don't feel guilty. Just get back on track as soon as possible.

A fad diet is one that promotes an approach to eating that depends on one food (for example, grapefruit), a special combination of foods, or the elimination of or dependence on one major food group. These types of diets are not based on sound nutritional practices. Fad dieting ultimately leads to failure, because any weight loss is usually not permanent. The main shortcoming of fad diets is that they do not bring about a change in basic eating habits and lifestyle. Again, the best strategy for a lifetime of successful weight control is a sound, nutritious diet combined with regular, vigorous exercise.

Actually, it is fortunate that so few people can stay on a fad diet. Most quick reducing diets lack the necessary nutritional balance and may cause great harm if followed for long periods of time. Remember there is no magic combination of foods to cause weight loss and no one food can help break down fat.

A weight loss plan should NOT:
- emphasize a particular food (grapefruit, yogurt, cabbage soup, etc.).
- guarantee a weight loss of specific pounds.
- eliminate one major food group (for example, carbohydrates).
- say it is "fast," "easy," or "quick." Permanent weight loss takes time.

- be linked to a food product that is only available through the diet program.

Diet Aids (Pills, Candy, Gum, etc.)

The goals of diet aids are to curb the appetite, numb the taste buds or provide a feeling of fullness. Just because these aids are sold over-the-counter (that is, without a prescription) doesn't mean they are completely safe. Certain individuals may be sensitive to a particular chemical contained in the product, may unintentionally overdose on the product or may develop other side effects. The major drawback of these plans, however, is that they do not contribute to permanent weight loss.

Fasting and Extreme Calorie Restriction

Some people mistakenly seek self-starvation or **fasting** as a means of quick weight loss. Fasting tends to confuse the body and it starts burning up the wrong tissue. Weight lost by fasting and other drastic measures such as extremely low calorie diets is mainly lean body mass or muscle—not fat.

Another problem from a severe calorie cutback is that the body decreases the rate at which calories are burned and actually stores fat more efficiently. Fasting is not an effective or safe approach to weight loss.

There is also no evidence that fasting can cleanse your body of toxins. Most of the loss from fasting is fluid and minerals needed by the body—not fat.

Myths about Weight Control

Fad Diets Can Lead to Permanent Weight Loss

Fad diets are not the best way to lose weight and keep it off. You may lose weight at first on one of these diets, but most people get tired of them and regain any lost weight.

Remember This ✓

Excuses, excuses. . .

- Do you avoid exercising because you say you don't have time?
- Are you afraid of failure?
- Have you tried and failed before?

Now is the time to establish a weight loss plan and follow it. Don't make excuses—make the time!

Did You Know?

Starvation and extreme calorie reduced diets cause substantial losses of water and fat-free tissue. On the other hand, exercise and burning more calories results in weight loss consisting primarily of fat.

Eat a variety of foods to get the nutrients you need.

Fad diets may also be unhealthy if followed for a long time because they may not provide all of the nutrients your body needs.

High-protein/low-carbohydrate diets are a healthy way to lose weight.

The long-term health effects of a high-protein/low-carbohydrate diet are not known, and it is definitely not a balanced eating plan. High protein foods such as meat, cheese, and eggs may raise heart disease risk by including too much fat and cholesterol. Eating too few fruits, vegetables and whole grains may lead to constipation due to lack of dietary fiber.

Certain foods, like grapefruit, celery, or cabbage soup, can burn fat and make you lose weight.

No foods can burn fat. Some foods with caffeine may speed up your metabolism for a short time, but they do not cause weight loss. The best way to lose weight is to cut back on the total number of calories you eat and be more physically active.

Specific food combinations can cause you to lose weight.

There is no scientific evidence that eating foods in certain sequence or in a specific combination will burn fat or cause weight loss.

Natural or herbal weight-loss products are safe and effective.

A weight-loss product that claims to be "natural" or "herbal" is not necessarily safe. You should talk with your doctor before using any weight-loss product. Many of these products have not been scientifically tested to prove that they are safe or that they work.

Remember This ☑

Quick weight loss usually turns into quick weight gain.

Skipping meals is a good way to lose weight.

Studies show that people who skip breakfast and eat fewer times during the day tend to be heavier than people who eat a healthy breakfast and eat four or five times a day. It is better to eat small meals throughout the day that include a variety of healthy, low-fat, low-calorie foods.

Over-the-counter diet pills suppress appetite or raise metabolic rates.

These pills can cause high blood pressure, dehydration and poor nutrient absorption. There is a risk of dependency as stronger doses are needed.

Meal replacement products such as liquid drinks can control calories by replacing regular meals and snacks.

These products alone cannot help you lose weight. Most people cannot stay with these plans over time because they eliminate flexibility of food choices.

Spot Reducing

Spot reducing is an attempt to lose fat in a particular area of the body by exercising the muscles in that area. It is impossible to spot reduce. Exercising the muscles in a particular area will not cause the fat around that muscle to be broken down for energy. During vigorous exercise the muscles call upon fat storage deposits throughout the body for fuel. The best way to lose fat is to participate in vigorous activities that can be performed for long periods of time.

For Your Information

Rather than cutting your calories on a restricted diet (which will lead to fewer vitamins, minerals and nutrients), try adding 400-500 calories of exercise and cutting out 400-500 calories of food from your diet.

The best way to lose fat is vigorous activities.

For Your Information

When you stop exercising muscle does not turn to fat. Muscle and fat are two different types of tissue. Your muscles may shrink because of inactivity and then fat can fill the space which leads you to think the muscle has turned to fat.

Eliminating Cellulite

There is really no such thing as **cellulite**. The term is used frequently to describe fat that appears to cause ripples and bumps on the thighs and buttocks. These fat dimples are caused by the way fat gets trapped between connective tissues that lay between your skin and other muscles. When the tissues are weak, the fat pushing against them causes a dimpled look. Fat is fat. It is additional weight gain that causes the bulging look. Since females tend to store more fat in the thighs and buttocks ("pear shape"), they may be more likely to have this dimpled look. The many special cures which are advertised for cellulite (massages, scrubbing, creams, supplements and injections) are not effective. The fat causing this dimpled look is lost just like all other fat in the body—by burning more calories than you take in—by losing weight through diet and exercise.

Special Equipment

Advertisers make many claims and promises for exercise equipment to aid in weight loss. It is important to recognize the limitations and dangers of using these techniques. Equipment such as electric stimulators, plastic or rubberized sweat suits, inflated belts, body wraps and steam baths are totally ineffective in helping lose fat tissue and can be harmful. Refer to Chapter 17 for more information about various types of gimmicks and gadgets.

Excessive dehydration caused by wearing rubberized or plastic clothing is extremely dangerous and does not contribute to a permanent weight loss. Wearing such clothing causes the body temperature to rise to a potentially dangerous level, because the sweat cannot evaporate and evaporation is the body's cooling mechanism. As the temperature continues to rise, sweating increases, leading to excessive water loss. Many people, in their eagerness to lose weight, mistake water loss caused by excessive sweating with fat loss.

Special Dangers of Dieting

The advertising media places considerable attention on the personal appearance of young people—especially young females. Advertisements of all types show slender females and muscular, athletic males. It is important to realize that not everyone can attain this type of body build. You must consider realistic goals for yourself.

If you decide to lose weight, do it for the right reasons and in the right way. Don't feel pressured by others to look a certain way.

Eating disorders such as anorexia nervosa and bulimia can be caused by an obsession with losing weight. Make certain you are following a healthy weight management plan.

Anorexia Nervosa

Although it is important to maintain an optimal body weight level and an acceptable body fat level, it is not healthy to become obsessed with weight loss or employ extreme measures to attain weight loss. Some weight loss methods are extremely dangerous, can lead to serious health problems and can even be life-threatening. **Anorexia nervosa** is a condition of self-imposed starvation in order to maintain an extremely low body weight. An anorexic has an obsession to become thin and have a "perfect body." This disease, which is particularly common among young females, is characterized by an intense fear of becoming obese—even after losing a considerable amount of weight.

An anorexic usually begins with a normal dieting program, then begins to skip one or more meals a day, and then may not eat for several days. Anorexics often use methods such as excessive exercising, self-induced vomiting, laxatives or diuretics (substances that cause water loss) to speed up weight loss.

Characteristics of individuals who have anorexia nervosa include: an unusually stressful life, social

Did You Know?

It's never too late. . .

Even if you are very obese or have not established a regular exercise plan, you can begin today to develop a weight loss program that will work.

STRESS Stopper

Some people create their own stress by believing they should be able to control all areas of their life. This week try to be realistic about the things that occur which are out of your control. Accept the things you cannot change. Keep a list of the items that continue to frustrate and stress you.

Maintain optimal body weight, but do not become obsessed with weight loss.

Did You Know?

Men with eating disorders usually rely on excessive exercise to stay slim. Women rely more on diet pills and laxatives.

For Your Information

What can you do to overcome an eating disorder?

- Learn to take care of yourself physically and emotionally.
- See a physician.
- Consult a counselor to help you build life skills that will be more effective for you.

Asking for professional help may be difficult, but it is essential and will help you recover faster.

rejection, loss of a boyfriend, poor self-esteem, depression, an obsessive/compulsive personality, a perfectionist attitude, and a mother-dominated family.

Typically, an anorexic cannot overcome the disorder without treatment, yet it is often difficult for the person to accept help and seek treatment. A trained counselor can provide psychological and medical therapy to assist the individual in overcoming the disorder and reversing the physical damage. Some anorexics may require hospitalization and long-term treatment.

Recognizing Anorexia Nervosa

Someone with the following behaviors may be anorexic:

- Refuses to maintain body weight over a minimal normal weight for age and height.
- Intense fear of gaining weight or becoming fat (even though underweight).
- For females the absence of at least 3 consecutive menstrual cycles (when they are otherwise expected to occur).
- Wearing baggy clothes to hide the body.

People who exhibit the following characteristics may be anorexic:

- Rigid dieting causing dramatic weight loss.
- Inaccurate body perception—believing they are fat even when underweight.
- Rituals involving food, excessive exercise and other aspects of life.
- Maintaining rigid control of lifestyle.
- Feeling of panic after a small weight gain.
- Preoccupation with food, its preparation and observing others eating.
- Feeling of helplessness in the presence of food.
- Empowered by self-denial and strict discipline.
- Mood swings.
- Obsession with weighing themselves.
- Obsession with calorie counting.

Bulimia

Another eating disorder which is particularly common among young women is **bulimia**. Bulimia is a pattern of binge eating and purging (eliminating) the food by vomiting and laxatives. As with anorexics, bulimics are preoccupied with food and body image. However, it may be more difficult to identify individuals who are bulimic, since they typically maintain a body weight that is near normal.

A bulimic may binge eat 1,000 to 20,000 calories in a one or two hour period. This is followed by purging or fasting.

As with anorexics, early treatment by trained professionals is vital to overcome this dangerous eating disorder.

Recognizing Bulimia

Someone with the following behaviors may have bulimia:

- Recurrent episodes of binge eating (rapid consumption of large amounts of food in a short period of time).
- A feeling of lack of control over eating behavior (during the eating binge).
- Regularly engaging in self-induced vomiting, use of laxatives or diuretics, strict dieting or fasting, or vigorous exercise to prevent weight gain.
- A minimum average of two binge eating episodes a week for at least three months.
- Persistent overconcern with body shape and weight.

People who exhibit the following characteristics may have bulimia:

- Eating when depressed.
- Low self-esteem and guilt.
- Loss of control.
- Perfectionism—trying to be a "people pleaser."
- Use of food as an escape from an otherwise carefully controlled and regulated life.
- Never overeating in front of others—secretive binge eating.

For Your Information

About one out of every 200 women between 12 and 30 years old has anorexia nervosa.

About 5% of college aged women have bulimia.

Inaccurate body perception may be a sign of an eating disorder.

Muscle building exercises are an excellent way to gain weight.

Gaining Weight Safely

Some individuals have difficulty gaining weight and feel they are too thin or underweight. This person may be an athlete who burns an excessive number of calories during workouts or someone whose heredity or metabolism rate contributes to a lower weight. Although some individuals may be unhappy about being "underweight," if you regularly eat a healthy selection of foods, it is important to be cautious in undertaking a program to gain weight. You may be unhappy about being thin now, but you naturally gain weight as you grow older and mature. Many overweight adults remember when they could eat anything and never gain an ounce, but now have great difficulty controlling their weight.

Follow these suggestions to gain weight safely:

- Use muscle building exercises to stimulate muscular development. Remember good muscular development contributes to a better looking physique and muscle is heavier than fat deposits.
- Substitute fruit juices and skim milk for beverages such as coffee and tea. Fruit juices and frozen yogurt shakes can greatly increase your calorie intake.
- Drink a commercial nutritional supplement.
- Eat healthy snacks between meals—low-fat fruit yogurt, hot or cold cereal, muffins, bananas, dried fruit, baked potatoes topped with cottage cheese, vegetable pizza.
- Eat three meals or more per day consistently. Do not skip a meal—make mealtime a priority.
- Eat larger portions.
- Drink extra fluids such as low-fat milk or juices. Cranberry juice is particularly high in calories.
- Don't gain weight by eating more high-fat foods. This can lead to high cholesterol.

Remember This ☑

Gain Muscle—Not Fat!

Make certain you gain muscle by exercising. Just eating more without activity will cause you to gain fat weight.

Get the Body You Want:

Picture yourself as you would like to look and feel. Create this vision and then decide what it would take to get there. You can become a little fitter, stronger, leaner and healthier!

Did You Know?

Food Labels

Buying fat-free or reduced fat versions of foods such as ice cream and chips can be a little misleading. For instance, a serving size of regular potato chips has 120 calories. One and a half servings of fat-free potato chips also has 120 calories. Be careful that you don't eat more because a food has less fat.

Summary

Weight control is a problem you may encounter at some time in your life. By establishing sound eating habits, you can gain control of your weight now and for the future.

Begin by understanding your body composition and knowing whether you are overweight, overfat or at your optimal weight and fat level.

There are many health dangers associated with being obese or overfat. The major cause of overweight is inactivity.

You can use this basic rule: balance your calorie intake with your calorie expenditure (what you burn) to control your weight at an optimal level.

While exercise and certain diet plans can contribute to weight loss, the most effective method is a combination of exercise and sensible diet adjustment. You must avoid fad diets, fasting, diet aids and other gimmicks that are ineffective and can be dangerous.

Chapter 9 Review

Lesson Checklist

- Do you know how to determine your body composition?
- Do you know the importance of maintaining appropriate body weight and fat levels?
- Do you know the importance of exercise to a diet plan?
- Can you describe several of the keys to permanent weight control?
- Can you recognize the signs of anorexia and bulimia?

Chapter Projects

Write a response to each of the following:

1. Describe the difference between obese, overfat and overweight.
2. How does calorie intake affect weight?
3. Why are fad diets discouraged?
4. Why do fasting diets fail to achieve a loss of fat?
5. Describe one potential danger of using over the counter diet aids.
6. Why is spot reducing ineffective?
7. How does exercise contribute to fat loss?
8. Describe three guidelines for permanent weight control.

Behavior Change Evaluation

Review the following items to see if you have gained an understanding of fitness and wellness. On a piece of paper briefly state how you will make these changes.

- I will include daily activity in my schedule to help balance my caloric intake.
- I will not be fooled by advertisements for fad diets, fasting and extreme calorie reduction plans, or diet pills.
- I will not be misled by ads for products to spot reduce or eliminate "cellulite."

Critical Thinking

Using the information you have gained from this chapter, describe your body type, body composition, weight loss or gain needs, and the weight control plan you intend to follow.

Chapter 9 Review

Test Your Knowledge

Read the questions below and select the best possible answer for each.

1. The storage of fat necessary for normal body functioning is called
   a. storage fat
   b. essential fat
   c. nonessential fat
   d. excess fat

2. The fat in the body that is storage fat and exists primarily within fat cells just below the skin and around major organs is called
   a. nonessential fat
   b. essential fat
   c. primary fat
   d. unnecessary fat

3. Drastically reducing your calorie intake will
   a. insure permanent weight loss for most people.
   b. shrink your stomach
   c. slow metabolism and cause loss of lean tissue
   d. burn up only body fat

4. Which is true regarding fasting diets?
   a. They cleanse the body.
   b. They cause and increase in the rate at which calories are burned.
   c. They are effective for permanent weight loss.
   d. They cause loss of lean muscle tissue.

5. Which of the following will result in weight loss?
   a. calories taken in are equal to calories burned
   b. calories taken in are greater than calories burned
   c. calories taken in are less than calories burned
   d. calories taken in are less than 4000

6. Which is NOT a guideline for permanent weight control?
   a. weight loss should be gradual
   b. regular exercise should be included
   c. maintain intake of required nutrients
   d. limit calorie intake to one meal a day

7. Which type of exercise will help burn the greatest number of calories?
   a. aerobic
   b. stretching
   c. strength training
   d. all are the same

8. How many calories are in a pound of body fat?
   a. 2,000
   b. 3,000
   c. 3,500
   d. 5,000

Handling Stress

10

Chapter Topics

- What is Stress?
- What Causes Stress?
- The Body's Reaction to Stress
- The Effects of Stress on the Body
- Finding Your Stress Zone
- Preventing and Coping with Stress
- Avoiding Negative Coping Strategies
- Controlling Your Anger
- Dealing with Peer Pressure

Chapter Objectives

After completing this chapter, you will be able to:

- Define stress.
- Understand the causes of stress.
- Explain how stress affects you.
- Describe how stress management activities can be helpful to you.
- Describe how physical exercise helps relieve stress.
- Describe positive and negative coping strategies.

Key Words

adrenaline

alarm stage

assertive behavior

distress

endorphins

eustress

exhaustion stage

fight or flight

homeostasis

resistance stage

stress

stressor

Suggested Physical Activities

Try exercise as a stress-reliever the next time you feel tense. Observe how you feel after exercise.

Healthy People 2010 Goals

◆ Reduce substance abuse to protect the health, safety and quality of life for all, especially children.

◆ Increase the age and proportion of adolescents who remain alcohol and drug free.

◆ Increase the proportion of adolescents who disapprove of substance abuse.

◆ Increase the proportion of adolescents who perceive great risk associated with substance abuse.

Use the *Personal Fitness for You* Student CD for:

◆ Lab 10-1: Handling Your Stress

◆ Lab 10-2: Stresso: A Game to Determine Stress

◆ Lab 10-3: Stress Awareness

◆ Lab 10-4: Assertive Behavior

◆ Lab 10-5: A Method of Relaxation

◆ Chapter Practice Test

◆ Chapter Study Guide

◆ Chapter Crossword Puzzle

◆ Vocabulary Flash Cards

◆ Chapter Power Point Review

Making a class presentation can be stressful for some people.

What Is Stress?

You experience stress everyday. Life would be boring without it! **Stress** is a nonspecific response of the body to any demand made upon it. This means that the body will react in a similar manner whether the stress is good (positive) or bad (negative).

Stress response can vary from one individual to another. Something which may be extremely stressful to one person may cause very little reaction from another person. Some people seem to accept situations and may even feel challenged by changes in their lives, while others may become upset, confused and uptight. For instance, being asked to make a class presentation may cause one student extreme anxiety and nervousness, while another student may become more creative and produce better work under stress.

What Causes Stress?

Stressors are the things that cause stress. Stressors cause positive stress (**eustress**) and negative stress (**distress**). Examples of stressors which cause eustress for some people could be going to the prom, playing in a championship game and starting a new job. However, these same stressors could result in distress for other people. Remember, response to stress varies from individual to individual. Examples of negative stressors include failing an exam, being fired from a job and breaking up with a boyfriend or girlfriend.

Stress caused by a personal relationship is an example of distress.

Types of Stressors

Stressors cause the **homeostasis**, or internal balance of the body, to be upset. The following are types of stressors:

- **Psychological**—such as love, fear, anxiety
- **Environmental**—such as excessive heat, cold, noise, overcrowding
- **Social**—such as personal relationships, family problems, loneliness, discrimination
- **Physiological**—such as illness, injuries, fatigue, drugs, foods such as caffeine, salt, sugar and alcohol

Stressors upset your internal balance.

The Body's Reaction to Stress

The body reacts to stress, whether eustress or distress, in three stages or levels.

Level 1—The Alarm Stage

The **alarm stage** is the first level of stress. During this stage, the body recognizes the stressor and prepares for "**fight or flight**" (dealing with or escaping the situation) by releasing hormones such as **adrenaline**. The body's immediate physical responses to stress are shown on the next page.

Family Activity

Have a family discussion about each family member's stressors. Talk about ways to reduce or cope with these stressors.

STRESS Stopper

5 Stress Busters:
- Exercise
- Deep Breathing
- Meditate
- Get a massage
- Progressive muscle relaxation

The Body's Response to Stress

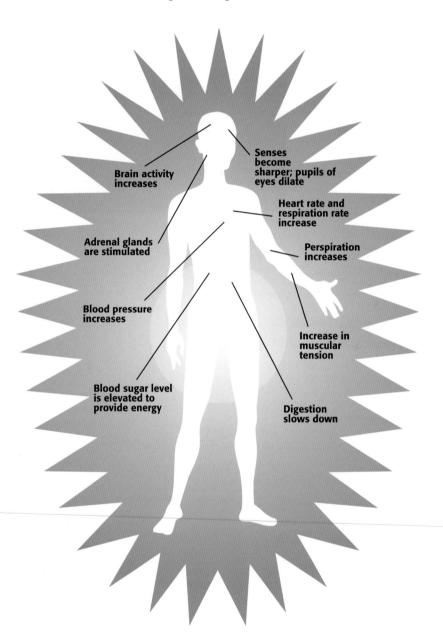

Brain activity increases

Senses become sharper; pupils of eyes dilate

Heart rate and respiration rate increase

Adrenal glands are stimulated

Perspiration increases

Blood pressure increases

Increase in muscular tension

Blood sugar level is elevated to provide energy

Digestion slows down

Everyone has daily experiences which stimulate muscle-producing tensions. For instance, an argument with your parents or a fight with a close friend will cause tension which may trigger such short-term symptoms as tense neck and shoulder muscles, inability to sleep, constipation, irritability and fatigue. These symptoms usually disappear as a person copes with his or her particular problem.

Level 2—The Resistance Stage

During the **resistance stage**, the body attempts to adjust to the stressor and return to normal. The heart rate and respiration rate decrease and hormones are secreted which give the body the energy to cope with the stressor. This phase may be of very short duration and may use only a small amount of energy which is easily replaced. However, if intense or long-term stress exhausts the amount of stored energy available and the problem persists, the body enters the third stage of stress.

Level 3—The Exhaustion Stage

The third stage of stress is the **exhaustion stage** and may lead to disease. Prolonged stress can affect the body in a number of ways. If stress continues long enough, and your body cannot cope with it, you may suffer from short-term or long-term effects of stress which are described in the next section.

If stress persists, you may experience long-term effects.

The Effects of Stress on the Body

Overcrowding, noise, traffic, pollution, overwork, competition and money problems are among ongoing stressors. As the human body tries to deal constantly with these stressors, it experiences a continual state of arousal. This can cause a loss of energy and possibly lead to nervousness, pain and disease. Over a long period of time, cardiovascular, kidney and glandular diseases may also develop.

The relationship of stress and disease is complex. Factors which may determine if a person becomes sick as a result of stress, include:
- the number of stressful events
- the severity of stressful events
- how the person perceives the stressful events
- how the person responds to the stressful events
- how the person copes with the stressful events

Short Term Stress Symptoms:
- Headaches
- Diarrhea
- Dizziness
- Fatigue

Long Term Stress Symptoms:
- Severe headaches
- Depression
- Fatigue
- Weight control problems
- May affect the heart, blood pressure, stomach, muscles and joints

STRESS Stopper

Even small changes can help reduce stress. Try:
- Leaving earlier for school.
- Taking breaks between tasks.
- Letting the phone ring a few times before answering it.

Finding Your Stress Zone

As noted earlier, not all stress is harmful - some actually helps us perform at a higher level. The key is to find your desirable stress zone. The chart below shows that a person with no motivation or stress has a low performance level. As motivation or stress increases, performance increases. Moderate stress results in optimal performance for most activities. As stress increases to excess, performance declines.

For example, an athlete who is not motivated and does not try very hard will often perform poorly. If he or she is overstressed, poor performance is also likely to occur. A similar situation may occur when you take a test. If you are not motivated, you may not put forth your best effort. Being nervous or tense may interfere with your performance as well.

HIGH

PERFORMANCE LEVEL

UNDERSTRESSED ZONE	DESIRABLE STRESS ZONE	OVERSTRESSED ZONE
Dissatisfaction	Good Self-Esteem	Tiredness
Bored	Ability to Change	Illness
Easily Fatigued	Effective Problem-Solving Skills	Low Self-Esteem
Frustrated	Creativity	Extreme Tension
	Self-Motivated	Irrational Behavior

LOW

Low   Moderate **Stress Level**   High

Keep Things in Perspective

Perception, or how we see a problem, determines our stress level. In other words, what might be a problem for one person, may not be for another. Since stress is so individualized, it is important to keep your problems in focus or perspective.

Try not to let minor irritations or hassles cause an unnecessary amount of anxiety. Everyone experiences annoyances such as having to wait in lines, losing your keys or being stuck in traffic. Instead of worrying about things which are beyond your control, realize that you have to put up with them and relax. Look around and see how tense other people are getting and be proud of the fact that you can control your emotions. Try to evaluate each situation in relationship to the big picture.

Practice Assertive Behavior

Another strategy to cope with a stressful situation is to practice **assertive behavior**. The theory of assertive behavior is that every person has certain basic rights. When you give into pressures and do things which are against your basic beliefs, you are setting up a guilt/stress situation which may cause possible ill effects to your mind and body.

For example, you are with a group of friends who are experimenting with mood altering substances (alcohol or drugs). They pressure you to join them. You do not believe in what they are doing but value their friendship. Your choices are:

1. Leave your friends to avoid having to make a decision.
2. Deny your own wishes and beliefs to satisfy theirs (non-assertive behavior).

STRESS Stopper

If you're angry at someone, write down your feelings in a letter. Don't hold back—tell it like it is. Put the letter in a drawer and two days later, read it. Do you still want to send it? Probably not!

Remember This ✓

Let other people do their own thing. Things don't always have to be done your way.

3. Express yourself by saying why you do not care to participate, but in a way that meets your needs to feel good about yourself and not hurt others in the process (assertive behavior).

Of course, it is not as easy for some people to say "no" as it is for others. Remember that assertiveness is not only what you say but how you say it. Body language is as important as what you say. Note the body language difference between these assertive and non-assertive behaviors:

Assertive	Non-assertive
Faces person talking to	Does not face person
Maintains eye contact	Avoids eye contact
Stands straight and steady	Sways and shifts weight
Speaks confidently, clearly	Does not talk loud enough
Does not hesitate	Lacks confidence, is uneasy

If you say one thing and behave differently, you will probably have trouble convincing your friends that you mean what you say.

Establish Challenging and Attainable Goals

Be realistic when setting goals. Don't add to your frustration by overextending yourself and then not being able to accomplish your goals as quickly as you would like. Aside from school, you may also be involved in clubs, athletic teams, jobs, hobbies, chores at home, church and other activities. Decide which activities are most important to you. Make sure that you have the time and energy to devote to the activities you choose.

Learn Time Management

Time management techniques are very helpful. Keep an appointment book or calendar to organize your time and remind yourself of important dates and events.

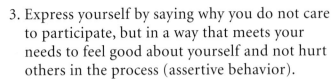

STRESS Stopper

5 More Stress Busters:
- Listen to Music
- Play with your cat or dog
- Take a hot bath
- Connect spiritually
- Limit caffeine, greasy foods

Keep an appointment book or calendar to organize your time.

Knowing when tests and assignments are due and allotting time to study is a great stress reducer.

Learn to say "no" and set priorities. Don't agree to do more than you have time or energy to do. Avoid crowding too many things into one day. Allow yourself time to relax each day.

Limit Certain Foods

Eating foods with high amounts of caffeine, such as soft drinks, chocolate, coffee and some teas can cause you to be irritable and unable to cope with stress. Foods with high concentrations of sugar, such as many packaged snacks and candies, can have the same effect. Eating a nutritious, balanced diet will help you look good and perform better, making you less susceptible to stress.

Foods with a high sugar content can increase your stress level.

Share Your Stress

Just talking to someone about your concerns and worries often helps alleviate stress. A trusted friend, family member, counselor or teacher may be able to help you view your problem in a different way.

Learn Stress Diversion Activities

Another approach to coping with stress is to participate in activities that can reduce, eliminate or divert tension. By filling your leisure time with a variety of activities, it is possible to reduce the effects of stress, both physiologically and psychologically. Identify specific activities which are most enjoyable and relaxing for you.

Spending time with a pet is a good stress diversion.

To learn more about stress management, visit the following web site:
www.pp.okstate.edu/ehs/links/stress.htm

Examples of diversion activities include:
- listening to your favorite music or playing an instrument.
- taking a long walk—going to the beach, a park or shopping mall.
- enjoying nature; studying or reading outside.
- spending time with a pet.
- going to a movie or to the zoo.
- working on a hobby or craft—writing, painting, creating something.
- finding time to be alone and get your thoughts together.
- participating in sports or recreational activities.
- doing yoga or tai chi.

Use Exercise to Reduce Stress

Vigorous exercise is a very beneficial way to relieve stress. Exercising uses up the excess adrenaline produced to prepare you for the fight or flight response, allowing your heart rate, respiration rate and blood pressure to return to normal following the exercise. In addition, as you exercise you improve your fitness level, which keeps you from becoming easily fatigued and enables you to cope with negative stressors.

Benefits of Exercise to Reduce Stress

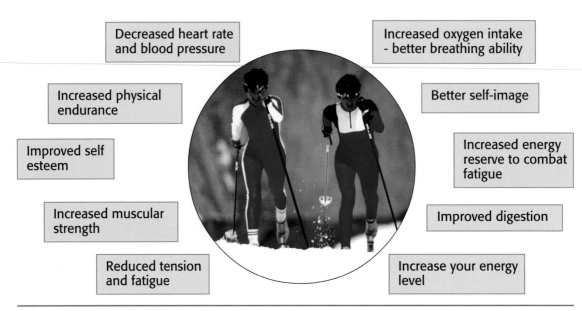

Decreased heart rate and blood pressure

Increased oxygen intake - better breathing ability

Increased physical endurance

Better self-image

Improved self esteem

Increased energy reserve to combat fatigue

Increased muscular strength

Improved digestion

Reduced tension and fatigue

Increase your energy level

Endorphins are stress and pain-relieving substances produced naturally by the body. When comparing physically active and inactive people under stress, it has been found that endorphins are produced faster and in greater amounts among active people. Regular exercise fine-tunes the endorphin producers. During vigorous exercise, endorphins are released, causing changes in a person's mental attitude. For example, during a workout runners may experience "runner's high," which is a state of increased energy and mental alertness due to the release of endorphins. There are also other chemicals that, as they are released during exercise, produce mental alertness and the ability to think and react quickly.

Exercise does not have to be strenuous to reduce stress. Working in the garden, walking with a friend or any other type of moderate exercise can make you feel better. If you select an activity that is enjoyable for you, you will enjoy working out and at the same time eliminate feelings of stress.

Meditation

Meditation is an easy relaxation technique to learn. It requires no special equipment and once learned, can be practiced almost anywhere. The relaxation response brought about by meditation causes a decrease in heart and respiratory rates, blood pressure and muscle tension.

To meditate:
1. Sit in an upright position in a chair with your hands resting on the arms of the chair or in your lap.
2. Close your eyes and repeat the word "one" to yourself each time you inhale and the word "two" as you exhale.

Try to practice meditation for 15-20 minutes twice a day, if possible. Don't be concerned with timing yourself. This defeats the purpose of meditation.

Remember This ☑

Make an appointment with yourself if you're putting off something you need to do. Treat the appointment as seriously as you would an appointment with a boss or teacher.

Meditation is an excellent positive method of controlling stress.

STRESS Stopper

Think of a place where you feel at peace. Maybe it is by the beach, a stream, in the woods or by a garden. Find a picture (or take one) that represents the place and keep it on your desk, in the bedroom or bathroom or even in a notebook, so you can look at it frequently. Let seeing the picture trigger you to feel relaxed and at peace.

Progressive Muscle Relaxation

Progressive muscle relaxation is a very effective technique developed by Dr. Edmund Jacobsen and involves tensing and relaxing all the muscle groups in the body. This technique makes you aware of how high levels of muscular tension feel and teaches you how to relax your body at will and release tension from the muscles. It is especially useful for athletes and other performers to control pre-competition anxiety and can also help you sleep better.

Devote at least twenty minutes to this relaxation exercise which is best conducted in a warm, dark room. The exercise sequence can be memorized, read to another person or played on a tape recorder.

To perform the progressive relaxation technique:

1. Lie on your back with a pillow or blanket under your head and/or knees and your arms at your sides. This technique may also be done sitting in a chair, but the back of the chair must be high enough to support your head.
2. Contract the muscles in the toes. Hold the contraction for five seconds and then allow the muscles to totally relax.
3. Contract the muscles in the lower leg. Hold the contraction for five seconds and then allow the muscles to totally relax.

Continue contracting the muscle groups moving up the body. Perform each contraction twice.

Deep Breathing

Deep breathing exercises relieve stress by concentrating on breathing and increasing oxygen to the body. These exercises may be performed in any position.

To deep breathe:

1. Inhale slowly and deeply through the nose.
2. Slowly exhale through the mouth.
3. Repeat about ten times.

STRESS Stopper

Stand with your back straight and place your right hand on your chest and your left hand on your stomach. Breathe so that only the hand on your stomach moves. Take a breath from your diaphragm, exhale, then relax. Focus only on your breathing. Don't get distracted by outside thoughts or sounds.

Deep breathing exercises help relieve stress.

Imagery

Imagery can help you deal with stressful situations.

To practice imagery:

Relax, close your eyes and think about a beautiful, peaceful scene such as a forest, lake or mountain. Imagine the details of the scene; pay attention to the smells, sounds and colors.

Continue the imagery until your mind and body are relaxed.

Imagine you are in a stress-free place.

Avoiding Negative Coping Strategies

Everyone has a pattern for coping with stress, but not all patterns are positive. To successfully cope with stress, identify negative coping patterns and replace them with positive ones.

Too often people try to escape stress through substances such as alcohol, drugs, muscle relaxants, tranquilizers and sleeping pills. These "wonder drugs" do not eliminate stress, but are addictive and can actually lead to more stress. Only you can overcome your own stress.

Negative and ineffective coping strategies include:

- too much alcohol
- too much television
- dependence on chemicals or drugs
- tobacco use
- withdrawal or avoidance
- excessive gambling
- overspending

Positive coping strategies such as physical exercise and relaxation techniques are the best ways to combat stress.

Avoid negative coping strategies.

Controlling Your Anger

We see examples of anger in our society every day. Coaches scream at officials, athletes fight during games, drivers yell at each other from their cars. This hostility (called "road rage" when driving a car) draws attention and is meant to intimidate other people. Often the other person becomes defensive and angry which makes it difficult to discuss the problem and arrive at a solution.

When you become angry, your attitude becomes negative and you see yourself as a victim. You may look for ways to "get even" with the person causing your anger, instead of trying to find a constructive solution to the problem. Anger can affect your health, put you at a higher risk for heart disease, cause ulcers and lead to depression.

In order to control your anger you must be aware of your emotions and recognize that they are causing problems in your life. Once you realize that you have a problem controlling your temper, you can help yourself deal with it.

You can help yourself become a calmer person by practicing these strategies:

1. Know what triggers your anger—keep a journal and write down what happens when you're really angry.
2. Try to put yourself in the other person's place. Look at the situation from his or her point of view.
3. Look for humor in the situation—maybe the laugh is on you!
4. Try to be constructive when you express your displeasure. Instead of pointing out someone's mistake, ask "how can we fix this?"

It is important to learn to control your anger.

Practice strategies that will help you become a calmer person.

5. Try to "relabel" a situation or behavior that makes you angry. If someone cuts in front of you in traffic, don't label him or her as a bad person, instead tell yourself that he or she is in a hurry for a good reason.

6. Keep your voice down. Speaking quietly and calmly will help keep the situation under control.

7. Put up a shield. For instance, if someone is yelling at you, remember that he or she is angry at the situation, not at you personally.

8. Practice relaxation techniques. Focus your thoughts on something pleasant and breathe deeply.

9. Walk away or call back later. If you can't control your emotions, tell the other person that you would prefer to make an appointment for a time to sit down and resolve the problem.

10. Remind yourself that other people and things can not make you angry—only your mind can do that. You can choose to react in a stressful way or you can choose to react in a calm way.

It may take some time to change your behavior. You may want to seek help from a counselor. However, seeing the world from a positive angle instead of a negative one will help you become a happier, healthier person.

It is important to control your emotions in stressful situations.

Dealing with Peer Pressure

Your peer group can encourage you to try new activities, volunteer to help others, and offer you support and friendship. But your peer group can also try to make you do things that you would not normally do and could possibly cause you harm. The best way to deal with potentially harmful peer pressure is to avoid it in the first place. Associate with people who have the same interests as you and who like you. Good friends won't make you do things you don't want to do and will respect you when you say no.

Choose your friends wisely.

Did You Know?

Healthy People Exhibit the 3 C's:

1. **C**ontrol over their health.
2. **C**ommitment to work, school, activities and relationships.
3. The ability to see stress as a **C**hallenge rather than a threat.

Make Good Choices

Ask yourself if something is worth doing? Should you go out with your buddies rather than write that paper that is due the next day? Should you skip class and miss a test?

Look at your options. What can go wrong? Will the choice result in a positive outcome?

How do you say no? Use a truthful excuse or just simply say no, thanks. Offer an alternative suggestion to the group. Others in the group may welcome your suggestion.

For Your Information

Stress-related Illnesses:

- Heart disease
- Stroke
- High blood pressure
- Migraine headaches
- Stomach ulcers
- Kidney problems
- Neck or lower back pain
- Chronic fatigue
- Bowel problems
- General anxiety

Handling stress involves making good choices in many areas of your life.

Summary

Stress is the nonspecific response of the body to any demand placed upon it. Stress may be positive (eustress) or negative (distress). Response to a stressor varies from one person to another.

Your body responds to eustress and distress in the same manner. You respond to stress both physically and mentally. If the body fails to adjust to the stressor, short-term effects occur. More harmful long-term effects of stress can seriously affect your health.

Keeping things in perspective, goal setting, assertive behavior, eating correctly, physical exercise, relaxation techniques and other enjoyable activities will help you cope with stress in a positive manner.

Negative coping techniques contribute to further problems and more stress. It is very important to use positive coping strategies to deal with stress rather than negative coping strategies such as using alcohol, tobacco or drugs.

Portfolio Idea

Controlling Your Stress

Record the results of this activity in your personal portfolio or follow the instructions from your teacher.

◆ What types of stressors do you encounter most often?

◆ What coping strategies do you use to deal with your stressors? (Include positive and negative strategies.)

◆ Do you feel stress is affecting your schoolwork, job, relations at home or with friends? If so, how and what do you think you can do to cope with it more effectively?

◆ Is frequent anger a problem for you? If so, what strategies could you try to overcome it?

Chapter 10 Review

Lesson Checklist

- Do you know the difference between eustress and distress?
- Can you list some common causes of stress?
- Can you explain the three stages of stress?
- Do you understand the effects of long-term stress on the body?
- Do you know how physical exercise helps relieve stress?
- Can you describe some positive coping strategies?
- Can you describe how stress management activities can be helpful?
- Can you describe how negative coping strategies can add to a person's stress?
- Do you understand the effects of uncontrolled anger?

Chapter Projects

Keep a journal or diary for two weeks describing your feelings about your physical and psychological well-being before, during and after activity. Describe your level of satisfaction, fulfillment and enjoyment.

Behavior Change Evaluation

Review the following items to see if you have gained an understanding of fitness and wellness. On a piece of paper briefly state how you will make these changes.

- I will try to deal with the minor irritations of life.
- I will make realistic goals and try to accomplish them.
- I will try to use time management techniques, such as an appointment book.
- I will set priorities and will not put things off until the last minute.
- I will learn at least one new activity that I can use to relieve stress.
- I will exercise on a regular basis to help me control stress.

Critical Thinking

- Make a list of three stressors which currently affect you. Then write down the strategies that will help you deal with the stressors.
- How can time management techniques help you control your life?

Test Your Knowledge

Read the questions below and select the best possible answer for each.

1. Which of the following is a symptom of stress?
   a. inability to sleep
   b. headaches
   c. fatigue
   d. all of the above

2. In which stage of stress does the body attempt to adjust to the stressor and return to normal?
   a. alarm
   b. resistance
   c. exhaustion
   d. reaction

3. Which occurs during the first stage of stress?
   a. heart rate increases
   b. blood pressure decreases
   c. digestive system speeds up
   d. muscles relax

4. In which stage of stress does the body prepare for "fight or flight"?
   a. alarm
   b. resistance
   c. exhaustion
   d. reaction

5. Positive stress is called
   a. good stress
   b. distress
   c. eustress
   d. stressors

6. Things or events that cause stress are called
   a. stressors
   b. distress
   c. eustress
   d. stress events

7. Which statement about stress is true?
   a. All stress is bad.
   b. Stress is a nonspecific response of the body to any demand made upon it.
   c. Stressors result from too much stress.
   d. Eustress is negative stress.

8. Which is a way to cope with stress?
   a. meditation
   b. deep breathing
   c. listening to music
   d. all of the above

9. Which is a stress related illness?
   a. heart disease
   b. stroke
   c. high blood pressure
   d. all of the above

10. When the body is subjected to prolonged stress, which stage of stress is entered?
    a. alarm
    b. resistance
    c. exhaustion
    d. reaction

Understanding the Cardiorespiratory System

11

Chapter Topics

- The Heart
- The Blood Vessels
- Blood Pressure
- The Blood
- The Respiratory System
- Effects of Training on the Respiratory System
- Aerobic and Anaerobic Activity
- Cardiovascular Disease
- Prevention of Cardiovascular Disease

Chapter Objectives

After completing this chapter, you will:

- Know the importance of cardiorespiratory fitness to good health.
- Know how the cardiorespiratory systems function.
- Be able to identify the health-related problems associated with an inadequate level of cardiorespiratory fitness.
- Be able to identify the contributions of physical activity to good cardiorespiratory fitness.
- Be able to identify the risk factors associated with cardiovascular disease.

Key Words

aerobic
alveoli
anaerobic
anemia
aorta
arteries
atherosclerosis
atria
bronchi
bronchioles
capillaries
cardiorespiratory fitness
cholesterol

coronary arteries
diaphragm
diastolic
hemoglobin
high blood pressure
hypertension
plaque
plasma
platelet
pulmonary
red blood cell
respiration
septum

stroke
systemic
systolic
trachea
triglycerides
vascular
veins
ventricle
white blood cell

Suggested Physical Activities

◆ Plan three blocks of time this week to perform aerobic activity. Remember to start slowly if you have not been exercising regularly.

◆ Try a new activity such as in-line skating, spinning or another type of exercise in which you have never participated.

Use the *Personal Fitness for You* Student CD for:

◆ Lab 11-1: Understanding How the Heart Works
◆ Lab 11-2: Charting Your Heart Rate
◆ Lab 11-3: Blood Cholesterol Levels
◆ Chapter Practice Test
◆ Chapter Study Guide
◆ Chapter Crossword Puzzle
◆ Chapter Power Point Review
◆ Vocabulary Flash Cards

Achieve cardiorespiratory fitness to look and feel better.

Cardiorespiratory fitness is the ability to perform moderate to high intensity exercise using the large muscles of your body for a prolonged period of time. It is the cardiorespiratory system which supplies the entire body with oxygen. The cells which make up the various tissues in the human body require a constant supply of oxygen to function. As physical activity increases, the oxygen requirement increases.

Cardiorespiratory fitness is a component of health-related physical fitness, because individuals who possess moderate to high levels of fitness tend to have a decreased risk of premature death from cardiovascular disease. Other benefits of moderate to high levels of cardiorespiratory fitness include weight control, stress reduction, more energy and increased self-esteem because you will look and feel better.

The heart, lungs, blood and blood vessels work together to provide the body with an adequate oxygen supply. As cardiorespiratory fitness improves with training, the efficiency and capability of these systems to deliver oxygen to the working muscles also increases.

The Heart

The heart (cardio means pertaining to the heart) is one of the major components of the cardiorespiratory system. It is the ultimate endurance muscle, because it must beat constantly in order to sustain life. It is a relatively small (fist-sized) but powerful pump which circulates approximately 2000 gallons of blood per day.

The heart consists of two pumps. The right side (**pulmonary** pump) sends blood to the lungs and the left side (**systemic** pump) sends blood throughout the body. Each side of the heart is divided into two chambers. The upper chambers are called **atria** and the lower chambers are called **ventricles**. The **septum** is the wall of muscle that separates the left and right chambers.

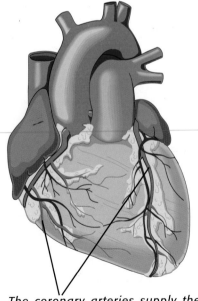

The coronary arteries supply the heart muscle with oxygenated blood.

How the Heart Works

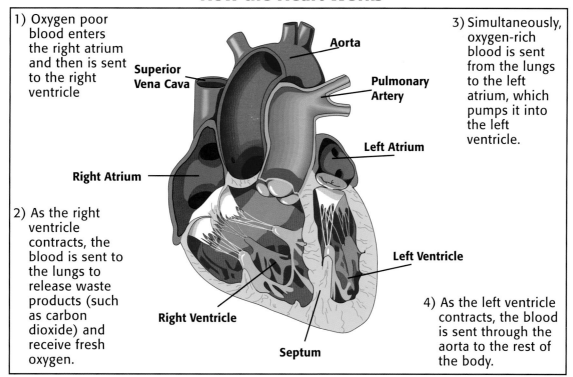

1) Oxygen poor blood enters the right atrium and then is sent to the right ventricle

2) As the right ventricle contracts, the blood is sent to the lungs to release waste products (such as carbon dioxide) and receive fresh oxygen.

3) Simultaneously, oxygen-rich blood is sent from the lungs to the left atrium, which pumps it into the left ventricle.

4) As the left ventricle contracts, the blood is sent through the aorta to the rest of the body.

Aorta

Superior Vena Cava

Pulmonary Artery

Left Atrium

Right Atrium

Left Ventricle

Right Ventricle

Septum

Blood which is low in oxygen is delivered by the veins into the right atrium, which pumps blood into the right ventricle. The **aorta** is the largest artery in the body. **Coronary arteries** branching out from the aorta supply the heart muscle with its own oxygenated blood supply. This is necessary because the heart receives no nourishment from the blood it pumps throughout the body.

Each time the heart beats or contracts, blood is sent out to the body. A simple way to measure heart rate without any equipment is by measuring your pulse, which is caused by the pressure of the blood on the walls of the arteries as the heart pumps. The radial artery in the wrist or the carotid artery in the neck are good pulse-taking sites.

The average resting heart rate is between seventy and eighty beats per minute. Measuring your resting heart rate will give you a good indication of the condition of your heart. A person in good physical condition often has a lower resting heart rate of

WEBSITE

To learn more about cardiorespiratory fitness, visit the following web sites:

American Heart Association:
www.americanheart.org

National Heart, Lung, and Blood Institute:
www.nhlbi.nih.gov/

American Stroke Association:
www.strokeassociation.org

National Stroke Association:
www.stroke.org

forty to sixty beats per minute. This low heart rate indicates a strong heart muscle which pumps more blood with each beat, so it does not have to pump as often to supply the body with the necessary blood. While at rest, your heart pumps about five liters of blood per minute.

The Blood Vessels

The **vascular** system distributes blood throughout the body and is composed of arteries, veins and capillaries.

Arteries carry blood away from the heart. They have thick, muscular walls which help blood move throughout the body. Arteries branch into smaller arterioles, continually decreasing in diameter until the smallest blood vessels, called **capillaries**, are reached. The capillaries are where the oxygen and nutrients are exchanged for carbon dioxide and waste products. They also connect the arterial and venous systems. The capillaries are so small that red blood cells must pass through them single file.

As the blood returns to the heart, it passes through tiny venules, which gradually increase in size and join together to form **veins**, eventually forming the vena cava. Veins do not have muscular walls like arteries, thus blood tends to pool, especially in the legs. There are valves inside the veins which keep blood from flowing backwards. As the skeletal muscles contract, this squeezing movement helps push the blood back toward the heart. People who stand or sit in one position for an extended period of time may feel fatigued because of the pooling of blood in the legs, which results in poor venous return and diminished blood and oxygen to the brain.

Family Activity

Discuss blood pressure with your family members—what it is and what their blood pressure is. Determine if anyone in your family has high blood pressure.

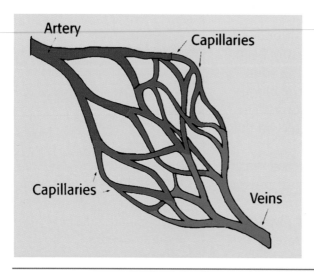

Blood Pressure

As the left ventricle contracts, blood is pushed into the aorta. This pressure on the arteries as blood leaves the heart is called **systolic** pressure. As the ventricle refills, arterial pressure falls, and the low point is called **diastolic** pressure. Normal systolic blood pressure is below 120 mm Hg and normal diastolic blood pressure is below 80 mm Hg. A systolic reading of 140 Hg and higher or a diastolic reading of 90 or higher taken on two separate occasions is classified as **hypertension** or **high blood pressure**.

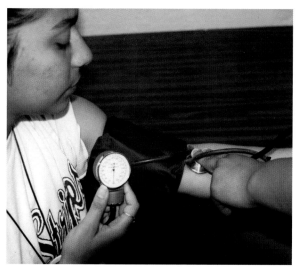

Do you know your blood pressure?

Category	Systolic (mm Hg)	Diastolic (mm Hg)
Normal	below 120	below 80
Prehypertension	120-139	80-89
Hypertension Stage 1	140-159	90-99
Hypertension Stage 2	160 and above	100 and above

The Blood

A person weighing 150 pounds has a blood volume of approximately ten to twelve pints. Blood transports oxygen, carbon dioxide, nutrients, waste products, hormones, antibodies and heat throughout the body. The cellular components (red cells, white cells and platelets) make up about 45% of the blood volume; the remaining 55% is composed of a watery fluid known as **plasma**.

Plasma has a water base, and helps regulate the body temperature. It contains essential minerals, enzymes, fats, sugars, oxygen and carbon dioxide. Suspended in the plasma are large proteins such as globulin, which is involved in the formation of antibodies, and fibrinogen, which plays an important role in the clotting mechanism.

Did You Know?

Over 61 million Americans have hypertension but only half know they have it. Generally there are no symptoms.

The main role of **platelets** is to stop the flow of blood when an injury occurs. The fibrinogen forms fibrin threads which catch the sticky platelets as they flow by, forming a blood clot.

Red blood cells have a life-span of about 120 days, but they are constantly replenished by the bone marrow. Red blood cells contain a substance called **hemoglobin**, which gives the cells their red color. Hemoglobin carries oxygen from the lungs through the blood stream to individual cells and also picks up carbon dioxide for transport back to the lungs to be exhaled. Hemoglobin increases the oxygen-carrying capacity of the blood by about seventy times. A lack of red blood cells or insufficient hemoglobin in the red blood cells results in a deficiency of oxygen being delivered to the muscles. The muscles therefore cannot burn enough fuel, which causes the body to feel tired and weak, a condition known as **anemia**. Adding foods rich in iron to a diet helps reverse hemoglobin deficiency.

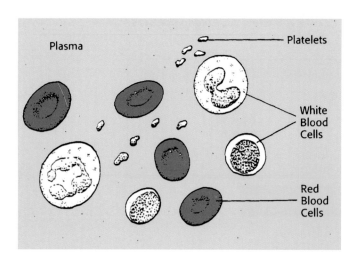

White blood cells help the body fight infection. They attack and consume bacteria and are involved in antibody reactions.

The Respiratory System

The respiratory system is responsible for supplying the entire body with sufficient oxygen to be able to function during rest and during activity. It is also responsible for the removal of carbon dioxide.

A strong muscle called the **diaphragm** separates the chest cavity from the abdominal cavity. As the diaphragm contracts, an area of lower pressure is created, allowing air to come into the lungs (inhalation). As the muscle relaxes, air is forced out (exhalation). As activity level increases, more oxygen is required, thus a greater volume of air is inhaled.

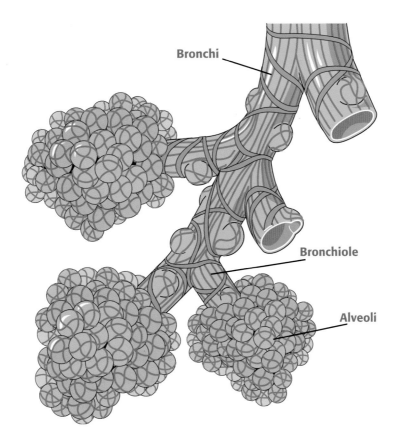

Bronchi

Bronchiole

Alveoli

- Air enters the body through the nasal passages and/or mouth, traveling down the **trachea** which branches into two **bronchi**, each of which leads to a lung.

- The bronchi split into many **bronchioles**, which branch into progressively smaller bronchioles, eventually ending in tiny air sacs called **alveoli**.

- It is in the capillaries in the alveoli walls where the oxygen and carbon dioxide exchange takes place. This exchange of gases between the lungs and the environment is called external **respiration**.

- The bronchial tubes are lined with tiny hairs called cilia which carry mucus up out of the lungs and into the throat. This mucus helps eliminate foreign matter such as dust and germs.

- The right lung has three sections or lobes, while the left lung has two lobes. These lobes are sponge-like and very elastic, capable of expanding and contracting. The lungs are normally capable of supplying more than enough oxygen to meet the needs of physical activity. The volume of air which can be inhaled or exhaled per minute is called ventilation. Respiration rate is the number of breaths per minute, normally about twelve to sixteen breaths per minute at rest.

During exhalation, the diaphragm muscle receives assistance from the muscles between the ribs (intercostal muscles) and the abdominal muscles to make it easier to expel a larger volume of air.

Effects of Training on the Respiratory System

During exercise, the body requires more oxygen but also produces more carbon dioxide, which must be removed. Exercise programs can increase the depth of breathing and decrease the breathing rate, resulting in more efficient breathing. As the heart rate increases during activity, more blood is sent to the lungs. As activity increases, ventilation increases. During maximal effort, ventilation can reach 120 liters of air per minute.

Effects of Exercise on the Heart and Blood Pressure

The amount of blood pumped by the heart increases during exercise, but there is a change in the distribution of blood. Less blood is sent to certain areas of the body (digestion slows down, for example) and more blood is sent to the active skeletal muscles and to the heart muscle. When a person begins to exercise, the blood vessels in the muscles dilate (enlarge) to allow more blood to flow into the working muscles. This causes a slight drop in blood pressure, which is detected by the pressure receptors and relayed to the brain, which sends a signal to the heart to beat stronger and faster to deliver more blood. When the blood pressure becomes too high, the brain signals the heart to slow down. As exercise intensity increases, the heart rate increases. Heart rate is a good measure of exercise intensity. The heart rate can gradually adapt to an increase in workload by beating faster proportionally to the intensity of the exercise, and it will level off (plateau) after about two or three minutes.

Exercise increases the depth of breathing resulting in more efficient breathing.

Did You Know?

Research shows that physical activity lowers resting blood pressure in people with mild or moderate hypertension by an average of 10 points.

The Cardiorespiratory System

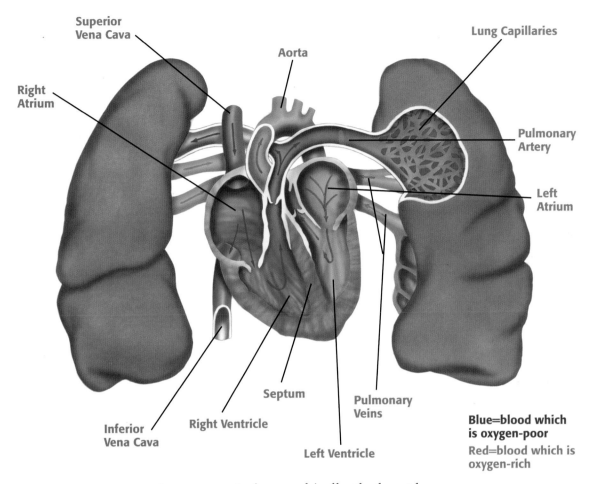

Superior Vena Cava

Aorta

Lung Capillaries

Right Atrium

Pulmonary Artery

Left Atrium

Inferior Vena Cava

Septum

Right Ventricle

Pulmonary Veins

Left Ventricle

Blue=blood which is oxygen-poor

Red=blood which is oxygen-rich

As a person trains aerobically, the heart becomes larger, stronger and more efficient, reducing the number of beats per minute and pumping more blood per beat. This is called a **training effect**. Another result of training is an increase in the formation of capillaries in the skeletal muscles and the heart muscle, which facilitates the exchange of gases between the blood and the muscles, resulting in less fatigue during aerobic activities and faster removal of waste materials.

An additional benefit of aerobic training is the decrease in recovery time after exercise. This means that all systems of the body which have been affected by exercise return to normal more rapidly.

Aerobic and Anaerobic Activity

Aerobic means with oxygen. Aerobic activities are those in which the oxygen supply is sufficient to meet the demands of the working muscle. This causes a steady state during which the individual's heart rate levels off or plateaus, indicating that sufficient energy is being produced to power the muscular contractions. To improve your cardiorespiratory fitness, you need to participate in aerobic activities or exercises which involve the continuous use of the large muscles of your body for a duration of several minutes. Examples of aerobic activities are walking, jogging, running, cycling, swimming, dancing, cross-country skiing, stair climbing, rowing and skating.

If the intensity of the activity is high or if the time (duration) is so long that there is not enough oxygen to meet the energy needs, the activity becomes **anaerobic**, meaning without oxygen. Activities in which sudden, intensive, explosive muscle contractions occur are anaerobic. When insufficient oxygen is available to the muscle tissue, an oxygen deficit occurs. Heavy exertion creates a large oxygen deficit. This oxygen debt must be replaced or paid back after exercise during the recovery. Examples of anaerobic activities are sprinting, weight lifting and jumping over hurdles.

Aerobic and anaerobic activities contribute to your cardiorespiratory fitness.

Most activities involve both anaerobic and aerobic metabolism and the intensity and duration of the activity determine the role each system plays in energy production.

Cardiovascular Disease

Cardiovascular disease (CVD) is the leading cause of death in the United States and most developed countries. Cardiovascular disease (heart attack and stroke) claims about as many lives each year as the next five causes of death combined (cancer, chronic lower respiratory diseases, accidents, diabetes, and influenza and pneumonia). The most prevalent type of cardiovascular disease is coronary artery disease.

Coronary Artery Disease

Coronary artery disease is caused by buildup of fatty deposits (**plaque**) inside the coronary arteries. These arteries provide the heart muscle (myocardium) with its blood supply. This buildup of plaque can begin in childhood and as it progresses, the arterial opening becomes narrower, leading to **atherosclerosis** (narrowing of the coronary arteries).

As plaque deposits continue to grow, blood clotting may occur as the blood platelets pass along the rough surface of the plaque. If a clot forms, it will move through the blood vessels until it reaches an artery that is too small for it to pass through, and it forms a blockage. The tissue that is supplied oxygen and nutrients by that artery will cease to function. If enough heart tissue is deprived of oxygen, a heart attack, or myocardial infarction, occurs.

Family Activity

Find out if any of your family members have high blood pressure or diabetes or have had a stroke or heart attack. Tell them about lifestyle changes they can make to reduce their risk of cardiovascular disease.

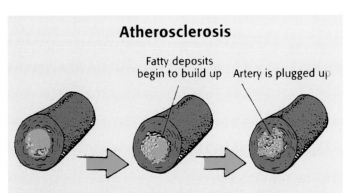

Atherosclerosis

Fatty deposits begin to build up   Artery is plugged up

The fatty deposit buildup in arteries: The normal artery (left) begins to show signs of atherosclerosis as fatty substances are deposited and the lining of the artery thickens (middle). On the right, the artery has been totally plugged up and blood can no longer travel through it.

Heart Attack Warning Signs
- Chest discomfort
- Pain in arms, back, neck, jaw or stomach
- Shortness of breath
- Cold sweat, nausea, or light-headedness

Out of the 1.5 million Americans who have heart attacks each year, slightly more than a third die.

Strokes occur when the blood supply to part of the brain is blocked. Atherosclerotic deposits in the carotid arteries in the neck or arteries in the brain can cause strokes, as can a blood clot (a thrombus) which forms and closes off an artery. Another type of stroke occurs when a blood clot (embolus) travels to a spot in an artery and blocks it (an embolism). If a weak spot in the wall of an artery bulges, it is called a cerebral aneurysm, and if it ruptures, it is a cerebral hemorrhage.

Strokes can affect the body in many ways, ranging from instant death to loss of memory, speech, hearing, vision or muscular function, depending on which part of the brain was damaged. Small strokes can result from partially occluded arteries. Warning signs of a stroke include:
- numbness or weakness on one side of the body
- feeling dizzy or falling for no reason
- loss of speech or memory
- temporary problem with vision in one eye

Prevention of Cardiovascular Disease

Knowledge of cardiovascular disease risk factors has changed the lifestyles of many people. This is evident in the decline of cardiovascular disease in the United States over the past twenty-five years, but still it causes almost half of the deaths in this country each year.

Uncontrollable Risk Factors

Heredity (Including Race)

Individuals with relatives who contracted cardiovascular disease prior to age sixty have a greater risk than those with no family history of heart disease. Also, the younger the relatives were when they had cardiovascular problems, the greater the heredity risk. Sometimes it is impossible to know if a person's cardiovascular disease was caused by genetics or lifestyle. Being overweight, smoking, inactivity and poor eating habits also contribute to cardiovascular disease. Individuals with a family history of cardiovascular disease should be especially aware of these controllable factors and strive for the lowest possible risk level. In the United States, African Americans have higher rates of high blood pressure, heart disease, and stroke than other ethnic groups. Hispanic Americans (Puerto Rican, Cuban, and Mexican) also have higher incidences of high blood pressure.

Age

As people age, they experience lifestyle changes. They may become sedentary, gain weight and eat poorly. These factors lead to a higher risk of cardiovascular disease. Certain cardiovascular problems are products of a lifetime of poor habits.

Many people are becoming more active and making other lifestyle changes to lower their risk for cardiovascular disease.

Other Heart Disease Risk Factors

Stress can cause:

Overeating
Increased smoking
Raised heart rate
Raised blood pressure
Raised blood sugar levels

Drinking Alcohol

can raise blood pressure
can cause heart problems
increases risk of stroke
increases triglycerides
contributes to obesity

More women die of cardiovascular disease than the next six causes of death combined.

Atherosclerosis can begin at a very young age and some elementary school children have elevated blood cholesterol levels. Regular exercise, weight control and good nutrition can help a person stay in optimal condition as he or she grows older.

Gender

Men have a greater risk of cardiovascular disease than women, and they have heart attacks earlier in life. Even after menopause, when women's death rate from heart disease increases, it is not as great a risk as for men. However, heart attack is the leading cause of death for women.

Controllable Risk Factors

Smoking

Smokers have 2 to 4 times greater risk of developing cardiovascular disease than nonsmokers. As a person smokes, nicotine and over a thousand toxic compounds are released into the bloodstream. These substances can damage the arterial walls, which allows cholesterol to be more easily deposited, forming atherosclerotic plaque. In addition, smoking increases the risk of the formation of blood clots, which can cause complete blockage of a blood vessel. The carbon monoxide produced by cigarette smoke replaces some of the oxygen carried by the red blood cells throughout the body. Other effects of smoking include an increased heart rate, increased blood pressure and decreased HDL (good) cholesterol levels.

People who chew tobacco or smoke pipes or cigars also increase their risk of heart disease. Toxic chemicals are absorbed through the mouth and are transported through the bloodstream. Incidences of mouth and throat cancers are much greater for these individuals.

Did You Know?

Smoking is the most preventable cause of death in society. Tobacco use is responsible for almost 1 in 5 deaths in the U.S.

Breathing environmental tobacco smoke can cause narrowing of arteries and lead to heart attack and stroke.

About 40,000 non-smokers die each year from CVD as a result of environmental tobacco smoke.

High Blood Pressure

High blood pressure is a disease itself as well as a cardiovascular disease risk factor. With high blood pressure (hypertension), too much pressure is exerted on the walls of the arteries. This scars the lining of the arteries and they become harder. As your heart works harder to push blood out, it strains and weakens and tends to enlarge.

Unhealthy Cholesterol Levels

High total cholesterol, high LDL cholesterol, low HDL (good) cholesterol and high triglyceride levels are directly related to your risk of heart disease. A blood chemistry test can determine your **cholesterol** levels. Ask your doctor to explain the results to you.

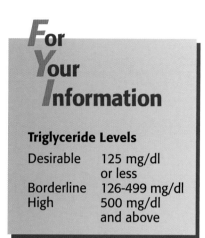

For Your Information

Triglyceride Levels

Desirable	125 mg/dl or less
Borderline	126-499 mg/dl
High	500 mg/dl and above

LDL - the bad cholesterol - excess amounts can accumulate in deposits (plaque) on artery walls.

HDL - the good cholesterol - helps transport excess cholesterol out of the arteries.

High Triglyceride (blood fat) levels are associated with a high risk of heart disease.

Improving Your Blood Fat Levels

1. Regular aerobic exercise
2. Reducing body fat
3. Quit smoking
4. Reducing intake of dietary fat, saturated fats, trans fats, and cholesterol
5. Increase dietary fiber
6. Cutting down on refined sugars and alcohol
7. Include antioxidants such as beta-carotene and vitamins C and E in your diet

LDL

Total Cholesterol Levels for Teens

Normal	120 to 170 mg/d
Borderline	171 to 200 mg/dl
High	201 and higher

HDL

Make being active a part of your lifestyle.

Lack of Physical Activity

Aerobic exercise aids in the control of most of the cardiac risk factors. Benefits of aerobic exercise include:

- increase in cardiorespiratory fitness
- decrease in blood pressure
- lower blood lipids (triglycerides and cholesterol)
- increase in "good" cholesterol (HDL)
- decrease in body fat
- increase in ability to handle stress
- help in preventing or controlling diabetes

Obesity

Obesity, or excess body fat, is a major risk factor for heart disease. Excess fat causes the heart to work harder. Obesity can also increase the risk of diabetes. Chapter 9 provides guidelines for altering your body composition and achieving your weight goal.

Diabetes

People with diabetes mellitus have blood sugar levels that are not properly controlled by the hormone insulin. These individuals are more susceptible to atherosclerosis and have a high incidence of death from cardiovascular disease. Adult-onset diabetes is often developed in individuals who overeat, are obese and sedentary. Those with a family history of diabetes need to have their blood glucose levels checked periodically, maintain normal body weight and participate in a regular exercise program.

What You Can Do About Your Risk

You can prevent or control many of the risk factors for heart disease. Begin a regular exercise program, don't use tobacco products, learn how to deal with stress, maintain a good body weight and eat correctly. You can't control genetic predisposition for a disease, but if you know you have a family history of heart disease or diabetes or some other condition, you should make sure that your lifestyle consists of healthy habits which will help prevent the onset of disease.

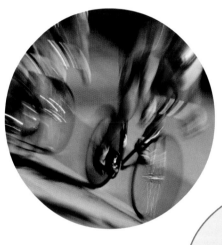

Achieve Cardiovascular Fitness Now to Look and Feel Better

You Can Stop!

There are many effective treatments to help you stop smoking. Find one that works for you.

- Counseling
- Medication

    Nicotine Replacement Therapies (gum, inhaler, nasal spray and patches)

    Non-Nicotine Agent called Buproprion (acts on pathways in the brain involved with nicotine addiction.)

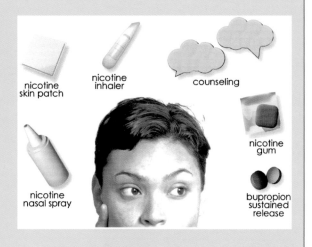

Healthy People 2010 Goals

- ◆ Improve health, fitness, and quality of life through daily physical activity.
- ◆ Increase the proportion of children and adolescents who view television 2 or fewer hours per day.
- ◆ Reduce lung cancer death rate.
- ◆ Promote respiratory health through better prevention, detection, treatment and education.
- ◆ Reduce stroke deaths.
- ◆ Reduce the proportion of adults with high blood pressure.
- ◆ Reduce the mean total blood cholesterol levels among adults.
- ◆ Reduce tobacco use by adolescents.
- ◆ Reduce initiation of tobacco use among children and adolescents.
- ◆ Increase the average age of first use of tobacco products by adolescents and young adults.
- ◆ Increase tobacco cessation attempts by adolescent smokers.
- ◆ Increase adolescents disapproval of smoking.

Stay active to feel better and achieve cardiorespiratory fitness!

Summary

Cardiorespiratory fitness is considered the most important aspect of physical fitness. A high level of cardiorespiratory fitness means that your heart, lungs and blood vessels are functioning effectively. Cardiorespiratory fitness enables you to have more energy, a lower level of body fat and a lower risk of cardiovascular disease.

Your heart is a two-sided pump. The right side supplies the lungs with blood and the left side sends blood to the various systems of the body. The vascular system distributes blood to all the tissues of the body through arteries, veins and capillaries. Blood is made up of plasma, white blood cells, red blood cells and platelets. Hemoglobin gives red blood cells their color and carries oxygen and carbon dioxide throughout the blood stream. A lack of red blood cells or hemoglobin is called anemia.

Most cardiovascular problems are related to lifestyle—lack of exercise, tobacco use, diet and stress problems. Cardiovascular disease is the leading cause of death in the United States. Coronary artery disease is the most common type of cardiovascular disease.

You should do everything you can to reduce your chances of dying of cardiovascular disease, especially if you have a family history of heart disease or diabetes.

Chapter 11 Review

Lesson Checklist

- Do you know why cardiorespiratory fitness is important for your health?
- Can you explain how the heart functions?
- Can you explain how oxygen is delivered to body tissues?
- Do you know why high blood pressure is a risk factor for cardiovascular disease?
- Can you identify the risk factors which are associated with cardiovascular disease?
- Can you explain how exercise helps prevent cardiovascular disease?

Chapter Projects

1. Explain how atherosclerosis occurs.
2. Explain the differences between aerobic and anaerobic activities.
3. Why do we need to breathe?
4. How does atherosclerosis affect blood pressure?
5. What are the functions of red blood cells?
6. What are acceptable ranges for blood pressure?
7. Explain the functions of the two sides of the heart.
8. Which cardiovascular risk factors can you control?
9. Why does obesity increase your risk of cardiovascular disease?
10. What role does stress play in heart disease?

Behavior Change Evaluation

Review the following items to see if you have gained an understanding of fitness and wellness. On a piece of paper briefly state how you will make these changes.

- I will measure my resting heart rate periodically.
- I will measure my blood pressure periodically.
- If I have a blood test performed, I will ask the doctor to explain the results.
- I will try to find out if I have a family history of cardiovascular disease.
- I will analyze my lifestyle and try to reduce or eliminate any controllable risks associated with cardiovascular disease.

Critical Thinking

Based on what you have learned about the cardiorespiratory risk factors, analyze your lifestyle and describe the changes you should make to lower your risk for cardiorespiratory disease. Based on your family history, describe any special factors that increase your risk.

Test Your Knowledge

Read the questions below and select the best possible answer for each.

1. Which is an example of normal blood pressure?
   a. 150/86
   b. 138/92
   c. 130/84
   d. 110/70

2. The recommended Cholesterol Level for teens is:
   a. Below 100
   b. Between 120 - 170
   c. Between 140 - 180
   d. Above 200

3. Which are the major cardiovascular disease risk factors that can be controlled?
   a. Smoking, heredity, hypertension, obesity, lack of exercise, diabetes
   b. Diabetes, age, obesity, hypertension, high cholesterol, gender
   c. Smoking, hypertension, high cholesterol, lack of physical activity, obesity, diabetes
   d. Stress, obesity, high blood pressure, lack of exercise, smoking, diabetes

4. Which fats have a negative effect on blood cholesterol levels?
   a. Monounsaturated
   b. Polyunsaturated
   c. Saturated and trans fat
   d. All are equally bad

5. The good cholesterol is:
   a. Plaque
   b. Low density lipoproteins
   c. High density lipoproteins
   d. Triglycerides

6. Which is another term for high blood pressure?
   a. Hyperplasia
   b. Hypertrophy
   c. Hypertension
   d. Hypotension

7. The blood vessels which supply the heart with blood are the:
   a. Coronary veins
   b. Coronary arteries
   c. Pulmonary veins
   d. Pulmonary arteries

8. Atherosclerosis is:
   a. A build up of fatty deposits in the coronary arteries
   b. A disease of the liver
   c. Congestive heart failure
   d. A bulge in the wall of an artery in the brain

9. Which part of the blood carries oxygen and carbon dioxide?
   a. Hemoglobin
   b. White blood cells
   c. Plasma
   d. Platelets

10. What cardiovascular disease risk factor cannot be controlled?
    a. Smoking
    b. Obesity
    c. Lack of exercise
    d. Heredity

Achieving Cardiorespiratory Fitness

12

Chapter Topics

- Physical Activity and Cardiorespiratory Fitness
- Applying the Principles of Training
- Determining Your Target Heart Rate Training Zone
- Measuring Your Heart Rate During Exercise
- Recovery Heart Rate
- Guidelines for the Exercise Session
- Guidelines for Setting Goals to Improve Your Cardiorespiratory Fitness
- Suggested Cardiorespiratory Programs

Chapter Objectives

After completing this chapter, you will

- Know how to determine your target heart rate zone.
- Know the importance of the warm-up and cool down periods of a workout.
- Know how to plan an exercise session with time allotted for each phase: warm-up, exercise, cool down, muscle toning.
- Understand exercise considerations for those with special needs.
- Know a variety of aerobic activities which promote cardiorespiratory fitness.
- Understand the correct technique for participating in a variety of cardiorespiratory activities.
- Develop a personal fitness plan for cardiorespiratory fitness

Key Words

aerobic capacity
cool down
heart rate monitor
interval training

maximal oxygen uptake
  (VO$_2$ max)
pooling of blood
pedometer
rate of perceived exertion

recovery heart rate
talk test
target heart rate
warm-up

Suggested Physical Activities

At least three days during the week, do a vigorous activity and record your rate of perceived exertion (see page 246). Did you reach at least 4 on the scale?

Use the *Personal Fitness for You* Student CD for:

◆ Lab 12-1: Your Target Heart Rate Zone
◆ Lab 12-2: Effect of Activity on the Heart Rate
◆ Lab 12-3: Rate of Perceived Exertion
◆ Lab 12-4: Recovery Heart Rate
◆ Lab 12-5: The Exercise Session
◆ Lab 12-6: Analyzing Your Walking/Jogging Form
◆ Lab 12-7: An Interval Training Program
◆ Lab 12-8: Swimming or Water Exercises
◆ Lab 12-9: Par Course or Fitness Trail
◆ Lab 12-10: Video Analysis of Performance
◆ Lab 12-11: Cardio Workout
◆ Lab 12-12: School/Community Activities
◆ Lab 12-13: Home Exercise Programs
◆ Lab 12-14: Aerobic Activity Option Day
◆ Chapter Practice Test
◆ Chapter Study Guide
◆ Chapter Crossword Puzzle
◆ Vocabulary Flash Cards
◆ Chapter Power Point Review

Achieving cardiorespiratory fitness is a big step towards total fitness.

Physical Activity and Cardiorespiratory Fitness (Aerobic Capacity)

The terms **aerobic capacity**, maximal oxygen uptake, and VO$_2$ Max are terms that mean the same thing as cardiorespiratory fitness: the ability to perform large muscle, dynamic, moderate to high intensity exercise for long periods. Cardiorespiratory fitness is an indication of how well your heart, lungs, blood vessels, blood, and muscles function during exercise.

The key to achieving cardiorespiratory fitness is leading an active lifestyle. A wide range of physical activities performed throughout the day can help to improve your cardiorespiratory fitness. Even moderate activity (such as walking to school, gardening, doing housework, washing the car, and performing physical activity at school or work) is beneficial. However, it is important to apply the principles of training in order to achieve significant improvements in your cardiorespiratory fitness. By applying these principles you can reach or maintain a cardiorespiratory score in the Healthy Fitness Zone on the health-related fitness tests.

Applying the Principles of Training

As described in Chapter 6, exercise programs must follow the principles of training to be effective. Apply these principles to your cardiorespiratory fitness program.

Overload Principle

Frequency: The number of exercise sessions per week will depend on the exercise preference, lifestyle and the caloric expenditure goal. For most people, at least three to five exercise sessions per week are recommended. If your goal is weight loss,

Achieving Cardiorespiratory Fitness

Frequency	3-5 days per week
Intensity	60-85% of maximum heart rate
Time	20-60 minutes of continuous activity
Type	Large muscles movement - walkiing, cycling, jogging, swimming, aerobic exercise to music, - that can be maintained at the appropriate intensity

participate in your aerobic activity at least 30 minutes for five days each week.

Intensity: Cardiorespiratory fitness may be improved by using low intensity, long duration exercise sessions as well as higher intensity, shorter duration sessions. However, the risk of injury is greater using high intensity sessions. Most individuals should begin with low to moderate intensity exercise sessions with longer training duration. The intensity of a cardiorespiratory workout is determined by the degree to which the heart rate is increased during exercise. For most people, 60-85% of their maximum heart rate is a good range of intensity.

Time: The American College of Sports Medicine recommends that you maintain your exercise intensity from 20 minutes to 60 minutes. Several shorter sessions may also provide a cardiorespiratory benefit. For example, fifteen minutes of cycling and fifteen minutes of aerobic dance during one day would meet the recommendations, as would three ten-minute sessions of cycling. If you train at a low intensity, you should exercise for 30 minutes or more.

Type: Aerobic activities are the most effective type of activities to develop cardiorespiratory fitness. Aerobic activities are those which involve rhythmic use of large muscle groups over a prolonged period of time. Examples of aerobic activities are walking, running, stair-climbing, cycling, swimming, rowing, dancing, skating, cross-country skiing, jumping rope and endurance games.

> ## Remember This ✓
>
> Plan sports parties, such as skiing or skating, for birthdays and other occasions. Spend more time exercising and less time watching television.

Vary the intensity of your workouts to achieve total fitness.

Participation in some of these activities may not maintain the heart rate in a pre-selected training zone for twenty minutes, but as long as the activity is continuous and moderate to vigorous, you will still benefit.

Principle of Progression

If you want to continue to improve your fitness, you must place additional overload on the body. Listed below are several ways to create a progressively more demanding cardiorespiratory program:

- Run or walk a longer distance.
- Run or walk the same distance in a faster time.
- Swim more laps.
- Swim the same number of laps in a faster time.
- Push yourself harder during an aerobic exercise program to music or a step training program.
- Increase the number of days you work out.

Whichever technique you select, the progression should be gradual to prevent strain and soreness.

Family Activity

With your family, make a list of aerobic-type activities in which you can participate together.

Try to exercise together at least once a week.

Moving from a walking program to a jogging program is an example of the principle of progression.

Principle of Specificity

The type of training or exercise program in which you participate determines which fitness component improves. Therefore, if cardiorespiratory fitness is your goal, it is necessary to participate in activities that condition the heart, circulatory system and lungs. Aerobic activities such as walking, jogging, aerobic exercise to music, swimming, cross-country skiing and bicycling are specific activities that contribute to improved cardiorespiratory fitness.

Use the principles of training in your exercise program.

Principle of Regularity

It is important to exercise 3 to 4 days a week at the beginning of your exercise program, progressing to 4 or 5 days a week as your fitness improves. Once you reach your target level, training 3 to 5 days a week will help you maintain your cardiorespiratory endurance level. Keep a training log to monitor your progress.

Principle of Individuality

It is important to consider your individual goals for cardiorespiratory fitness when selecting activities to include in your program. You might want to improve athletic performace, increase your aerobic capacity, and/or lose weight. Choosing activities that you enjoy will improve your chances of reaching your goals. Your rate of improvement may be affected by how your body responds to frequency, intensity, and duration to exercise. Individuals with low levels of cardiorespiratory fitness will show greater gains in VO_2 Max than those who begin with higher fitness levels.

Aerobic exercise such as step aerobics contributes to improved cardiorespiratory fitness.

Family Activity

Teach your family members how to count their pulse. Then help them determine their resting heart rate and target heart rate.

Determining Your Target Heart Rate Training Zone

While all physical activity is beneficial, if your goal is to improve your cardiorespiratory fitness; your heart rate must reach your **target heart rate** zone. This means you are exercising hard enough to make your heart stronger, but not so hard to exceed a safe upper limit for your heart rate.

To calculate your target heart rate training zone, it is necessary to know your resting heart rate. Chapter 4 gives information on how to accurately obtain your resting heart rate. There are two methods for calculating your target heart rate zone. Each uses a percentage of your maximum heart rate zone. See the *Personal Fitness for You* Student CD for a form to help you calculate your target heart rate zone.

The Heart Rate Maximum Method

1. Find your maximum heart rate (MHR) by multiplying your age by .7 and subtracting the answer from 208.
2. Multiply by appropriate training percent (use 55% for low fitness, 65% for moderate fitness, and 75% for high fitness)

The answer is your lower number of your target heart rate zone.

Repeat with training percent (65% for low fitness, 75% for moderate fitness, and 90% for high fitness) for your upper number of your target heart rate zone.

The example on the next page is a moderately fit 15 year old student, using training percents of 65% and 75%.

Lower Target Heart Rate	Upper Target Heart Rate

1. 15 (your age)
    x 0.7
    ——————
    10.5
	1. 15 (your age)
	    x 0.7
	    ——————
	    10.5

208
- 10.5 (answer from above)
——————————
    197.5 or 198 (Maximum Heart
                    Rate or MHR)
	208
	- 10.5 (answer from above)
	——————————
	    197.5 or 198 (Maximum Heart
	                    Rate or MHR)

2. 198
    x   0.65 lower training percent
    ——————————
    128.7 or 129
Lower Heart Rate is 129 beats per minute
	2. 198
	    x 0.75 lower training percent
	    ——————————
	    148.7 or 149
	Upper Heart Rate is 149 beats per minute

To gain cardiorespiratory fitness benefits, the 15 year old in the example above should exercise at an intensity that will raise his/her target heart rate zone between **129** and **149** bpm.

The Heart Rate Reserve Method

This method uses the resting heart as a part of the calculation.

1. Measure your resting heart rate prior to getting out of bed in the morning.
2. Find your maximum heart rate (**MHR**) multiplying your age by .7 and subtracting the answer from 208.
3. Subtract your resting heart rate (**RHR**) from your maximum heart rate (**MHR**) to get your Heart Rate Reserve (**HRR**).
4. Multiply the answer by training percent of **40% for low, 50% for moderate or 60% for high fitness.**
5. Add your resting heart rate (**RHR**).
6. The answer is the **lower number of your target heart rate zone.**
7. Repeat with training percent of **50% for low, 60% for moderate, or 85% for high** fitness for your upper number.

The example below is a moderately fit student 15 years old with a resting heart rate (RHR) of 75 beats per minute.

Lower Target Heart Rate   **Upper Target Heart Rate**

1. Resting Heart Rate 75 bpm

2. 15 (your age)
   x 0.7
   ‾‾‾‾‾
    10.5

    208
   - 10.5
   ‾‾‾‾‾‾
     197.5 or 198 (Maximum Heart Rate or MHR)

3. 198 (MHR)
    - 75 (Resting Heart Rate or RHR)
   ‾‾‾‾‾
    123 (Heart Rate Reserve or HRR)

Repeat steps 4 and 5, using upper training %

4. 123 (HRR)   4. 123   (HRR)
   x   0.50 (lower training percent)   x   0.60 (RHR)
   ‾‾‾‾‾‾   ‾‾‾‾‾‾
    61.5   73.8

5. 61.5 (HRR)
   + 75   (RHR)   5. 73.8
   ‾‾‾‾‾   + 75   (RHR)
    136.5 or 137 Lower Number of   ‾‾‾‾‾
            Target Heart Rate Zone   148.8 or 149 Upper Number of
                                                 Target Heart Rate Zone

The 15 year old with the resting heart rate of 75 and moderate fitness level has a target heart rate zone of 137 to 149.

There are several types of heart rate monitors to help you check your pulse rate during activity.

Measuring Your Heart Rate During Exercise

It is difficult to count your pulse during exercise. However, by using a heart rate monitor you can accurately monitor your heart rate before, during, and after exercise. Many exercise machines such as treadmills, exercise bicycles, steppers, etc. have built in pulse rate monitoring devices. Keeping a log of your resting heart rate, exercise heart rate, and recovery heart rate is a good way to monitor your progress.

Talk Test

The talk test is a method of measuring the intensity of your workout. When you participate at a moderate intensity level, you should be able to carry on a conversation comfortably while engaging in the activity. Your activity becomes **vigorous** if you become winded or too out of breath to carry on a conversation.

Rate of Perceived Exertion

As you participate in an exercise program, pay close attention to how hard you feel the workout is for you. This feeling should take into consideration the total amount of exertion, stress and fatigue you feel. Don't become concerned about an individual factor such as shortness of breath, but try to concentrate on your total inner feeling of how hard you are working or exerting yourself. It is important to be as accurate as you can—try not to underestimate or overestimate your feeling of exertion. Listen to your body.

At a moderate intensity level you should be able to carry on a conversation comfortably.

"Listen" to your body to assess your rate of perceived exertion.

The **Rate of Perceived Exertion** Scale (below) can assist you in monitoring your exercise tolerance. It provides you with guidelines regarding exercise intensity. Refer to the scale to determine the rating for your workout.

The rate of perceived exertion scale is also an excellent way to measure the intensity of your workout. As you learn to use the scale, compare your exercise heart rate with your rate of perceived exertion—it should be 4 to 5. If they both indicate your workout was intense enough for fitness improvement, you may find it more convenient to only use the rate of perceived exertion scale so that you do not have to stop exercising to take your pulse.

Rate of Perceived Exertion		
Rate of perceived exertion is the assessment of the intensity of a workout compared to how you feel.		
0	**No activity**	Warmup and cool down zone
0.5	**Very, very light activity**	
1		
2	**Very light activity**	
3	**Moderate activity**	**Training Zone** This is the target heart rate zone that you are striving to achieve. 3 is easy—only a moderate workout 4 and 5 are the ideal levels for a training effect without straining—you can breathe and speak easily but are beginning to sweat.
4	**Somewhat hard activity**	
5		
6		7 and 8 are at the upper limit of your training zone. You may be having trouble carrying on a conversation and you are sweating more.
7	**Hard activity**	
8		
9	**Very hard activity**	This is beyond your target heart rate or workout training zone. Your breathing is more difficult and you can not talk. Your muscles may begin to have a burning sensation. 10 is considered a maximal workout.
10		

Adapted from Noble, B.J., Borg, G.A.V., Jacobs, I, Ceci, R., Kaiser, P. "A category-ratio perceived exertion scale: Relationship to blood and muscle lactates and heart rate." Medicine, Science, Sports and Exercise 15:523-528, 1983.

Recovery Heart Rate

Checking your **recovery heart rate** at the end of each exercise session gives you information regarding the quality of the exercise you performed. When you check your heart rate at the end of your exercise session, your recovery heart rate should be 120 beats per minute or below after five minutes and should be 100 beats per minutes or below after ten minutes. If your recovery heart rate is higher, it is possible that the intensity of your workout was too high and/or the duration was too long. It is very important to remember that your training program should be challenging but not too uncomfortable—you should enjoy it!

Recovery Heart Rate

5 minutes after end of exercise HR= 120 bpm or less

10 minutes after end of exercise HR= 100 bpm or less

Guidelines for the Exercise Session

A typical exercise session should include a warm-up (approximately five to ten minutes), the selected exercise program (from twenty to thirty minutes), the cool down (approximately five to ten minutes), and the muscle toning phase (approximately ten minutes).

The chart on the next page illustrates how the heart rate gradually increases during the warm-up until it is in the training zone, levels off during the workout and then gradually returns to the starting level during the cool down.

Did You Know?

Being physically fit will help you get through your daily work and play activities.

The Exercise Session

Activity	Time (min.)
Warmup	5-10
Exercise program	20-60
Cool down	5-10
Muscle toning	10

The Workout Session

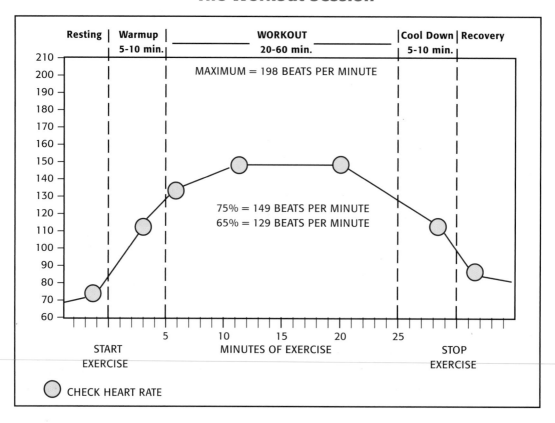

| | Resting | Warmup 5-10 min. | WORKOUT 20-60 min. | Cool Down 5-10 min. | Recovery |

MAXIMUM = 198 BEATS PER MINUTE

75% = 149 BEATS PER MINUTE
65% = 129 BEATS PER MINUTE

START EXERCISE

MINUTES OF EXERCISE

STOP EXERCISE

◯ CHECK HEART RATE

During the warm-up, stretch the muscles to be used in the workout session.

The Warm-up

The purpose of the **warm-up** is to prepare the body for the increased stress which will be placed upon it during the exercise session. If possible, the warm-up activity should relate specifically to the exercise to be performed. Prior to a cardiorespiratory workout, warm up with low intensity, large muscle activity such as brisk walking or easy jogging in place. Stretch the muscles to be used. The warm-up session provides three important benefits.

1. The heart rate gradually increases from the resting pulse.
2. The temperature within the muscles increases.
3. Chances of muscle soreness and injury are reduced.

The Exercise Program

The purpose of this phase is to raise the heart rate to the target zone to achieve cardiorespiratory fitness. As noted earlier, this phase should be vigorous enough to increase the heart rate to the target zone and maintain it at the recommended rate for at least twenty minutes. Activities which may be included in this phase are walking, jogging, swimming, bicycling, rope skipping and aerobic exercise to music. Guidelines and specific information for a variety of exercise programs are included later in this chapter. Remember to follow the principles of overload, progression and specificity as you prepare your workouts.

The Cool Down

The **cool down** allows the body to gradually return to its starting point. During the cool down gradually decrease your pace of exercise until the pulse rate lowers to 100-120 beats per minute.

One important reason for the cool down is that it prevents possible **pooling of blood** in the lower extremities which can cause dizziness or fainting. It may occur when a person stops exercising suddenly and the blood is not returned to the heart and brain fast enough.

The next phase of your cool down should involve some of the same stretching exercises you did in warm-up. Gentle stretching assists in cooling the body and helps prevent soreness from unaccustomed use of muscles. The cool down is an excellent time to improve flexibility. The entire cool down process should last from five to ten minutes.

Muscle Toning (Optional)

The purpose of this phase is to work on muscular strength and endurance. You should perform isolated exercises for the various muscle groups: legs, hips, buttocks, arms and abdominals.

The exercise phase should include activity to raise your heart rate.

After large muscle activity, it is a good idea to stretch the muscles.

SAFETY TIP After the workout use a cool down program to lower your pulse to 100-120 beats per minute.

Abdominal curl-ups are an important part of the muscle toning phase.

Each day alternate which muscle group is used. Try doing sets on each side and stretch out the muscles before moving to the next group.

Although optional, it is beneficial to include this phase of the workout on a regular basis. Maintaining good muscle tone is important for many daily activities. In addition, increased muscle mass will cause you to burn more calories even when you are not exercising.

Safety Considerations

To get the maximum benefit from your cardiorespiratory exercise program and reduce your risk of injury, keep these factors in mind:

Visit the Mayo Clinic web site at:
www.mayoclinic.com

- Follow the guidelines for your warm-up, exercise session and cool down.
- Observe the correct techniques for the specific exercises.
- Remember the safety precautions regarding clothing and weather conditions explained in Chapter 3.
- Keep in mind that overtraining can be harmful. Follow the guidelines for overload and progression.

Exercise for Special Groups

Groups with special needs due to illness, disability or temporary disabling conditions are still encouraged to seek the highest possible level of cardiorespiratory fitness. Students with special needs should seek the advice of a doctor before developing a cardiorespiratory fitness plan. The following guidelines may be helpful for those with asthma and diabetes in planning a cardiorespiratory workout.

Asthma (and other chronic pulmonary diseases). Many people, including some famous athletes, have asthma and exercise at high levels. If you have asthma, you should talk with your doctor about your limitations. The exercise program must be based on the degree of respiratory difficulty. Cycling, walking and swimming are appropriate types of exercise. Upper body exercises such as arm cranking or rowing may not be desirable. Modifications in the intensity, duration and frequency of an exercise may be necessary. If a duration of at least 20 minutes of continuous exercise is not realistic, a goal of two ten-minute sessions or four five-minute sessions may be better. A walking test is a good method of evaluating progress.

Diabetes (a disease associated with problems in controlling the blood glucose level). In general, a diabetic can participate in the same types of activities as other individuals. Daily exercise is recommended. The exercise intensity may need to be at the lower end of the target heart rate. In addition, some individuals may need to start with a duration of 5 to 10 minutes gradually increasing to 30 minutes. An individual with diabetes must "listen to his or her body" for signs of whether the workout is too intense.

Learn more at:
www.diabetes.org

Guidelines for Setting Goals to Improve Your Cardiorespiratory Fitness

Now is the time to set your goals for improving cardiorespiratory fitness. Use the chart on the next page to complete the *My Activity Plan* form. Remember to include activities which you will enjoy.

Walking or jogging on a treadmill is an excellent cardiorespiratory fitness activity.

Initial Fitness Level	Cardiorespiratory Goal
Below the recommended Healthy Fitness Zone	Decrease your time 1-4 minutes
At or near the recommended Healthy Fitness Zone	Decrease your time 1-2 minutes
Higher than the recommended Healthy Fitness Zone	Decrease time 30-60 seconds

My Activity Plan (MAP)

My goal is to do the following activities:

Type of Activity	Frequency: Times per Week	Intensity of the Workout (heart rate, perceived exertion)	Time: Number of Minutes per Day
Walking	4 days	129-149 bpm	30 minutes
Soccer	2 days	RPE = 5	60 minutes
Cycling	2 days	129-149 bpm	20 minutes

Refer to the student *Personal Fitness for You* CD for the *My Activity Plan* form.

Suggested Cardiorespiratory Exercise Programs

The following programs illustrate a basic progression for use in planning your aerobic exercise.

Walking

Begin your walking program by just going for a walk—don't think about stopwatches or heart rates. The main idea is to walk at a comfortable pace—but faster than a stroll. Try walking for at least 20 to 30 minutes. For maximum gain from your walking program and to lower the risk of injury, using correct technique is important. Use the information below to help you safely increase the intensity of your walking.

For Your Information

People with knee, ankle or back problems often find that jogging or walking on a treadmill is easier on their joints than exercising on hard surfaces such as concrete or asphalt roads.

Source: Fitness for Dummies by Suzanne Schlosberg and Liz Neporent, IDG Books, 1996.

Technique:
1. Walking for fitness is not the same as pleasure walking. No shuffling, strolling or sauntering is allowed!
2. Concentrate on really using (contracting) your muscles in the feet, thighs, calves, buttocks and diaphragm.
3. Make certain you are in an upright position and that your entire foot is placed on the ground—heel first, then toes.
4. Stand tall with shoulders back and relaxed. Keep your head level and your chin up. Focus your eyes about ten feet in front of you.
5. Include an arm swing to make it a total body activity. With the elbows bent at 90 degrees, swing them from the shoulder. The upper arm should be almost parallel to the ground on the backswing. Increasing the arm swing generally leads to faster movement by the legs.
6. The stride should be long and smooth. The best way to increase speed is not to overstride but to take quicker steps. The supporting leg should be straight as your body passes over it. Avoid excessive side-to-side movement.
7. Avoid leaning forward. This can cause low back problems.

Procedure:
1. Start slowly and use the first three to five minutes as a warmup. Increase your pace gradually.
2. Try to move with a natural, effortless motion.
3. Use a stride that is natural for you but gradually take quicker steps to increase the speed of your walking.
4. As you quicken your pace, thrust harder with your legs, increase your arm swing and breathe naturally.

Walk with purpose, moving your arms as well as your legs. At the end of a brisk walk, you should be perspiring and breathing harder, but not so hard that you can't carry on a conversation.

Types of Walking

Strolling (2 m.p.h.) Good for sedentary people or those recovering from illness.

Fitness Walking (3-4 m.p.h.) Fast enough to elevate heart rate into the training zone. Stride is faster and longer, and arms swing.

Power Walking (5 m.p.h.) heart rate is in the middle to top of the heart rate training zone. Stride is longer and arm swing more exaggerated.

Racewalking (6-9 m.p.h.) Competitive walking for conditioned athletes. One foot must always be in contact with the ground and the support leg must be straight in the vertical position for one moment.

Waterwalking in chest-deep water is good for those individuals who have leg or back problems. There is less strain on the joints of the body because of the buoyancy of the water. The water creates resistance which increases the intensity of the cardiorespiratory workout.

Using Pedometers

Pedometers are an excellent way to measure how active you are - in and out of class. Every activity can be measured using a pedometer. Everyone can be active - including the unskilled and overweight - and your activity can be meaured objectively with pedometers.

Walking is an excellent cardio-respiratory activity.

Family Activity

Walking with a dog is fun for both you and the dog! It is also safer to walk with a dog.

Pedometers can be used to track your steps, calories, and minutes of activity

Interval Walking

A program for advanced walkers, interval walking involves five sets of one minute intense walking with two minutes of recovery walking between sets. Perform interval walking every other day, with rest or slow long distance walking on the other days.

Jogging

Jogging is a form of exercise that involves alternate walking and running at a slow-to-moderate pace or running at a slow, even pace.

Jogging is useful in maintaining weight. It helps with general muscle tone and contributes to overall fat reduction. Jogging is one of the best methods of developing the cardiorespiratory system for people without physical problems or limitations.

Clothing for jogging should be loose and comfortable. Avoid wearing rubberized clothing since this material does not allow sweat to evaporate, causing excessive salt loss and dehydration, which may result in heatstroke. Choose shoes that have a good arch support and a firm sole.

Family Activity

Have each family member wear a pedometer for one day. Keep a log of total steps for each person. Set a family goal based on this total. A 10% increase in total steps is a good start. Let each person wear the pedometer for several more days to see if everyone can reach their goal.

Sample Jogging Program

Start by walking 10 minutes and jogging 1 minute
by 6 weeks jog 10 minutes
by 12 weeks jog 20 minutes
by 18 weeks jog 30 minutes

Jogging shoes should have good arch support and a firm sole.

The beginning jogger should run on a track, grass or dirt and not on a hard surface. Start the program by walking, walking and jogging, or slowly jogging every other day until your body adjusts. Increase the frequency and intensity of your program depending on your needs and interests.

The following procedures suggested by the President's Council on Physical Fitness describe basic jogging technique:

1. Warm up, stretch and walk before jogging.
2. Keep the back as straight as is comfortable with the head up.
3. Bend the elbows and hold them slightly away from the body.
4. The best way for your feet to hit the ground is to first land on the heel and then rock forward on the ball of the foot. Avoid landing on the ball of the foot, as this puts excessive strain on the calf muscles.
5. At the end of the jogging session, cool down with a walk.

Interval Training

Interval training involves alternating periods of exercise with periods of rest. It is done at a very high intensity level. Interval training can be used with activities such as walking, jogging, running, cycling and rope jumping.

As you have already learned, an aerobic exercise program is one in which the body is able to provide sufficient oxygen for the workout. An interval training program is an example of an anaerobic exercise program. Anaerobic exercise means that the exercise is so intense that the body cannot supply the amount of oxygen needed during the workout.

SAFETY TIP To avoid injury, it is important to follow the suggested biomechanical technique for jogging. Use proper foot and knee action to help absorb the force of landing.

A common interval workout consists of three to seven work periods which are three to five minutes long. These periods of work are broken by short rest periods of walking or jogging to partially recover for the next work period. The length of the rest or recovery period is usually based on a heart rate recovery plan, with 120 beats per minute classified as minimal. That is, if your heart rate reaches 160 during the work period, you must jog or walk until your heart rate drops to 120 beats per minute. As your system becomes more efficient, your recovery rate time will decrease.

The advantages of interval training over continuous training include:
- accomplishing more work in less time.
- reducing boredom by providing greater variety.
- achieving greater intensity of the work, because of the short work periods.

Sample Interval Training Program

Session	Activity	Time
1	Walk	3 minutes
	Jog	1 minute
	Walk	3 minutes
	Jog	2 minutes
2	Walk	3 minutes
	Jog	3 minutes
	Walk	2 minutes
	Jog	3 minutes
3	Walk	2 minutes
	Jog	3 minutes
	Walk	2 minutes
	Jog	4 minutes
4	Walk	2 minutes
	Jog	4 minutes
	Walk	2 minutes
	Jog	4 minutes

Requirements for an effective progression in the interval program include:
- reducing the length of the recovery period.
- increasing the intensity of the work period.
- increasing the number of work periods.
- increasing the length of the work period.
- or any combination of the above.

Short periods of walking allow for recovery before the next exercise period.

Cycling

Technique:
1. Clothing for cycling should allow evaporation of perspiration. Bicycle shorts help prevent chafing. Helmets are an important safety measure.
2. Make certain the seat height is correct for you. Comfortable padding on the seat is a must for long rides!
3. Adjust the handlebars to a position which is comfortable for your riding style.
4. Pedaling must be vigorous and sustained to achieve real benefits.
5. Try to relax and enjoy the sights!

Procedure:
1. Start with a moderate pace so your leg muscles can adjust gradually to the increased activity.
2. Remember it takes skill to handle a bike safely in traffic, on narrow roadways and in tight places. Learn how to handle your bike effectively before you attempt difficult situations such as heavy traffic or steep, winding roads. Be alert to holes or objects on the road.
3. Generally, you need to cycle twice as fast as you would jog to achieve your target heart rate. In the beginning, strive for a sustained ride and gradually increase your time or distance.

Using an exercise bicycle is another excellent aerobic activiy.

SAFETY TIP Good biomechanical technique for cycling involves using a bike that is properly adjusted to avoid knee strain and back pain. It is also important to avoid leaning too far forward.

Rope Jumping

Rope jumping is a form of endurance training in which various rhythmical jumping, hopping and gymnastic dance steps are performed over a steadily rotating or swinging rope held in the hands of the individual. The rope should be the same length as from the armpits to the feet of the individual.

Jumping rope is a good aerobic exercise.

Technique:
1. Exercise on a cushioned surface wearing athletic shoes.
2. Practice the footwork and rope work separately.
3. Don't jump too high—about a half inch above the floor is sufficient.
4. Combine footwork with the rope twirling; one jump for each rotation of the rope. The rope should hit the floor as you are in the air.
5. Avoid large arm circling in twirling the rope; emphasize wrist action.
6. When an error or "miss" occurs, continue footwork while you recover rope action.

Procedure:
1. Warm up for three minutes by slow skipping or walking briskly.
2. Start with the rope behind you, one end in each hand forming a loop.
3. Jump over the rope as it is rotated over your head and beneath your feet. Skip with both feet together, or step over the rope, alternating feet.
4. Cool down for three minutes after jumping by slow walking.

To achieve an aerobic training effect, determine if the rope jumping produced your target heart rate. If this level was not reached immediately after jumping, then you must increase the load by jumping faster or for longer periods of time. After the appropriate jumping pattern has been found and is followed for a period of time, increase the intensity of the jumping session. Alternate various combinations of activity, such as walking briskly, with periods of rope jumping.

SAFETY TIP
Jump rope on a cushioned surface.

Family Activity

Teach the water exercises to family members the next time you go swimming together.

Did You Know?

It's 12 times more difficult to walk through water than through air, which is one reason for the popularity and effectiveness of aqua aerobics. Water also supports your joints, greatly reducing exercise-related stress.

Source: Self. July 1997.

Water sports are fun and provide a good workout.

Water Activities

Aquatic programs include everything from aerobics, step training, walking and running to aquatic line dancing, water Tai Chi, water boxing, ski conditioning and sports specific training.

Water exercise provides dynamic conditioning for the trunk muscles which function as stabilizers. When water resistance exercise is performed, water currents act constantly against the body, and the trunk muscles must respond continuously.

Not only do water exercises and/or lap swimming improve cardiorespiratory fitness, they are also great for increasing muscle tone, improving flexibility, burning calories and releasing tension. Water exercises can be performed by almost all people—swimmers and non-swimmers—regardless of age and physical condition.

Water Exercise

Procedure:
1. If possible, stay in water that is shoulder-level. The resistance of the water increases the strenuousness of your workout.
2. Select a variety of exercises and perform them in a sequence that will keep your heart rate in the target zone.
3. Consider having music available and combining aerobic exercise steps with the usual water exercises.

Lap Swimming

Procedure:

1. Before each workout, warm up by walking back and forth across the shallow end of the pool for a minimum of five minutes.

2. Choose a variety of strokes and make your workout continuous. Alternate strokes when you need a change. The breaststroke and backstroke are less demanding than the front crawl. The butterfly is considerably more demanding. See the suggested starter program below.

3. Cool down by walking slowly for three minutes at the end of the exercise.

Swimming laps using a variety of strokes is one way to maintain a continuous workout.

During the first six weeks, try to swim the distance that is comfortable, rest, then continue the swimming-resting cycle until the required distance is covered. Beginning with the seventh week, attempt to cover the distance without stopping.

Swimming Exercise Program

Week	Distance (yards)	Time Goal (minutes)	Frequency (days per week)
1	300	12:00	4
2	300	11:00	4
3	400	15:00	4
4	400	13:00	4
5	500	20:00	4
6	500	18:00	4
7	600	23:00	4
8	600	20:00	4
9	700	22:00	4
10	800	24:00	4
11	900	26:00	4
12	1000	28:00	4

The butterfly is a very demanding swimming stroke.

Aerobic Exercise to Music

Aerobic exercise to music incorporates a variety of movements—hopping, high stepping, jumping, twisting, stretching, swinging and skipping—set to almost any type of music. The appeal of music and dance make aerobic exercise and training enjoyable. Once you have learned the basic steps, you can combine dozens of movements into routines or use a tape to guide you.

It is important to remember that, just as with all aerobic programs, there are also three phases of an aerobic exercise workout to music—warm-up, the workout and cool down.

Low Impact Aerobics

Low impact aerobics refer to those programs in which the stress and shock to the participant's joints are minimized. In low impact aerobic dance one foot is always on the floor.

SAFETY TIP If you do high impact aerobics your risk for injury is higher. To avoid injury use good biomechanical technique: proper vertical alignment of feet, knees and hips.

SAFETY TIP Low impact aerobics is less stressful on your joints.

Maintain good posture when performing step aerobics.

Step Aerobics

Step aerobics, bench stepping or step training is included in many aerobics classes. The participant steps on and off a step bench while working to music and attempts to maintain a rate of 80-120 steps per minute. Not only does a pumping action of the arms contribute to the workout, but light weights can add to the calorie expenditure.

Technique:
1. Beginners should use a four-inch step bench and gradually increase to eight to twelve inches.
2. Wearing the proper shoes is important—those made for aerobics or cross-training are recommended. Running shoes and those with extensive treading may not be safe for stepping.
3. To avoid the risk of knee strain and injury, do not flex (bend) the knee beyond 90° as you step up. Slightly bend the knee and place the entire foot (not just the toes or ball of the foot) on the center of the step bench.
4. Land on the floor with the ball of the foot first and then the heel, bend the knee to help absorb the impact.
5. Maintain good posture—lean forward slightly at the hips (not the waist). Keep the chest up and hips tucked under.

The step bench can also be used for stretching by placing the toes on the edge and dropping the heels toward the floor and for exercises such as push-ups (place hands on the step) or curl-ups (place feet on the step).

Some commercial step benches are 42 inches long and 14 inches wide with an adjustable height. Those with a nonskid top surface are best. One word of caution: to lessen the chance of overuse injuries, limit step workouts to no more than three per week.

For Your Information

Hand weights can add 10-15% more intensity to your aerobic or step workout.

SAFETY TIP Good biomechanical technique for step aerobics includes keeping the knees bent and maintaining erect posture.

In-line Skating

One of the fastest growing sports in the world, in-line skating is an excellent way to improve cardiorespiratory fitness. Skating is an activity that can be enjoyed with family and friends. All age groups may participate. Many athletes use skating as a cross-training activity. Studies show that skating can compare with running and bicycling as an aerobic activity. Inline skating is considered a low-impact aerobic activity. The stroke, recovery and glide motion is easier on the joints of the body than running.

Remember that it is important to warm up and stretch prior to skating. Jogging in place for 5 minutes and then stretching will improve your range of motion. As you improve the flexibility of the skating muscles, you will be able to apply more force over a greater range of motion and you will be able to skate faster. You will also find that you are able to skate for a longer amount of time, because more flexible muscles use less energy to move the muscle through the full range of motion.

It is necessary to learn safety techniques and street awareness prior to skating where there are motor vehicles, bicycles and pedestrians. Perform the following safety check prior to skating:

Wheels: secure, turn freely, not worn

Skates: fastened properly

Helmet: securely on head

Knee and elbow pads: fit correctly

Wrist guards: hard plastic piece is on the palm of the hand. (Put these on last, otherwise it may be difficult to adjust the rest of your equipment.)

In-line skating is an enjoyable way to build cardiorespiratory fitness.

Be aware of automobile traffic and pedestrians when skating in public areas.

Proper safety gear is essential.

Take your time and study the models carefully when shopping for skates.

Skating Safely:

SKATE SMART by wearing protective gear.

SKATE ALERT by controlling speed and watching out for hazards.

SKATE LEGAL by obeying all traffic regulations.

SKATE COURTEOUS by skating on the right, passing on the left and always yielding to pedestrians

Source: International In-Line Skating Association.

Spinning

Spinning was originally invented to simulate bicycle racing in a controlled environment. It is an aerobic workout that utilizes a special stationary bicycle which has a knob to change the pedaling resistance. The bikes are very simple with no calorie counters, computers, digital profiles, etc. Since people can set the workload to suit their own ability and level of difficulty, individuals of all ability levels can train together. During spinning classes there is usually music and a leader who speaks to the class (sometimes through headphones) and sets the mood for the ride. To motivate the participants, the leader may tell the riders that they are going up a hill, sprinting or going down a mountain. Depending on what level of difficulty the resistance is set, a 45 minute spinning class can burn between 400 and 800 calories.

Spinning is a high-intensity workout that simulates a bike race.

Rowing is a good all-body workout that won't put stress on your joints.

Rowing

Rowing is an excellent aerobic workout, comparable to cross country skiing. Rowing machines enable you to work your entire body without much impact on your joints. As you pull the handle, you glide back and forth on the seat which creates a feeling of rowing on open water. You can adjust the stroke speed and resistance to suit your ability and fitness level.

Rowing vigorously can burn approximately 800 calories per hour. Rowing strengthens the back, arms, shoulders and abdominal muscles. Keeping the elbows close to your body maximizes the strengthening of the arm muscles. It is important to use proper rowing technique to prevent knee and lower back pain.

Remember This ☑

When the weather is bad. .

Move your walk indoors. Shopping malls are a popular alternative—many malls let walkers in before shopping hours, usually between 6:30 and 10:00 A.M. Call local malls to see if any have such a program. If no mall in your area has walking times, find a local health club that has an indoor track or treadmill.

Elliptical Trainer

1. Be sure you know how to use the controls that increase speed and resistance and make sure that the emergency shutoff switch works.
2. Maintain good posture
   - Shoulders back
   - Head up and slightly forward, chin up, look forward
   - Abdominals tight
   - Lightly grip handrails
   - Your lower body should support most of the weight
3. Relax as you maintain a good stride through your normal range of motion.

Stair Stepper/Climber

1. Understand how to increase and decrease the intensity of the workout.
2. Wear athletic shoes that support your feet, heels, and ankles. Dress comfortably.
3. Stand tall and look forward. Keep posture upright.
4. Choose a stepping rate that slightly raises your heart rate. The faster the pedals move, the faster you must step.
5. More pedal resistance allows you to slow your stepping rate.
6. The height of each step should be about the same as stepping on a normal step. You knees and ankles should feel comfortable.

Sports Activities

Soccer, basketball, team handball, lacrosse, hockey, tennis, badminton, squash and racquetball are other examples of popular sports which are excellent activities for cardiorespiratory fitness. Find an activity that you enjoy and make fitness fun!

Soccer and other team sports can provide excellent cardiorespiratory exercise.

Healthy People 2010 Goals

◆ Improve health, fitness, and quality of life through daily physical activity.

◆ Increase the proportion of adolescents who engage in moderate physical activity for at least 30 minutes on 5 or more of the previous 7 days.

◆ Increase the proportion of adolescents who engage in vigorous physical activity that promotes cardiorespiratory fitness 3 or more days per week for 20 or more minutes per occasion.

Summary

Regular moderate physical activity can improve your general health and well-being. Exercise and training programs can improve the efficiency of your cardiorespiratory system. It is especially important to follow the principles of training: overload, progression, specificity, regularity and individuality when training. Aerobic exercise is the best type of program to improve your cardiorespiratory fitness.

When participating in a cardiorespiratory workout, it is important to know your target heart rate and strive to reach your target heart rate training zone while you work out.

A typical exercise session should follow a specific plan and include four phases: warm-up, exercise, cool down and muscle toning.

There are a variety of aerobic activities you can include in a cardiorespiratory fitness program. Select a program that is right for you and then follow the suggested progression and tips provided in this chapter.

Portfolio Idea

Your Cardiorespiratory Workout

Record the results of this activity in your personal portfolio or follow the instructions from your teacher.

◆ Describe the workout sessions -- warm up activities, activity phase, cool down, muscle toning (if any), and safety considerations.

◆ Did you enjoy the workouts? Why or why not?

◆ Did you achieve your target heart rate zone as measured by pulse rate or rate of perceived exertion during each session?

◆ Descibe how you felt after each session.

◆ What changes do you think you should make in the workout session?

Chapter 12 Review

Lesson Checklist

- Do you know why brisk walking is such a good activity for improving cardiorespiratory fitness?
- Can you list the most important points to remember when cycling?
- Can you explain why a warm-up is beneficial?
- Do you know why it is important to stay within your target heart rate training zone when you are working out?
- Do you know why it is important to cool down after exercise?

Chapter Projects

Write a response to each of the following:

1. How can aerobic exercise improve your breathing efficiency?
2. Why is jogging such a good cardiorespiratory activity?
3. Describe the three essential phases of an exercise session.
4. Explain why a warm-up is beneficial.
5. Explain the importance of the cool down.
6. Why is it important to monitor your heart rate during aerobic exercise?
7. Why is it important to check your recovery heart rate after each exercise?

Behavior Change Evaluation

Review the following items to see if you have gained an understanding of fitness and wellness. On a piece of paper briefly state how you will make these changes.

- I will try to include at least 30 minutes of moderate intensity activity in each day.
- I will try to participate in moderate to vigorous activities at least three times a week for at least twenty minutes per session.
- I will calculate my target heart rate training zone.
- I will try to improve my cardiorespiratory fitness by exercising using the FITT formula guidelines.

Critical Thinking

Based on what you have learned about cardiorespiratory fitness training, design a program that you would like to follow that meets the guidelines of the FITT formula.

Chapter 12 Review

Test Your Knowledge

Read the questions below and select the best possible answer for each.

1. A person who wants to participate in a vigorous intensity workout should select target heart rate training percents of:
   a. 40 to 50%
   b. 50 to 60%
   c. 60-85%
   d. 90-100%

2. You should recalculate your target heart rate zone:
   a. as you get more fit
   b. as you age
   c. as your resting heart rate decreases
   d. all of the above

3. Which is not considered when calculating target heart rate?
   a. Age
   b. Weight
   c. Fitness Level
   d. Maximum Heart Rate

4. Which is the best way to determine intensity of an aerobic workout?
   a. Distance covered
   b. Minutes of exercise
   c. Heart Rate
   d. Number of times per week

5. Which of the following is not a cardiorespiratory endurance activity?
   a. Pushups
   b. Swimming
   c. Bicycling
   d. Running

6. The most important factor for achieving a training effect is
   a. duration
   b. intensity
   c. frequency
   d. repetition

7. In addition to pulse counting, one may monitor exercise intensity by using
   a. Ratings of perceived exertion
   b. Duration of exercise
   c. Heart rate reserve
   d. Frequency of exercise

8. The type of training in which you participate determines which fitness component improves, which is known as
   a. progression
   b. specificity of training
   c. personal training
   d. duration of training

9. How many sessions of aerobic exercise per week are recommended?
   a. 2 to 3
   b. 2 to 4
   c. 3 to 5
   d. 5 to 7

10. How many minutes of aerobic activity per session are recommended
    a. 10
    b. 15 to 60
    c. 20 to 60
    d. 40 to 60

Understanding the Muscular System

13

Chapter Objectives

After completing this chapter, you will be able to:

- Describe the difference between muscular strength and endurance.
- Identify the health-related problems associated with inadequate muscular strength and endurance.
- Identify the basic structure of the muscle.
- Understand the effects of exercise on the muscular system.

Key Words

atrophy
cartilage
concentric contraction
eccentric contraction
fast-twitch muscle fiber
hypertrophy

intermediate fast-twitch
  muscle fiber
ligament
muscle
muscular endurance
muscular strength

slow-twitch muscle
  fiber
static contraction
tendon
testosterone

Suggested Physical Activities

Try to add at least one activity each day that will help improve your muscular strength and/or endurance. (Hint: yard-work and housework count!)

Healthy People 2010 Goals

◆ Increase the proportion of adolescents who engage in moderate physical activity at least 30 minutes on 5 or more of the previous 7 days.
◆ Increase proportion of people who perform physical activity that enhances and maintains muscular strength, muscular endurance and flexibility.

Use the *Personal Fitness for You* Student CD for:

◆ Lab 13-1: Identifying the Major Muscles
◆ Chapter Practice Test
◆ Chapter Study Guide
◆ Chapter Crossword Puzzle
◆ Vocabulary Flash Cards
◆ Chapter Power Point Review

Understanding Muscular Fitness

Muscular fitness is a term used to describe the relationship between muscular strength and muscular endurance. **Muscular strength** is the amount of force that can be exerted by a single contraction of the muscle. Strength allows you to lift a heavy load, such as a box, bag of groceries or furniture. **Muscular endurance** is the ability of a muscle group to continue muscle movement over a length of time. Endurance allows you to keep going in an activity, such as lifting things over a period of time. Both are integral parts of muscular fitness and are health-related components of fitness.

Weight training will help you look and feel better.

Benefits of Strength and Endurance

In addition to allowing you to lift heavy objects and continue an activity over long periods, obtaining an optimal level of muscular strength and endurance is essential to achieving total fitness.

For instance, weak abdominal muscles strain the muscles in the back. While back pain may not be a problem to you now, it is a frequent problem of adults. Long-term back strain caused by weak abdominal muscles can take its toll.

One of the most important benefits of obtaining muscular strength and endurance is improved physical appearance. You will:
- develop better posture.
- look firmer and trimmer.
- feel better.

In addition, achieving a good level of muscular fitness will:

- reduce risk of muscle injury.
- increase capacity to perform daily tasks and activity by reducing fatigue.
- reduce bone and muscle loss as you age.

The following health-related problems can be avoided by maintaining an adequate level of muscular strength and endurance:

- low back pain
- abnormal movement due to muscular imbalance
- poor posture due to muscular weakness
- inability to function effectively on a daily basis
- muscular injuries

These benefits are especially important for active people whose days are filled with school, sports, club meetings, jobs, homework, shopping and leisure time activities.

Good muscular fitness will enable you to participate in a variety of activities.

Low back pain can be avoided with an adequate level of strength and endurance fitness.

To learn more about muscles, visit the following web site: **www.exer.net/exercise.html**

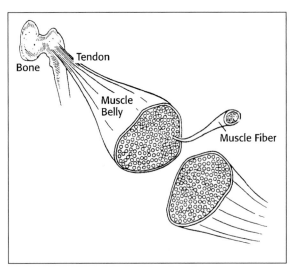

A muscle is connected to the bones by a tendon. The muscle fiber is covered by connective tissue.

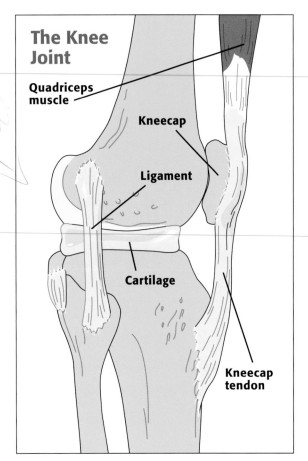

The Knee Joint

Quadriceps muscle

Kneecap

Ligament

Cartilage

Kneecap tendon

Muscle Basics

A **muscle** is a band of muscle fibers which contract (shorten) and produce movement. These long, thin fibers extend the length of the muscle. The muscle has blood vessels which supply oxygen and fuel and remove waste products. Nerves send signals to each muscle fiber to contract. Connective tissues attach bones and muscles together. One type of connective tissue is a **ligament**, which connects bones together in a joint. Another type of connective tissue is a **tendon**, which attaches skeletal muscles to bones. A third type is **cartilage**, which is found in a joint between the bones and acts as a cushion between the ends of the bones.

The human body has three types of muscles: cardiac, smooth and skeletal. Cardiac muscle is only found in the heart. Smooth muscles are in arteries and internal organs and help control many bodily functions, such as digestion. Skeletal muscles are located around joints and bones of the body and enable us to move. Weight training programs affect skeletal muscles.

The Muscle Fiber + Activities

The basic unit of the muscular system is the muscle fiber. There are three types of muscle fibers.

Slow-Twitch Muscle Fibers

- Slow to contract
- Can continue working for long periods of time
- Fibers have a rich blood supply
- Needed for endurance-type activities such as distance running and cross country skiing

Fast-Twitch Muscle Fibers

- Good for fast, short-term contractions
- Fibers are well supplied by blood vessels
- Have a reduced capacity for using oxygen
- Needed for fast, short burst activities requiring speed and power, such as sprinting and shot putting

Intermediate Fast-Twitch Muscle Fibers

- Have characteristics common to both slow-twitch and fast twitch fibers
- Better blood supply than fast twitch fibers so they can process oxygen better
- The function of these fibers can be altered to meet the specific exercise program
- They can be trained to perform like slow twitch fibers in an endurance program
- Used in activities of high intensity and moderate duration such as middle distance running

Def on this page

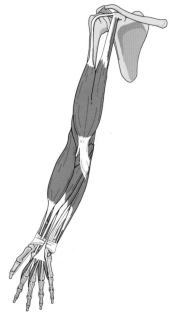

Achieving a good level of muscular fitness reduces the risk of muscle injury and fatigue.

Muscle Performance and Muscle Fiber Distribution

The amount of fast, intermediate and slow fibers in a skeletal muscle can be quite variable. If a muscle has mostly white, fast twitch fibers, it will appear white, such as a chicken breast. Chickens flap their wings only for a short period of time, using their breast muscles for short flights. Muscles dominated by slow twitch fibers will appear dark red, due to the number of blood vessels and myoglobin in slow fibers. Since chickens walk around all day, the fibers in their legs are dark colored, slow twitch fibers or dark meat. Most human muscles contain a mixture of all types of fibers and are usually pinkish in color.

Muscle Growth

Each person is born with a different number of slow-twitch, fast-twitch and intermediate fast-twitch fibers in the muscle tissue. An individual with a large proportion of fast-twitch fibers will tend to perform best in speed or power activities. These fast-twitch fibers adapt to training by increasing their mass and strength, resulting in an increase in the size of the muscle. This enlargement of the diameter of the muscle fiber is called **hypertrophy**. Slow-twitch fibers increase their diameter only slightly as they adapt to training by increasing their oxygen capacity. Those people who have more slow-twitch fibers have an advantage in endurance-type activities such as marathon running.

When a muscle is not used, the muscle fibers become smaller in diameter, a condition known as **atrophy**. If you break your arm and it is put in a cast, the muscle size will shrink because of lack of use. Once the arm is placed back into use, the muscle will regain its normal size. **Muscles do not turn into fat if you stop training.** Muscle cells have a much different structure than fat cells.

As you weight train, the muscle fibers grow thicker. There are thousands of fibers in each muscle and when each one thickens slightly, the diameter of the muscle increases. Heredity determines the number and type of muscle fibers you have and has some influence on the potential for muscle growth. An individual born with a great number of fast-twitch muscle fibers has a greater capacity to develop large muscles. A good weight training program, however, can help all individuals increase their muscle mass. The size of the muscle has a direct relationship to its ability to exert force (strength). In other words, the larger the size of the muscle, the stronger it will be able to become.

As you weight train, the size of the muscle increases.

Another way that strength can be increased is through regular weight training sessions that improve the efficiency of the messages sent from the brain via the nervous system to the muscles. When the messages are received faster, more muscle fibers will contract and the result will be a smoother performance and an improvement in strength.

A good weight training program can help you increase your muscle mass.

Strength Training and Women

Men have thicker muscle fibers and more muscle fibers than women have; therefore, men have an inherited capacity to develop larger muscles than women. The hormone **testosterone** is necessary for the development of large muscles. Women do not have this hormone in sufficient quantity to develop large muscles. Male testosterone levels increase upon reaching puberty during adolescence, thus enhancing muscular development. Women can develop some hypertrophy of muscles if they engage in a weight training program, but not nearly to the extent of males. A weight training program can also help women improve their strength, especially those women who start with low levels of strength.

Women can improve strength by engaging in a weight training program.

Types of Muscle Contractions

There are three basic types of muscular contraction: shortening, lengthening and maintaining a static position.

1. Shortening, or **concentric contraction**. During this type of contraction, one end of the muscle remains stationary, while the other end pulls the bone and turns it about the joint. This type of contraction is required for activities such as pull-ups, curl-ups and lifting weights.

2. Lengthening, or **eccentric contraction**. The term "lengthening" is misleading since the muscle does not actually lengthen. It gradually returns to its resting or original length. When you lower a weight slowly or lower your body during a chin-up, you are using an eccentric contraction.

3. **Static contraction**. During a static contraction, the muscle remains in partial or complete contraction without changing its length. This type of contraction is performed when muscles opposite each other contract with equal strength, thus balancing each other, or when the muscle is held in partial or complete contraction against another immovable force. An example of a static contraction is placing one hand against the other and pushing hard for ten seconds.

Not all muscular action is for the purpose of causing movement. Some muscles have other functions, such as steadying and supporting a body part, stabilizing a bone to which another muscle is attached, or neutralizing the unwanted action of a muscle which normally causes several movements.

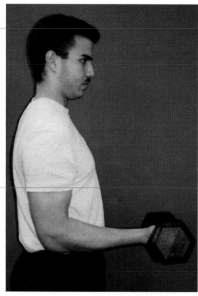

Lifting the weight shortens the muscle and is an example of a concentric contraction.

Lowering the weight lengthens the muscle and is an example of an eccentric contraction.

A static contraction maintains the muscle at the same length.

Effects of Exercise on the Muscular System

As you exercise a muscle, several changes take place.

- The size of the muscle temporarily increases as the blood flow to it increases.
- The body temperature rises, due to the increased activity in the muscle tissue.
- The increased temperature causes the muscles to become more flexible, able to contract and relax more easily, and contract at a faster rate.

In muscular endurance activities, additional changes occur.

- The number of red blood cells increases.
- Additional capillaries develop.

These changes mean the muscle fibers are receiving a richer blood supply and the muscle is better able to use oxygen. Thus, the muscle increases its capacity for long-term physical activity.

STRESS Stopper

Becoming too wrapped up in yourself can create stress. Try to look outside your own world and help others. Volunteer your time and your problems will seem smaller.

Summary

Both muscular strength and muscular endurance are important to achieve an optimal level of fitness and to meet the demands of daily living. The relationship between muscular strength and muscular endurance is called muscular fitness. Adding muscle mass increases the amount of calories burned each day.

There are three types of muscles—cardiac, smooth and skeletal. Weight training can lead to hypertrophy of the skeletal muscles.

There are three types of muscle fibers—slow-twitch, fast-twitch and intermediate fast-twitch. Slow-twitch fibers are used in long duration, aerobic activities. Weight lifting, jumping and sprinting use fast-twitch fibers. Activities such as middle distance running use intermediate fast-twitch fibers. The proportion of muscle fiber types you possess partially determines your success in certain activities.

Since the hormone testosterone is necessary for the development of large muscles, women usually do not achieve the muscular size of males, but can still increase strength through weight training programs.

The three types of muscular contractions are concentric (shortening), eccentric (lengthening) and static (no change in length). Exercise causes many changes to occur in the muscles and leads to increased strength and endurance.

Chapter 13 Review

Lesson Checklist

- Do you know the difference between muscular strength and endurance?
- Can you describe some health problems associated with inadequate muscular fitness?
- Can you identify the basic structure of the muscle?
- Do you know how different types of muscle fibers function?
- Can you describe the effects of exercise on the muscular system?

Chapter Projects

Write a response to each of the following:

1. What are the benefits of improved muscular strength?
2. How does increase in muscle mass help with weight control?
3. Will weight training develop large muscles on most females?
4. Describe the functions of the types of muscles found in the human body.
5. Describe the three types of muscular contractions.

Behavior Change Evaluation

Review the following items to see if you have gained an understanding of fitness and wellness. On a piece of paper briefly state how you will make these changes.

- I will increase my muscular fitness to develop better posture.
- I will increase my muscular fitness to help me look firmer and trimmer.
- I will increase my muscular fitness to reduce my risk of muscle injury.
- I will increase my muscular fitness to reduce muscular fatigue and make it easier for me to perform daily tasks.
- I will increase my muscular fitness to reduce bone and muscle loss as I get older.
- I will increase my muscular fitness to add muscle mass which will help burn more calories.

Critical Thinking

Based on what you have learned about the muscular system, describe how a muscular fitness program could personally benefit you.

Chapter 13 Review

Test Your Knowledge

Read the questions below and select the best possible answer for each.

1. Weight training programs have a direct effect on
   a. cardiac muscles
   b. smooth muscles
   c. skeletal muscles
   d. none of the above

2. Fast twitch fibers would be used in:
   a. walking a mile
   b. jogging a mile
   c. sprinting 100 yards
   d. swimming a mile

3. Slow twitch muscle fibers would be used in
   a. weight lifting
   b. 50 yard dash
   c. walking 3 miles
   d. 100 meter hurdles

4. Tendons connect
   a. bones to bones
   b. muscles to bones
   c. bones to ligaments
   d. motor nerves to muscle fibers

5. Ligaments connect
   a. bones to bones
   b. muscles to bones
   c. bones to tendons
   d. muscle fibers together

6. Muscular force exerted as a muscle shortens is called
   a. concentric
   b. eccentric
   c. static
   d. isometric

7. When a muscle remains in complete or partial contraction without changing length, it is called:
   a. a concentric contraction
   b. a static contraction
   c. an eccentric contraction
   d. an isotonic contraction

8. The hormone necessary for the development of large muscles is
   a. estrogen
   b. adrenaline
   c. insulin
   d. testosterone

9. Muscular strength is
   a. the maximum amount of force that can be exerted by a single contraction of the muscle.
   b. the ability of a muscle group to continue muscle movement over a length of time.
   c. the ability to exert force rapidly.
   d. The maximum amount of force one can produce in 10 repetitions.

10. Muscular endurance is
    a. the maximum of force that can be exerted by a single contraction of the muscle.
    b. the ability of a muscle group to continue muscle movement over a length of time.
    c. the ability to exert force rapidly.
    d. The maximum amount of force one can produce in 10 repetitions.

Achieving Muscular Fitness

14

Chapter Topics

- Muscular Fitness
- Applying the Principles of Training
- The Warm-Up and Cool Down
- Types of Weight Training Equipment
- Safety Precautions
- Spotting Techniques
- Methods for Developing Muscular Strength and Endurance
- Muscular Strength and Endurance Exercises
- Major Muscles of the Body
- Exercises for the Major Muscle Groups

Chapter Objectives

After completing this chapter, you will be able to:

- Describe how the principles of training are applied to muscular strength and endurance programs.
- Describe safety procedures which should be followed in a weight training program.
- Apply proper spotting techniques.
- Develop a personal fitness plan for muscular fitness.

Key Words

1 RM	isokinetic	plyometric
abdominal	negatives	progression
concentric contraction	overload principle	repetitions
eccentric contraction	pectoral	set
isometric	periodization	specificity
isotonic	pilates	spotter

Suggested Physical Activities

Test yourself to see how well you perform the various muscular fitness exercises in this chapter. Make sure you warm-up properly before exercising.

Healthy People 2010 Goals

◆ Increase the proportion of adolescents who engage in moderate physical activity for at least 30 minutes on 5 or more of the previous 7 days.

◆ Increase the proportion of people who perform physical activity that enhances and maintains muscular strength, muscular endurance and flexibility.

Use the *Personal Fitness for You* Student CD for:

◆ Lab 14-1: Muscular Fitness Exercises Without Equipment
◆ Lab 14-2: Muscular Strength and Endurance
◆ Lab 14-3: Your Weight Training Program
◆ Lab 14-4: Muscle Training for Two People
◆ Chapter Practice Test
◆ Chapter Study Guide
◆ Chapter Crossword Puzzle
◆ Vocabulary Flash Cards
◆ Chapter Power Point Review
◆ The Muscle Game

Muscular Fitness

As you learned in Chapter 4 and 13, muscular fitness includes muscular strength and muscular endurance.

- **Muscular strength** is the amount of force that can be exerted by a single contraction of the muscle.
- **Muscular endurance** is the ability of a muscle to perform repeated contractions over an extended period of time.

There are many types of activities that can help you improve your muscular fitness, but once again it is important to apply the principles of training in order to achieve the best results.

Applying the Principles of Training

Muscle growth occurs when a muscle lifts more weight.

Overload Principle

In order for a muscle to grow and become stronger, it must be challenged by making it lift more and/or work longer than usual. Assuming it receives sufficient nutrients and rest, muscle growth will occur. The next time it is subjected to that same workload, it will better be able to handle it.

Frequency. A frequency of two to three times per week is recommended for general muscular fitness. A minimum of 48 hours of rest is necessary between workouts to allow the muscle group **recovery time** from the work. If you want to strength train every day, work out different muscle groups on alternate days. For instance, on Monday work the upper body, on Tuesday work the lower body, on Wednesday work the upper body, etc.

Intensity. This is the amount of weight or resistance. To increase muscular strength, you should lift about 80% of your maximum lift.

The most weight you can properly lift through the full range of motion one time is referred to as **1 RM**—one repetition maximum.

To increase muscular endurance, you should lift 50-70% of your maximum lift. It is important to increase intensity gradually so that you do not injure muscles or connective tissues.

Time. This refers to the number of times or **repetitions** you perform an exercise. A group of repetitions is called a **set**.

Type. To increase muscular strength, use heavy weights with few repetitions (70-80% of maximum weight, one set of 8 to 12 repetitions or until unable to lift anymore, with occasional multiple sets). Training within the 8 to 12 repetition range is an appropriate strength stimulus for most people, as long as the weight is heavy enough so that you are unable to perform another repetition while maintaining good form.

To increase muscular endurance, use lighter weights and more repetitions (50 to 70% of maximum weight, three sets of 12 to 20 repetitions).

STRESS Stopper

Tensing and then relaxing the muscles is a great way to relieve stress. Try this the next time you are waiting in line or taking a test.

WEBSITE

To learn more about weight lifting, visit the following web site:

www.fitnesslink.com/ program/design.htm

You can increase intensity by:

- Increasing resistance (weight)
- Increasing number of repetitions
- Reducing momentum by decreasing the speed of movement
- Maintaining muscular tension throughout the movement (don't lock out joints) when performing multiple joint exercises such as bench press, leg press, military press, etc.

*It is important to perform the lifting (**concentric or positive phase**) and the lowering (**eccentric or negative phase**) parts of the exercise in a controlled manner. It should take about 3 seconds to lift the weight and 3 seconds to lower it.*

Achieving Muscular Fitness

Frequency	Muscular strength: every other day (2-4 times per week)
	Muscular endurance: every other day (3 days per week)
Intensity	Muscular strength: High resistance - heavier weights
	Muscular endurance: Low resistance - light weights
Time	Muscular strength: 8-12 repetitions
	Muscular endurance: 12-20 repetitions
Type	Muscular strength and endurance: resistance type activity (weights and weight machines)

Note: Exercises such as curl-ups, crunches and push-ups (no weights) can be performed daily.

Progression Principle

The muscle must lift more each time if it is to become progressively stronger. Begin with 8 repetitions, increase to 10 or 12, then increase the weight by 5% and drop back to 8 repetitions, building again to 10 or 12 before increasing the weight again. To increase muscular endurance, apply the same progression, only with more repetitions (10 or more).

Specificity Principle

You must work the exact muscle group that you wish to develop. If you can perform an exercise that isolates the muscle you intend to work, you will achieve greater improvement because the workload will not be shared by other secondary muscles. Most weight machines isolate a muscle or group of muscles (for example, the lower back machine or the biceps machine).

Regularity Principle

For general fitness, 2 to 3 days per week of weight training is sufficient. You will see a rapid improvement during the first couple of months of a weight training program and then gains will occur more slowly.

Individuality Principle ✳

Progress in your weight training program may be affected by the individual differences such as heredity, age and motivation. Your rate of improvement will depend on the way your body responds to training and how much effort you put into your training program.

Dumbbells can be found in many shapes, sizes, and weights.

The Warm-Up and Cool Down

You should perform a general warm-up (as with any type of exercise or activity) before your weight training session and cool down afterward. Walk, jog or bicycle for several minutes to warm-up. Before each weight training exercise, perform a set at a low weight for a warm-up.

After you complete your strength training workout, cool down for 5 to 10 minutes. This is a good time to perform stretching exercises to work on your flexibility. In addition, stretching after workouts may help prevent muscle soreness.

Types of Weight Training Equipment

Free Weights

Many weight training facilities have a variety of free weights such as barbells and dumbbells. This type of equipment is relatively inexpensive when compared to weight machines and is often purchased for home use. In addition, free weights are more versatile than machines; free weights can be moved in many different directions to challenge different muscle groups.

It is advisable to have a partner or spotter present when you lift barbells. A partner can check your form and make sure you are not lifting too much weight. Using correct techniques will also result in less chance of injury and greater strength gain.

Family Activity

Share the benefits of muscular fitness with your family. Make a chart for each member of your family of muscular strength and endurance activities, such as push-ups and crunches, which can be performed at home.

Olympic plates and barbells are used in many schools and health clubs.

Weight machines are an easy, safe way to develop muscular fitness.

Weight Machines

Weight machines are designed to work specific areas of the body. They are generally safer and easier to use than free weights, because the stack of weights slide up and down on a rod and are attached to the machine by a system of chains or cables and pulleys. To change the weight, you simply change the position of the pin on the weight stack. You usually do not need a spotter when working out on a weight machine, because the machine controls the direction in which the weights move.

Safety Precautions

- Warm-up properly before beginning the training program.
- As you are learning new exercises when starting a weight training program, use low weights and high repetitions. This will prepare your muscles and connective tissue for eventual strength training and reduce your chances of injury.
- Properly secure barbell plates to prevent slipping.
- It is important to breathe rhythmically as you exercise to avoid increasing internal chest pressure, which can cause you to faint or damage blood vessels. **Do not hold your breath.**
- When lifting a weight from the floor, keep the weight close to your body. Bending over and lifting a weight with straight legs may injure your low back.
- Unless spotters are present, do not perform the bench press or any other lift where you could be "pinned" if you lose control.
- For stability keep back straight and feet shoulder-width apart. Avoid twisting or shifting your weight during the lift or movement.
- Execute each movement under control. Reduce the weight if you cannot maintain correct form throughout the entire exercise.
- Moving through the joint's full range of motion will increase flexibility and strengthen connective tissue.
- Begin each workout by using the largest muscle groups, moving to the smallest.
- Don't train if you are ill or injured.
- Use proper techniques on all lifts.

Remember This ☑

When participating in any activity or sport with others it is important to be a responsible person. For example, when working out with weights, the spotter (a person who assists the weightlifter) is responsible for the safety of the weightlifter. The weightlifter must also be responsible by learning and using correct lifting techniques.

Spotting Techniques

A **spotter** is someone who assists the weightlifter. Depending on the type of lift, one or two spotters may be necessary. For a squat, two spotters should be used, one on either side of the weight to help if the lift cannot be completed. Some people prefer one spotter for the incline press or bench press, since it is easier for the weightlifter to coordinate the lift with just one spotter rather than two. Regardless of the number of spotters, the weightlifter must communicate with the spotter at anytime necessary during the lift. If a spotter removes the weight too soon, it may not allow the lifter to make his or her best effort. However, the spotter must be alert and not delay too long if help is needed to remove a weight, as an injury could occur to the lifter. Use a rack, if available, for all heavy lifts.

Spotters should:
- know how the exercise should be performed.
- help improve form when necessary.
- be physically able to assist with the weight.
- use correct lifting techniques, keep weight close to the body, keep the back straight and bend the knees.
- **communicate** with the lifter; assist when necessary.
- know the signals for starting and finishing the lift.
- check to make sure weight plates and collars are secure throughout the lift.

It is important to have spotters when performing squats.

Spotters should encourage partners to use good form when lifting weights.

Isometric exercises can be performed without special equipment.

Methods for Developing Muscular Strength and Endurance

Isometric Exercises

Isometric exercises are strength-building exercises in which you contract, or tighten, muscles without changing their length (static contraction). Pushing against a wall and pressing your palms together are examples of isometric contractions.

Basic Principles:

1. The duration of the contraction should last for about five seconds.
2. Several repetitions, adjusted to individual requirements, are recommended.
3. Strength gain is not developed through the entire range of motion but is specific to the position the exercise is performed. Therefore, contractions should be performed at various joint angles.
4. Normal breathing is essential during these exercises.

One advantage of isometrics is that they can be performed almost anywhere without elaborate and expensive equipment or special clothing. You can perform isometrics while riding in a car or sitting at your desk.

Some disadvantages of isometrics are that muscular endurance, cardiorespiratory fitness and flexibility are not improved; muscles and joints are not moved through the full range of motion; and the accompanying rise in blood pressure may be harmful to some people.

Pushing against a wall creates tension in the muscle, but no movement occurs. This is an isometric contraction.

Isotonic Exercises

Isotonic training involves lifting a resistance through a range of motion. Barbells, your own body weight and weight machines are examples of isotonic training resistance. An example of an isotonic exercise is a biceps curl. The bicep (the muscle located in the front of the upper arm) contracts and shortens to raise the weight (resistance). As the weight is lowered, the triceps (muscle located in the back of the upper arm) contracts and shortens while the biceps relaxes and lengthens. A pull-up is another example of an isotonic exercise, with the body weight as the resistance.

Many fitness centers and gyms have weight machines which provide varying resistance through a joint's complete range of motion. These machines put more stress on the muscles at the end of the range of motion where the muscle can exert more force because of better leverage. It is important to adjust the seat height of these machines to fit the lifter.

If your weight room has mirrors, use them to analyze your technique. Using proper form and lifting techniques will result in greater strength gains and less risk of injury.

For Your Information

Keeping a personal record of the amount of weight lifted and the number of repetitions performed on each machine is necessary to keep track of your progress. A personal weight chart will save you time because you will know how much weight you lifted during your previous workout. In addition, a weight chart is a good motivational tool, because you can see the improvement of each muscle group.

Strengthen Your Core

The muscles targeted in core strengthening exercises are those in your trunk–they're layered, overlapping and connected to each other. Twenty-nine muscles make up your body's core. Some of the major muscles include those in your back and your abdomen. Your core muscles work in harmony to provide stability to your body and protect you from injury. Strong core muscles keep your back healthy. They hold your body upright, improve your balance, and allow you to move your arms and legs freely. If the core muscles are weak, your body won't work effectively, and other muscles have to pick up the slack. A weak core could be why we 'hunch' our shoulders or get an aching back.

Strong core muscles keep your back healthy.

dif v/w 3

Biomechanical Principles of Muscular Strength

The following principles affect muscular strength:

- The length-tension relationship means that when a muscle is stretched, it can produce more force and as it shortens, it produces less force.
- The angle of muscle pull changes as a body segment moves through its range of motion. At a 90° angle, the muscle is most effective. As the angle decreases, the effectiveness of the muscle pull decreases.

The result of these two biomechanical factors is that the muscle's ability to produce force varies through the range of motion.

Isokinetic Exercises

An **isokinetic** exercise is one in which muscle tension is kept at a maximum through the full range of muscle movement. It differs from an isotonic exercise in which the tension varies at different points in the muscle movement.

Isokinetic exercise equipment provides for maximum resistance to be exerted throughout the range of motion of the muscle. However, since the exercise is performed at a constant speed, they are not as beneficial in developing strength for specific sports skills which involve accelerated movement such as throwing, rowing and kicking.

Muscular Strength and Endurance Exercises

It is best to perform weight training exercises in a certain order rather than just randomly. Muscle groups can be classified into small muscle groups (forearms, upper arms and lower legs) and large muscle groups (chest, back and legs). Exercise the large muscle groups before you workout the small muscle groups, because many of the exercises which involve large muscles also use small muscles. If you fatigue the small muscles by working them separately first, the small muscles will become tired and will not be able to continue, thus preventing the large muscles from being worked to their maximum. The following strength and endurance exercises will help you improve your muscular fitness.

The Biomechanical Principles

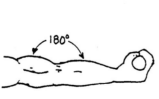

Weak angle of pull

Strongest angle of pull

Weak angle of pull

Abdominal Exercises

There are four **abdominal** muscles: rectus abdominis, external obliques, internal obliques and transverse abdominus. None of these muscles is responsible for the bending of the hip. In the full bent-knee sit-up movement, the abdominal muscles are only active during the first 30-45 degrees of bending. After that the hip flexor muscles complete the action of the sit-up.

Abdominal exercises develop abdominal muscles, but they will do very little to reduce fat deposits in the abdominal area. There is no such thing as "spot reducing." When you burn body fat as an energy source, the fat comes from all over the body, not just one spot. However, exercising a specific group of abdominal muscles by using effective techniques will help tone and strengthen the abdominal muscles. One reason many adults have low back problems is because of weak abdominal muscles. Abdominal muscles also help you to stand straight and reduce stress on the back muscles.

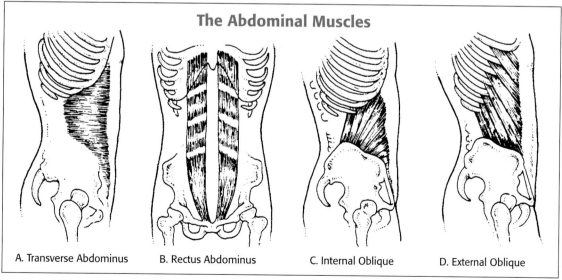

The Abdominal Muscles

A. Transverse Abdominus   B. Rectus Abdominus   C. Internal Oblique   D. External Oblique

Abdominal muscles help you stand straight and reduce stress on the back muscles.

It is important to develop both strength and endurance of the abdominal muscles. Start with one set of 20 reps for each of the exercises. If you are using your body weight only (crunches, etc.), you can perform those exercises every day. Using the stability ball is an excellent way to work on strengthening the abdominal muscles.

Crunch (abdominals)
- Lie on your back, legs bent, feet flat on the floor.
- Tilt your pelvis up as you press your lower back into the floor.
- Contract your abdomen and lift your upper back off the floor until the upper body reaches a 30-45 degree angle.

A variation is to place your feet up on a bench. You can also perform crunches on a slanted board or with a small weight held against your chest. Your arms may be crossed or you may support your head with your hands, but be careful not to pull on your neck. Keep your elbows out to the side.

The standard abdominal crunch.

A variation on the lift and twist.

Lift and Twist (obliques)
- Lie on your back and place the lower legs on a bench.
- Place the hands behind the head, fingertips touching and elbows out to the sides.
- Lift your head, shoulders and upper torso off the floor, twisting the torso toward the opposite knee. Do not move the hips.
- Return to center position and repeat in the opposite direction.

A variation is to place the feet in the air and lift reaching to the outside of one knee.

Upper Body Exercises

Push-Up Advanced:
- Perform a regular push-up, with these possible variations:
  1. A partner places his or her hand between your shoulder blades and exerts pressure.
  2. Place your feet on a box or low chair.
  3. Use only two or three fingers to support your body.
  4. Push up using only one arm.

Advanced push-ups may be performed by placing feet on a chair.

Modified Dip (triceps)
- Face away from a chair or bench.
- Place hands on a stabilized chair.
- Dip down to 90° at elbow joint.
- Return to starting position.

Modified Dip

Reverse Curl (forearms)
- Perform the same as the front curl, but use the overhand grip.

Overhead Press (deltoids, upper chest, triceps)
- Sit with back straight
- Press the bar upward until the arms are fully extended
- Return to starting position

Front Curl (biceps)
- Hold the bar using an underhand grip.
- Lift weight upward and forward.
- Lower with arms fully extended.

Dip (triceps)
- Place hands on parallel bars.
- Straighten elbows, support body weight.
- Dip down to 90° at elbow joint.
- Return to starting position.

Arm Curl (biceps)
- Use dumbbells or a bag filled with rocks or sand.
- With palm-up grip, curl-up as far as possible.
- Return to starting position.
- Repeat with other arm.

Wrist Curl (forearm flexors)
- Sit on bench, forearms resting on thighs.
- Hold the bar using the underhand grip.
- Curl the hands up toward the body.
- Lower slowly.

Reverse Wrist Curl (wrist extensors)
- Perform the same as the wrist curl, but use the overhand grip.

Triceps Extension (triceps)
- Lift weight above the head.
- Keep elbow close to the head; lower weight behind the head.
- Return to starting position by straightening the arm.

Shoulder Shrug (trapezius)
- Pick up bar from floor, bend knees, keep back flat.
- Use palm-down grip.
- Lift bar by raising shoulders toward ears, exhaling.
- Hold for 2 counts.
- Return to starting position by lowering shoulders.

Variation: Use dumbbells.

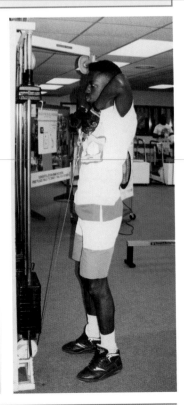

Upright Rowing (biceps, forearms, deltoids, trapezius)
- Grip handles with palms facing down.
- Pull up to the chin.
- Return to starting position.

Seated Rowing (upper back, arms)
- Place feet on pedals.
- Pull arms back toward chest.
- Return to starting position.

Seated Dip (triceps, deltoid, pectoralis major)
- Start with arms fully extended.
- Slowly lower the body until the upper arms are parallel to the floor.
- Press the body upward back to starting position.

Pull-downs (latissimus dorsi, pectoralis major, biceps)
- Sit facing the bar.
- With a wide grip on the bar fully extend the arms.
- Tilt the head forward and pull the bar to the base of the neck. Exhale as you pull the bar down; inhale as it goes up.

Triceps Press-down (triceps)
- Hold the bar with the overhand grip, hands close together, bar under the chin.
- Press the bar down until the arms are fully extended.
- Return to starting position.

Bench Press (pectorals, deltoids, triceps)
- Lie flat on the bench
- Extend arms and grasp bar
- Lower the bar to chest
- Return to the extended position

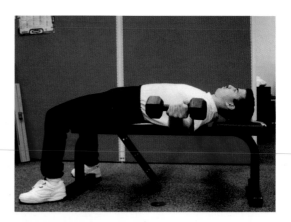

Flies (pectorals and arms)
- Lie on the bench with feet flat on the floor.
- Hold weight in each hand, straight up over chest, palms inward
- Slowly lower weights as far as possible, keeping arms straight
- Return to starting position

 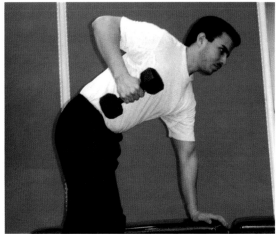

Bent-Over Row (trapezius, latissimus dorsi, deltoid, pectoralis, triceps, and biceps)
- Lean on a bench for balance, feet in stride position.
- Knees should be slightly bent, not locked.
- Raise weight toward side of chest; lower to starting position.

Lower Body

Leg Press (quadriceps, gluteus maximus)
- Start from seated position, knees flexed about 90°.
- Fully extend the legs; return to starting position.

Leg Curl (hamstrings)
- Lie on the bench, hands on hand grips, knees just off the end of the bench.
- Contract hamstrings slowly, curling legs and heels to buttocks.
- Return to starting position.

Leg Extension (quadriceps)
- Sit in seat; use extra pad for the back, if necessary.
- Place hands on hand grips.
- Contract quadriceps; hold.
- Return to starting position.

Hip Flexor (hip flexors and abdominals)
- Keep back straight, forearms on pads.
- Bend knees slowly upward as far as possible.
- Lower the legs slowly to starting position.

Half Squat (quadriceps, gluteals, hamstrings)

- Squat under the bar, grasp it with a shoulder width or slightly wider grip and lower it slowly until it rests on your trapezius muscles
- Toes should be slightly turned outward in line with the knees
- Stand up straight, step back slowly away from the rack
- Squat down slowly until your knee angle reaches about 90 degrees, and then return to the upright position
- As you progress, you may squat lower until your thighs are parallel with the floor. Correct form must be maintained. If your heels come off the floor or if you lean too far forward, you should limit your range of motion and use less weight.

Note: The squat is one of the best exercises for developing leg strength and power. It is best to have a competent person observe your technique at first, making sure your form is correct before increasing weight.

Heel Raise (calf muscles)

- Lean against a wall; raise heels by moving at the ankle joint.
- Lower slowly.

For more information about advanced training techniques, you should consult a certified strength coach. Remember to start off slowly to minimize injury and give your body time to adjust to the new program.

leg curl – hamstr
leg extension – quadr

triceps pull down

Circuit training helps develop muscular strength, muscular endurance and cardiorespiratory fitness.

Circuit Training

Six to twenty exercise stations are set up in a circuit. The weight trainer performs an exercise and then quickly moves to the next station performing a certain number of repetitions or doing as many reps as possible during a time period (from 20 to 60 seconds) at each station. This technique also develops cardiorespiratory fitness, but care should be taken to perform each exercise correctly. If the circuit involves weight machines, seat and weight adjustments should be made and belts (if any) should be fastened before each exercise is attempted. Participants should warm-up thoroughly before beginning the circuit.

Plyometrics

Plyometrics is a type of exercise used to develop explosive strength and also help develop bone density. In a plyometric exercise, the muscle exerts force while it lengthens (eccentric contraction), followed by a rapid shortening (concentric) contraction. An example is jumping off a bench and immediately jumping back on.

Pilates

Pilates is an exercise program which works the core muscles in the abdomen, back and buttocks. Emphasis is placed on maintaining correct posture throughout the exercises. Breathing techniques help improve concentration and control of movement. Some classes use special Pilates equipment, while others use mat and/or floor work. Pilates improves flexibility, muscular fitness and endurance.

*F*or *Y*our *I*nformation

Joseph Pilates was a German performer and boxer living in England in the early 1900's. Placed in an internment camp with other Germans at the outbreak of WWI, he taught other internees his system of matwork (exercises done on the floor). He later devised equipment to help patients rehabilitate from disease and injury, using springs to create resistance for bedridden patients.

Other Weight Training Devices

Stability balls can be used for abdominal exercises and also in place of a bench when you are doing strength training exercises. The instability of the ball forces you to use your core muscles. Select the correct size for you by sitting on the ball; your thighs should be parallel with the floor. Inflate the ball with more air to make the ball less stable and your workout is harder. Beginners should inflate the ball with less air until they get used to ball workouts.

Resistance bands are like giant rubber bands that you can pull against to strengthen muscle groups. They are available in a range of resistance levels, are portable and are convenient to use.

Exercise bars are used in many ways to tone and strengthen your body. They are foam covered steel and come in a range of weights from 4 to 27 pounds.

Resistance band

Exercise Bar

Stability ball

Knuu

Major Muscles of the Body

Front View

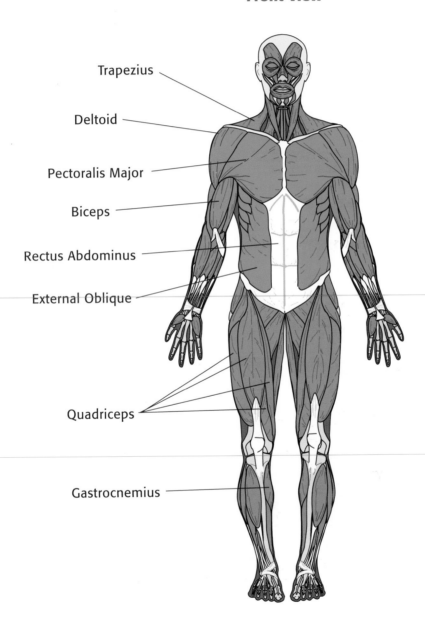

Trapezius

Deltoid

Pectoralis Major

Biceps

Rectus Abdominus

External Oblique

Quadriceps

Gastrocnemius

know

Major Muscles of the Body

Back View

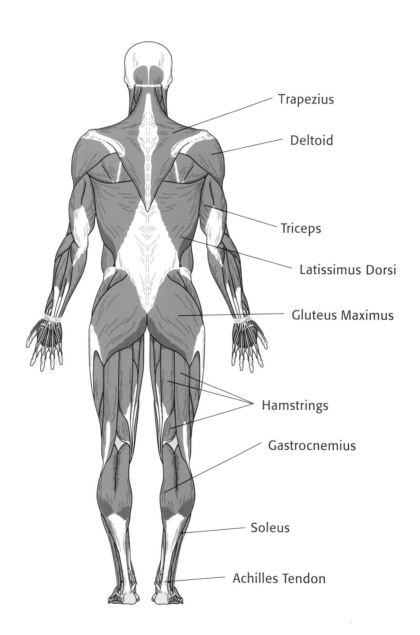

Trapezius

Deltoid

Triceps

Latissimus Dorsi

Gluteus Maximus

Hamstrings

Gastrocnemius

Soleus

Achilles Tendon

Exercises for the Major Muscle Groups

	Muscle Group	Exercises With Weights	Exercises Without Weights
Upper Body	Biceps	Front arm curl Reverse arm curls Upright rowing Pull-downs	Pull-ups
	Forearm	Reverse curls Wrist curls Reverse wrist curls	Squeezing a ball
	Deltoids	Upright rowing Seated dip Flies	Pull-ups
	Latissimus dorsi	Overhead press Rowing Pull-downs	Pull-ups
	Pectoralis major	Bench press Flies Overhead press	Push-ups
	Trapezius	Overhead press Shrug Upright rowing	Modified dips Dips Push-ups
	Triceps	Bench press Triceps extension Overhead press Seated dip Triceps press down	Dips Modified Dips Push-ups
Abdominals	Obliques	Twisting crunches Lift and twist	Twisting crunches Lift and twist
	Rectus abdominus	Crunch	Crunch Hip flexor
Lower Body	Gastrocnemius and Soleus	Heel raise	Heel raise Jumper Step-ups
	Gluteus maximus	Leg press Half squat	Step-ups Jumper
	Hamstrings	Leg curl Half Squat	Leg curl Curl-up
	Quadriceps	Leg extension Leg press Half Squat	Jumper Step-ups

The climbing wall is a challenging way to improve muscular fitness.

My Activity Plan (MAP)

My goal is to do the following activities:

Type of Activity	Frequency: Times per Week	Intensity of the Workout (high or low resistance)	Time: Number of Repetitions	Number of Sets
Bench Press	M W F	100 lbs	10	1
Bicep Curl	M W F	40 lbs	12	1
Crunch	M T W R F	_____	20	2

Refer to the student *Personal Fitness for You* CD for the *My Activity Plan* form.

Summary

Weight training helps you maintain strong bones and muscle as you age. It is a great way to improve your self image, help control your weight and enhance your performance in sports and other activities. Weight training is a lifetime activity—don't ever stop.

To develop muscular strength use heavy weights and few repetitions. To develop muscular endurance use light weights and many repetitions.

The three different methods of exercising your muscles are isometric, isotonic and isokinetic. A variety of exercises can be performed with and without special equipment to develop muscular strength and endurance.

It is very important to follow safety precautions while weight training. Warming up properly, starting at low weights, using correct body mechanics, breathing regularly and having a spotter present will help you lift safely. Never sacrifice **correct technique** while trying to lift heavy weights.

Chapter 14 Review

Lesson Checklist

- Do you know how the principles of training are applied to muscular strength and endurance?
- Do you know the safety procedures which should be followed while lifting heavy weights?
- Can you demonstrate proper spotting techniques?
- Can you identify exercise programs to develop strength, endurance and muscular mass?
- Can you demonstrate at least one exercise for each of the major muscle groups?

Chapter Projects

Write a response to each of the following:
1. Discuss the principle of progression as it relates to muscular strength.
2. What is the difference between isotonic and isometric exercise?
3. How does training for muscular strength differ from training for muscular endurance?
4. How do sit-ups and crunches differ when working the abdominal muscles?

Behavior Change Evaluation

Review the following items to see if you have gained an understanding of fitness and wellness. On a piece of paper briefly state how you will make these changes.
- I will assess my muscular strength and endurance goals based upon my personal needs.
- I will warm-up properly before lifting weights.
- I will use low weights and high repetitions when starting a weight training program.
- I will follow safety precautions and use good body mechanics when lifting weights.
- I will learn proper spotting techniques.
- I will learn the major muscle groups of the body and exercises to strengthen them.

Critical Thinking

Design a muscular fitness program for yourself. Analyze your strengths and weaknesses. Set short term and long term goals. Be realistic about the availability of equipment when planning your program. How many times per week will you train? Which exercises will you use? How many reps and sets will you begin with? How much weight will you start with for each exercise?

Chapter 14 Review

Test Your Knowledge

Read the questions below and select the best possible answer for each.

1. Isometric exercise is described as applying force
   a. with a movement
   b. at a constant speed
   c. without movement
   d. while a muscle is lengthening

2. Muscular force exerted as a muscle shortens is
   a. eccentric
   b. concentric
   c. isotonic
   d. isometric

3. Muscular force exerted as a muscle lengthens is
   a. eccentric
   b. concentric
   c. isotonic
   d. isometric

4. 1 RM stands for
   a. one range of motion
   b. one repetitive movement
   c. one repetition maximum
   d. none of the above

5. To increase muscular endurance, use
   a. light weights and 5 repetitions
   b. moderate weight (50-70%, 1RM) and 12-20 reps, multiple sets
   c. 70-80% of 1 RM and 8-12 reps
   d. 90% of 1 RM, 1-5 reps, multiple sets

6. To increase muscular strength, use
   a. 40-50% of 1 RM, 12-20 reps
   b. 80% of 1 RM, 8-12 reps, multiple sets
   c. 1 set of 100% RM
   d. 100% of 1 RM, 12-20 reps

7. The minimum number of training days per week for gaining strength is
   a. 2
   b. 5 to 6
   c. every day
   d. 1

8. A set is a
   a. group of exercises
   b. group of repetitions
   c. a single muscular contraction
   d. a group of similar exercises

9. A cool-down period after a weight training workout should include
   a. 30 minutes of aerobic activity
   b. 10 jumping jacks
   c. 5-10 minutes of relaxing and stretching
   d. sprinting

10. A minimum number of how many hours is necessary between weight training workouts to let the muscles recover?
    a. 24
    b. 36
    c. 48
    d. 72

Achieving Flexibility

15

Chapter Topics

- What Is Flexibility?
- Benefits of Flexibility
- Factors which Limit Flexibility
- Applying Training Principles to Flexibility
- Flexibility Techniques
- Biomechanical Principles of Flexibility
- Safety Precautions
- Stretching Exercises
- Potentially Harmful Exercises

Chapter Objectives

After completing this chapter, you will be able to:

- Define flexibility.
- Describe why flexibility is important.
- Identify health problems which may be related to poor flexibility.
- Identify factors which limit your flexibility.
- Explain how you can increase your flexibility by applying the principles of training.
- Define and identify static and dynamic stretching exercises.
- Describe safety precautions you should take when participating in flexibility exercises.
- Perform a variety of stretching exercises.
- Identify exercises that should be avoided.

Key Words

ball and socket joints
ballistic stretching
contract and relax stretching
dynamic stretching
extension
flexibility

flexion
hinge joints
hyperflexibility
ligaments
muscle imbalance
muscles

range of motion
static stretching
stretching
stretch reflex
tendons

Suggested Physical Activities

Try to find more time to stretch. You can stretch while watching television, talking on the telephone or listening to your favorite music. Take a stretch break while you are studying. Don't forget to stretch before AND after exercise!

Healthy People 2010 Goals

◆ Increase the proportion of adolescents who engage in moderate physical activity for at least 30 minutes on 5 or more of the previous 7 days.
◆ Increase proportion of people who perform physical activity that enhances and maintains muscular strength, muscular endurance and flexibility.

Use the *Personal Fitness for You* Student CD for:

◆ Lab 15-1: Flexibility Workout
◆ Lab 15-2: Your Flexibility Program
◆ Chapter Practice Test
◆ Chapter Study Guide
◆ Chapter Crossword Puzzle
◆ Vocabulary Flash Cards
◆ Chapter Power Point Review

What Is Flexibility?

Flexibility is a person's ability to move body joints through a full **range of motion**. Flexibility is specific to a joint or series of joints. For example, a person could have good range of motion in his or her back and hips, but poor range of motion in one or both shoulders.

Normal range of motion in joints is necessary to perform many necessary daily tasks. Better than normal flexibility is necessary to perform activities such as yoga, ballet, gymnastics and karate. Most people experience a decrease in flexibility as they age; however, if you maintain an active lifestyle you can enjoy a reasonable amount of flexibility throughout your life.

Benefits of Flexibility

Wellness

The ability to move your joints throughout their full range of motion is essential to optimal fitness and to healthy living. A high level of flexibility will help keep your muscles and joints moving without pain so that you can participate in all the activities that you enjoy. Maintaining flexibility is especially important as you get older.

Prevention of Low Back Pain

Adequate flexibility and strength in your lower back, abdomen, hips and thighs will improve your posture and help prevent the onset of lower back problems as you get older.

Healthy Joints

Poor flexibility in a joint can lead to joint damage. Tight muscles in your thighs can lead to a problem in your knees. Poor shoulder flexibility can lead to shoulder pains.

Injury Prevention

It is generally believed that maintaining flexibility can help prevent injury to the muscles and joints. If you have an optimal level of flexibility in a joint, you are less likely to become injured while participating in a sport or everyday activity. For example, reaching for a high object is easier and safer if you have good shoulder flexibility. In addition, as your flexibility increases, your performance will improve in many activities, especially those which involve running, jumping and throwing.

Stretching (extending the muscles) before and after aerobic and strength training sessions and other strenuous activities can help prevent sore muscles. Stretching can also help relieve tension in your muscles caused by stress or sitting for long periods of time in one position.

Poor flexibility can lead to knee and other joint pain.

Factors which Limit Flexibility

A number of factors may limit the range of motion of a joint. Some of these factors can be improved through exercise, others are based on the body's structure.

Bone Structure

Your bone structure may limit the range of motion of a joint. Your knee and elbow joints are examples of **hinge joints**, which have a definite limit to their ability to extend due to bone structure.

Stretching before and after your workout has numerous benefits.

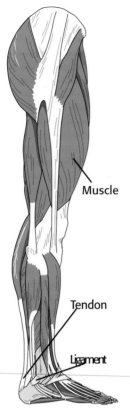

Muscle

Tendon

Ligament

Your shoulder and hip joints, which are **ball and socket joints**, operate differently in that the range of motion is partially governed by soft tissues such as tendons, ligaments and muscles.

Tendons: attach muscle to bone.
Ligaments: attach a bone to another bone.
Muscles: bands of fibers which enable us to move.

Muscles and Tendons

Muscles and their tendons are more commonly responsible for limiting the range of motion of a joint. It is possible to increase the elasticity (rubber band-like flexibility) or length of a muscle. **Extension** is the straightening movement of muscles at a joint. **Flexion** is the bending movement around a joint.

For example, when your biceps muscle contracts, the opposing muscle, the triceps, relaxes, which results in flexion or a bending movement of the elbow joint. Then when the triceps contracts, the biceps relaxes, and extension or straightening of the joint occurs.

Muscle imbalance occurs when one muscle group is worked much more than the opposing muscle group thus becoming much stronger. This can affect the range of motion of a joint and also increase the risk of injury to the weaker muscle group. Biomechanically, your quadriceps (front of thigh) are normally stronger than your hamstrings (back of thigh), but if you overdevelop your quadriceps and don't work out your hamstrings, muscle imbalance will occur and you will have a greater risk of hamstring injury.

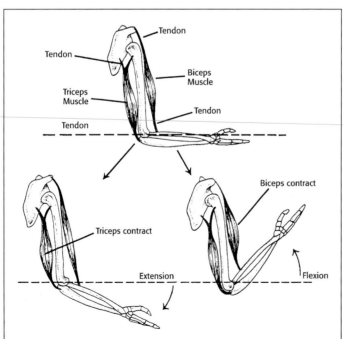

Tendon
Tendon
Triceps Muscle
Tendon
Biceps Muscle
Tendon

Triceps contract
Extension

Biceps contract
Flexion

Ligaments

Ligaments can lose their elasticity and shorten after long periods of inactivity. It is also possible to have slack, overstretched ligaments caused by improper exercises or injuries which result in too much motion in a joint, a condition called **hyperflexibility**. For example, an ankle which has been sprained several times is more prone to injury because the ligaments have been over stretched.

Fat

Excess fat can limit the range of motion of a joint, as can weight training which is not accompanied by flexibility training. Participating in activities and sports with wide ranges of movements increases flexibility.

Gender

Females generally are more flexible than males of the same age. Each person has a unique body structure; do not attempt to force a joint beyond its normal range of motion trying to stretch farther than someone else.

Injuries

Your flexibility can be affected by injuries to your joints, muscles, connective tissues or skin. Scar tissue that is formed as an injury heals can limit the range of motion of a joint. Proper use of flexibility exercises during and after rehabilitation from an injury can help a joint regain its normal range of motion. Physical therapists, physicians and athletic trainers can evaluate your flexibility after an injury and help you develop a program to improve your flexibility.

To learn more about fitness, visit the following web site:
www.fitnessonline.com

When using weights, a good stretching routine is also important.

After an injury, flexibility exercises can help you regain a full range of motion.

Keeping the abdominal muscles toned will decrease the risk of experiencing back pain.

SAFETY TIP

Large muscle activity before stretching is important.

Family Activity

Share your knowledge of flexibility principles with members of your family. Show them how to stretch properly and tell them about the benefits of attaining good flexibility.

Applying Training Principles to Flexibility

Whether you choose to combine your flexibility program with the warm-up and cool down portions of your cardiorespiratory and/or strength programs or work on your flexibility separately, it is very important to follow the principles of training.

Principle of Overload

If you want to increase your flexibility, the muscles, ligaments and tendons must be stretched slightly further than usual. Increasing frequency, intensity and/or time places overload on the muscles.

Principle of Specificity

Flexibility can only be gained in those joints of the body which are exercised. Extra attention should be given to those inflexible areas of the body. Areas which are related to your overall health fitness level, such as the lower back and hamstring muscles, should be given special attention. Based on the results of your flexibility tests, you may want to spend extra time on the less flexible joints of your body. However, it is important to stretch all areas regularly to maintain flexibility. You may want to increase your flexibility in specific areas in order to improve your performance in a particular sport or other activity.

Principle of Progression

Increase in range of motion will occur gradually as you continue to change the frequency, intensity and/or time of your stretching program. To avoid injury or extreme soreness, increase your stretching program slowly.

Principle of Regularity

Daily stretching is recommended by many experts. Maintaining your flexibility throughout your life will allow you to move your joints and muscles without pain, and you will be able to participate in the activities that you enjoy. A flexibility program needs to be done on a regular basis or you will lose the improvements in your flexibility.

Principle of Individuality

Flexibility is highly individual and specific to each body joint. It is important to design a flexibility program that will suit your individual needs. You may want to improve sports performance, maintain good posture or improve poor posture, relieve aches and pains that develop from sitting in one place for an extended period of time, or use stretching as a way to relax and reduce stress.

Warm-Up

A few minutes of jogging, bicycling, rope skipping or running in place causes an increase in blood flow to the muscles and a slight increase in body temperature. This increase in body heat causes your muscles to become more flexible, better able to contract and relax, and able to contract at a faster rate.

Achieving Flexibility

Frequency	At least 2-3 times per week Ideally 5 to 7 times per week
Intensity	Slow stretch until mild tension is felt
Time	Hold each stretch 15-30 seconds, 2 to 4 times
Type	Stretching should be slow and steady - no bouncing

My Activity Plan (MAP)

My goal is to do the following activities:

Type of Activity	Frequency: Times per Week	Intensity of the Workout	Time of Stretch and Number of Repetitions
Tricep	5 days	Until mild tension	15 sec/3 reps
Hamstring	5 days	Until mild tension	20 sec/4 reps
Quad	5 days	Until mild tension	20 sec/4 reps

Refer to the student *Personal Fitness for You* CD for the *My Activity Plan* form.

Yoga stretching emphasizes smooth, static stretches.

Safety Precautions

1. Perform stretching exercises within your own physical limitations. Do not compete with others.
2. Progression should be gradual. It is safe to stretch frequently, but increase intensity and time slowly.
3. Avoid ballistic stretching exercises which can cause damage to muscles, ligaments and tendons.
4. Partner stretching can be dangerous if your partner forces your body to stretch too far. Communicate with your partner.

Flexibility exercises should be performed at least three times per week.

Flexibility Techniques

Static Stretching

Static stretching is a safe method of increasing flexibility in which the muscle is gradually stretched so that a pull is felt but before it becomes painful. Hold the stretch for 15 to 30 seconds, performing each stretch two to four times.

Static stretching is the safe and recommended way to increase flexibility.

Dynamic Stretching

Athletes and others who are interested in achieving high levels of skill-related fitness may want to include some **dynamic stretching** in their fitness routines. Dynamic (moving) stretching is used to warm-up for practice or competition by mimicking sport-specific types of activities to increase the range of motion of a joint. This type of stretching helps performance by stimulating the nervous system activity in the joints. It is very important to warm-up properly and thoroughly by performing static stretching before dynamic stretching.

Dynamic stretching is a sport-specific stretch used to increase the range of a joint.

Contract and Relax Stretching

In **contract and relax stretching**, also called Proprioceptor Neuromuscular Facilitation (PNF), a muscle is contracted before it is stretched. The person stretching performs an isometric contraction, while a partner provides resistance. For example, to perform a calf muscle stretch, start in a seated position with your legs extended forward. Contract your calf muscles, with your partner applying force against your toes. Then pull the tops of your feet toward your body, which stretches out your calf muscles.

Practice contract and relax stretching with a partner.

Common Stretching Mistakes

- Not warming up before stretching
- Not stretching the muscles you are trying to stretch
- Placing too much pressure on ligaments or joints
- Using jerky, ballistic movements
- Not stretching to the point of maximum extension
- Not holding the stretch for 15 to 30 seconds, 2-4 reps each
- Not stretching often enough

Ballistic Stretching

Ballistic stretching involves bouncing or bobbing against the muscle and is harmful, can cause pain and muscle soreness and damage soft tissues. Ballistic stretching can trigger the **stretch reflex**, a painful muscle spasm. The stretch reflex is the body's protective reaction against overstretching. This is NOT a recommended method of stretching.

Biomechanical Principles of Flexibility

Force and Leverage

The structure of the joint has considerable influence on the range of motion possible.

Hinge joints (such as the elbow and knee joint) allow movement in only one direction.

Ball and socket joints (such as the shoulder and hip) allow movement in many directions. Therefore, a greater range of motion is possible.

Another factor that affects range of motion is that the muscles are arranged in sets so that when one set contracts and shortens, the other set lengthens and must relax. For example, when the biceps muscle contracts to flex the elbow joint, the triceps muscle relaxes.

The bones serve as the levers, the joints as the fulcrums (given fixed points) and the contracting muscles as the forces. The illustration on the next page shows this principle.

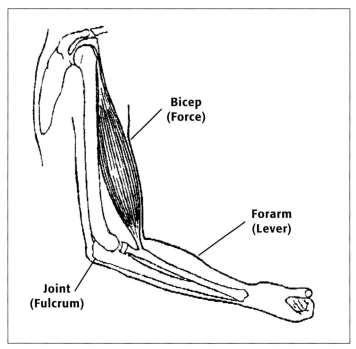

The forearm acts as a lever with the biceps providing the force.

Leverage is an important factor in determining the effectiveness of a particular stretching exercise. Leverage during a stretch means having sufficient control over how intense the stretch becomes and how fast it is performed. Better leverage enables you to achieve the desired intensity with greater control.

Isolating the muscles being worked in a given stretch is another important biomechanical concept of stretching. The fewer muscles you try to stretch at one time, the better. For instance, try stretching one hamstring at a time rather than both together. This gives you greater control and allows you to more easily change the intensity.

Try stretching one muscle at a time.

Lower Back and Hip Stretch (lower back and hamstring muscles, lumbar spine ligaments)
- Lie on your back with both legs bent.
- Grab the hamstrings just above the knee of one leg.
- Pull the knee to the chest, repeat with the other leg.

Pelvic Tilt (lower back muscles and ligaments)
- Lie on your back with your knees bent and feet flat on floor.
- Tighten the stomach muscles and flatten the small of your back against floor without pushing down on your legs.

Triceps Stretch (triceps muscles, shoulder joints)
- Place one hand on top of the back.
- Place other hand on elbow and press back.
- Repeat with other arm.

Shoulder and Chest Stretch (deltoid and pectoral muscles, ligaments of the shoulder joints)
- Clasp the hands together behind your back.
- Pull arms toward each other slowly.

Quadriceps Stretch (quadriceps muscles, knee ligaments)
- With one hand, grasp the opposite leg above ankle and pull back.
- Avoid bending knee beyond 90°.
- Repeat on the other leg.

Shin Stretch (tibialis anterior)
- Lean against a wall for balance.
- Place one leg with toes pointing back behind the other leg.
- Slowly bend knee of front leg until shin of back leg is stretched.
- Repeat on other leg.

Achilles Tendon Stretch (Achilles tendon, calf muscles)
- Face a wall two to three feet away with feet in forward stride position.
- Lean forward; place hands on the wall.
- Keep back straight, heels flat on floor.
- Bend elbows until you feel tightness in the calf and upper heel.

Inner Thigh Stretch (hip adductor)
- Sit on floor, bottoms of feet touching each other.
- Keep back straight.
- Press knees down.

Inner Thigh Stretch Variation (hip adductor)
- Lie on side, one arm stretched above head.
- Place other hand on floor in front to stabilize the body.
- Extend leg closest to floor.
- Bend top leg, placing foot behind extended leg.

Hamstring Stretch (hamstrings, lower back)
- Place one foot on a step.
- Bend the body forward from the hip joint over the foot on the step.
- Keep the leg on the floor straight.
- Repeat on the other leg.

Neck Stretch (neck flexors and extensors, cervical spine ligament)
- Slowly bend neck to one side; hold.
- Repeat to other side; hold.
- Slowly turn neck to one side; hold.
- Repeat to other side; hold.

Pretzel Stretch (hips, spine ligaments)
- Sit with legs extended in front of you.
- Place lower part of left leg over the right leg, right elbow behind the raised left knee.
- Slowly twist head and shoulders to the left.
- Repeat on the other leg.

Forward Hurdler Stretch (hamstring, lower back, lumbar spine ligaments)
- Sit with the back straight; bend one leg and place sole of foot against inside of straight leg at knee.
- Slowly reach down extended leg and hold.
- Repeat on other leg.

Hamstring Stretch

There are three ways to perform this stretch.
- Sit with the legs extended in front of you.

A) Pull the toes back toward the body to place emphasis on the hamstrings and calf muscles.

B) Grasp the ankle and flex the foot slightly to emphasize the middle portion of the hamstring.

C) Stretch the upper portion of the hamstring by fully flexing the foot and slightly bending the knee.

Partner Stretch

Be careful when performing partner exercises. If your partner pulls or pushes too hard and forces your joint outside its normal range of motion, you could be injured. Communicate with your partner if you experience pain while stretching. Partner stretching can be an effective way of increasing flexibility.

Potentially Harmful Exercises

Ballistic Arm Circles

Quadriceps Stretch with Heel Close to Buttocks

Neck Circles

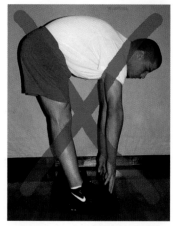

Toe Touch with Locked Knees

Yoga Plough

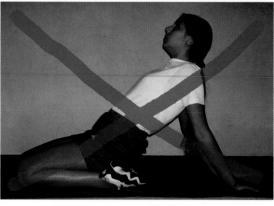

Sitting Quadriceps Stretch

Hurdle Stretch

Deep Knee Bends, Full Squats, Duck Walk

Ballistic Bar Stretch

Summary

Flexibility is the ability to move body joints through a full range of motion. The structure of a joint can limit the range of motion. Muscles, ligaments and tendons can also influence the range of motion of a joint. Stretching exercises can improve the flexibility of a joint that has a limited range of motion.

Flexibility influences our ability to work and play. Some of the benefits of adequate flexibility are fewer lower back problems, less chance of exercise-induced injury and reduced muscle soreness.

It is important to follow the principles of training in developing your flexibility. The degree of flexibility is specific to each joint in the body. Assessing your current level of flexibility in your shoulders, lower back and trunk will help you plan your flexibility program.

Increasing muscle temperature by jogging, cycling, brisk walking or running in place before stretching is recommended. A variety of static, dynamic and contract and relax stretching exercises may be used to improve each muscle group or joint. You can stretch as part of the warm-up and cool down of your cardiorespiratory and/or strength program, or you can design a separate flexibility program.

Avoid ballistic stretching and exercises which force sideways movement or more than normal extension or flexion of a joint. Use proper techniques when improving your flexibility. Make a commitment to yourself to stay flexible throughout your entire life.

Portfolio Idea

Flexibility Assessment

Record the results of this activity in your personal portfolio or follow instructions from your teacher.

Plan and participate in a flexibility workout for three days that follows the guidelines for achieving flexibility. After completing the workouts, respond to the following questions.

- Describe the flexibility sessions - warm-up activities, flexibility exercise phase (specific techniques used - static, dynamic, contract and relax stretching) and safety considerations.

- Did you apply the biomechanical principles of flexibility to your workout?

- Did you enjoy the workouts? Why or why not?

- Describe how you felt after each workout.

- What changes do you think you should make in the workout session?

Chapter 15 Review

Lesson Checklist

- Can you list some health problems which relate to lack of flexibility?
- Can you list factors which might limit a person's flexibility?
- Why is it important to warm-up before beginning a stretching session?
- Do you know the advantages and disadvantages of the different techniques of stretching?

Chapter Projects

Write a response to each of the following:

1. What is the "stretch reflex"?
2. Describe how the principle of overload is used to increase a person's flexibility.
3. What is the difference between a static stretch and a ballistic stretch?
4. What is the difference between tendons and ligaments?
5. What does warming up do to help your muscles?
6. What limits the range of motion of a joint?
7. What is the difference between static and dynamic stretching?

Behavior Change Evaluation

Review the following items to see if you have gained an understanding of fitness and wellness. On a piece of paper briefly state how you will make these changes.

- I will warm-up before stretching by jogging, bicycling, walking or rope jumping.
- I will perform flexibility exercises at least three times per week.
- I will avoid ballistic stretches.
- I will include stretching as part of my cool down routine after my cardiorespiratory workout.

Critical Thinking

A. Analyze your current flexibility in the following areas: arms and shoulders, torso, hips and thighs. List at least two exercises that will improve flexibility in each area.
B. Based on what you have learned about flexibility and the training principles, design a flexibility program based on your personal needs.

Chapter 15 Review

Test Your Knowledge

Read the questions below and select the best possible answer for each.

1. Which of the following is NOT a potential benefit of flexibility:
   a. Relief of aches and pains
   b. Maintenance of good posture
   c. Increased relaxation
   d. Improved energy production

2. Which of the following affects flexibility
   a. Tightness of the muscles
   b. Tightness of the ligaments
   c. Structure of a joint
   d. All of the above

3. Flexibility is determined by
   a. Heredity
   b. Joint structure
   c. Muscle elasticity
   d. All of the above

4. Good flexibility benefits all of the following EXCEPT
   a. Sports performance
   b. Injury prevention
   c. Muscle soreness prevention
   d. Body composition improvement

5. Ballistic stretching may be dangerous because
   a. It may cause a muscle to relax
   b. It may stimulate a muscular contraction during a stretch
   c. It has no influence on stretch receptors
   d. It doesn't increase flexibility

6. Which technique is most commonly associated with injury?
   a. Static stretching
   b. Dynamic stretching
   c. Ballistic stretching
   d. All of the above

7. Which stretching technique is safest and most often recommended?
   a. Static stretching
   b. Dynamic stretching
   c. Ballistic stretching
   d. All of the above

8. Flexibility exercises should be performed a minimum of how many days per week
   a. 1
   b. 2 to 3
   c. everyday
   d. 5 to 7

9. To improve flexibility, each exercise should be performed ___ times.
   a. 2 to 4
   b. 10
   c. 2
   d. 3

10. Back pain is likely to result from any of the following EXCEPT
    a. Increased flexibility
    b. Weak back muscles
    c. Poor posture
    d. Lifting a heavy object incorrectly

Designing Your Fitness Program

16

Chapter Topics	Chapter Objectives
◆ Goal Setting ◆ Why Set Goals? ◆ Long-Term, Intermediate, and Short-Term Goals ◆ Adding Activity to Your Life - Designing My Activity Plan (MAP) ◆ Evaluating Sports and Recreational Activities ◆ Maintaining the Program ◆ Evaluating Your Plan	After completing this chapter, you will be able to: ◆ Understand the importance of using goal setting to improve your health fitness level. ◆ Know how to set specific and realistic short-term, intermediate and long-term goals based on the health fitness assessment results. ◆ Know the importance of basing your fitness program on your individual fitness level, an understanding of the principles of training, your personal goals and availability of resources. ◆ Be able to design a personal fitness program that will lead to an optimal level of health-related fitness. ◆ Know how to maintain your personal fitness program in spite of obstacles that may occur.

Key Words

goal

long-term goal

intermediate goal

short-term goal

Suggested Physical Activities

Set a simple goal for getting started, such as "I will walk for 30 minutes 3 times a week after dinner."

Healthy People 2010 Goals

- ◆ Improve health, fitness, and quality of life through daily physical activity.
- ◆ Increase the proportion of adolescents who engage in moderate physical activity for at least 30 minutes on 5 or more of the previous 7 days.
- ◆ Increase the proportion of adolescents who engage in vigorous physical activity that promotes cardiorespiratory fitness 3 or more days per week for 20 or more minutes per occasion.
- ◆ Increase proportion of people who perform physical activity that enhances and maintains muscular strength, muscular endurance and flexibility.
- ◆ Promote health and reduce chronic disease associated with diet and weight.
- ◆ Reduce the proportion of children and adolescents who are overweight or obese.

Use the *Personal Fitness for You* Student CD for:

- ◆ Lab 16-1: Designing Your Fitness Program
- ◆ Lab 16-2: Planning an On-Going Physical Activity Program
- ◆ Lab 16-3: Evaluating Sports and Recreational Activities
- ◆ Lab 16-4: Sports Participation
- ◆ Lab 16-5: Daily Exercise Log
- ◆ Chapter Practice Test
- ◆ Chapter Study Guide
- ◆ Chapter Crossword Puzzle
- ◆ Vocabulary Flash Cards
- ◆ Chapter Power Point Review

Work hard to achieve your goals!

Goal Setting

What's next?

So far you have:

- learned why fitness and exercise are important.
- gained an understanding of your health fitness level.
- learned how to exercise using the principles of training.
- learned how to exercise safely.

Now you are ready to establish personal goals and to design an individualized program that will help you reach your highest level of fitness.

Each of us is different, but, regardless of our previous experience, disease or disability, everyone can improve his or her health and strive for optimal fitness. Remember, do not compare yourself to others—seek to achieve the highest fitness level possible for you.

Why Set Goals?

Perhaps this is the first time you have thought about specific goals you would like to achieve. No doubt you have general goals for yourself, such as pass this course, graduate from high school, get a summer job.

Designing your fitness program requires setting very specific individual goals, putting them in writing and making a commitment to yourself to seek a higher level of health fitness. A goal must be important to you-it must mean something special to accomplish your goal. You need to consider whether the benefits are worth the effort. Is it really worth your time to seek these goals? In addition, your goals must be personal and related to your specific needs and interests.

A **goal** is an outcome for which you are striving; something you want to achieve or intend to do in life.

A clearly stated goal is:
- Concrete—a definite objective you want to achieve.
- Measurable—a way of knowing when you have reached your goal.
- Related to a definite time frame—a deadline by which you intend to reach your objective.

Family Activity

Share some of your goals with your family members. They can help you stick to your program and achieve your goals.

Long-Term, Intermediate and Short-Term Goals

Long-term goals are those which involve a major change in lifestyle or behavior. They may be more general and take a longer time to achieve. Examples of long-term goals are:
- I will become a regular exerciser.
- I will feel better about myself.
- I will look better.
- I will be able to run a 10K race.

Intermediate goals can serve as milestone events along the way to achieving your long-term goals. For example, being able to run a 3K race after a month of activity might be a realistic intermediate goal as you work toward being able to run a 10K race. Suppose one of your long-term health fitness goals is to lose twenty-five pounds of fat by the end of the semester.

Intermediate goals might include:
- Maintain a consistent, vigorous aerobic exercise program.
- Avoid eating fast foods, processed foods and vending machine foods that are high in calories and fat.
- Begin a muscle training program doing muscular strength and endurance exercises-perhaps using weights.
- Lose twelve pounds by the end of eight weeks.

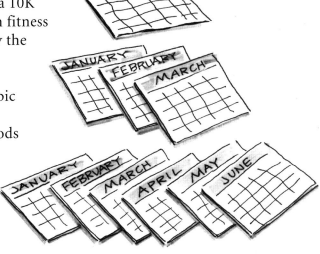

Goals may be short-term, intermediate or long-term.

Did You Know❓

If your time is limited, a shorter, more intense workout can burn the same number of calories as a longer, less intense session.

Working out with others in a class setting can motivate you.

As we describe each of these steps, it will help you to print out the *MAP* worksheet which is on the student *Personal Fitness for You* CD.

Short-term goals are attainable in a shorter time frame such as weeks or months. For example, using the 10K race long-term goal; your short-term goal might be: By the end of the next week, I will be able to run one mile or by next month, I will run 4 days a week. Other typical short-term goals for the long-term goal of losing twenty-five pounds of fat by the end of the semester might include:

- Begin an exercise program.
- Evaluate my diet for extra "fat" calories.
- Eat more fruits and vegetables every day.
- Lose five pounds by the end of three weeks.

Adding Activity to Your Life- Designing My Activity Plan (MAP)

In order for you to achieve your optimal level of fitness, you must design an activity plan which will lead to a healthier lifestyle. Your *MAP* for achieving the level of health and fitness you desire is an individualized plan. The key ingredient to the plan is movement. Just get moving! Develop a habit of being active. Devise a *MAP* that works for you! Developing your *MAP* involves the following steps:

Assessing Your Current Fitness and Activity Level

Use the Health Related Fitness assessment tests in Chapter 4 to frequently monitor your fitness level. Continue to use the Lab 2-1 *Making Physical Activity a Habit* in Chapter 2 to monitor your activity level.

Identifying Areas for Improvement

Using the previous assessment tools in Chapter 4, make a list of the areas in which you need to seek improvement. Note whether your activity level meets the guidelines of at least 30 minutes a day.

Determining Realistic Goals for You

When setting goals, first identify the areas in which you would like to improve, then apply the appropriate fitness component to achieve the goal. For example, if your personal goal is to reduce lower back problems, a program that will increase muscular strength and flexibility in the muscles and joints in the lower trunk should be part of your goal setting plan.

Use the chart below to identify your personal goals. Add other goals as needed.

> **Remember This** ☑
> You will be more successful if you attempt one major lifestyle change at a time. For example, first start an exercise program, then try to adjust eating habits.

Potential Personal Fitness Goals

- Look trimmer (firm muscles, reduce bulges, add muscle definition)
- Lose (or gain) weight (reduce fat)
- Become more muscular—increase muscle tone and bulk
- Improve muscular effectiveness for daily tasks, sports activities (overcome clumsiness)
- Increase stamina for activities such as dancing, swimming, long walks, jogging
- Prevent or reduce low back pain
- Increase resistance to muscular fatigue (in order to perform daily activities)
- Reduce or eliminate breathlessness from climbing stairs or walking a long distance
- Increase muscular strength to perform tasks—such as lifting, opening jars or moving objects
- Reduce or eliminate known health risks such as high blood pressure, high cholesterol, high fat intake
- Reduce discomfort from tension or nervousness
- Improve ability to handle stressful situations
- Increase range of movement and become more flexible
- Lower resting heart rate
- Reduce menstrual discomfort
- Improve posture
- Have more stamina and energy at the end of the day
- Eliminate use of dangerous substances—alcohol, steroids, illegal drugs, tobacco
- Get "in shape" to participate in a particular activity or sport

How do you know a goal is realistic for you? If you have a low level of fitness-far below the health fitness standards, your potential for large gains is much better than for those who are already at a good fitness level. Those at a good fitness level (at or above the recommended health fitness scores) may only achieve small gains in fitness. Those close to the recommended standards have the potential for moderate improvement. The chart on the next page provides assistance to you in identifying realistic goals.

Guidelines for Setting Goals to Improve Health Fitness Levels

Initial Fitness Level	Cardiorespiratory	Flexibility	Muscular Strength and Endurance		Body Composition
			Curl-up	Pull-up	
Below the recommended Health Fitness Standard	Decrease time by 1-4 minutes	Increase reach 2-8 cm	Increase 5-10	Increase 1-2	Decrease skinfold sum by 1-10
At or near the recommended Health Fitness Standard	Decrease time by 1-2 minutes	Increase reach 2-5 cm	Increase 3-7	Increase 2-4	Decrease skinfold sum by 1-5
Higher than the recommended Health Fitness Standard	Decrease time by 30-60 seconds	Increase reach 2-3 cm	Increase 2-5	Increase 1	Maintain or decrease by 1-2, if desired

Writing down your goals will help you stay focused on them.

Putting Your Goals in Writing

Use Lab 16-1 to record your goals and how you plan to achieve them. Writing your goals helps you make a commitment to reaching them. Think of your plan as a contract with yourself-a promise that you will keep!

Selecting the Type of Activity That Will Work for You

- Which activities do you most enjoy?
- Will the activities help improve your areas of weakness?
- Do you need special equipment for the activity? If so, is it easily available to you?
- How far must you travel to do the activity? Will transportation be a potential problem?
- Which days of the week and which time of day is best for you? Will you need to make changes in your schedule from week to week?
- Is your time schedule realistic? Will you be so rushed you are tempted to skip exercising?
- Do you need to have someone exercise with you or do you prefer to exercise alone? If you need others, do you have a partner or a group to join?

- What potential obstacles could interfere with your plan—illness, weather, injuries, school, job, other activities, home responsibilities? How can you overcome them?
- Do you need motivation to get you going? If so, how can you get assistance?
- Do you prefer to select one activity and stick with it or is a variety of activities more enjoyable?
- Do you need assistance in "staying with it"? If so, have you identified someone who will help you?
- Develop a plan for including these activities into your daily schedule-how will you find the time?

Even though our daily schedules will vary from week to week, the most successful activity plans establish a routine which includes a specific time schedule. Remember that even shorter spurts of exercise spaced throughout the day can be beneficial. Try including exercise with other activities such as doing curl-ups, stretching or lifting weights while watching television. Schedule blocks of activities on your calendar or in your appointment book. Have a designated exercise calendar. If necessary, vary the times and activities but keep your appointments! For some, finding a set time will be a challenge, but once you decide that you need to get more activity; you need to make the changes in your schedule in order to have time for activity.

Deciding How You Will Record Your Activities and Monitor Your Progress

- Will you keep an exercise and diet log?
- Will you chart your weight loss (or gain) and fat percentage change?
- Will you keep a log of the amount of time you are active during each day?

For some people, exercising with a partner is important.

Try exercising to television work-out programs.

Did You Know?

An excellent activity for most students is walking. Students who use wheelchairs, walkers, crutches or canes can participate at a rate comparable to students without disabilities.

Joining a class and trying a new activity is a good way to maintain interest in your plan.

Lab 16-5 will help you monitor your progress . See the *Personal Fitness for You* CD.

By monitoring your progress you can revise and build on your goals. For example, if you have been successfully participating in a walking program twice a week, you may want to add another day to the routine. As you continue your program, you may want to add a different activity on another day.

Identifying Potential Barriers and Obstacles and How You Will Overcome Them

What will you do if you are tempted to give up?

How will you deal with the following situations in order to maintain your plan?

You are too tired to exercise.

You are in a bad mood.

You don't have time to exercise because of the demands of family or school have increased.

You are on vacation.

You are bored with your program.

The weather is bad.

You have been sick or injured.

Here are some ideas which should help you:

Try doing a different activity - put variety in your schedule.

Set a date to start again if you have stopped for any reason.

Join an exercise class, club, church group, or neighbors who want to become active too.

Find friends who work out and join them.

Include activities which you can do indoors such as exercise videos.

You need to accept that lapses in your plan will happen. If you do lapse, just start back as soon as you can. Change is not easy and will take time to make a part of your routine. You need to plan for setbacks because things will happen.

Establishing a Reward System for Achievement of Your Goals

Once you have been successful in setting and achieving some specific goals, reward yourself! No matter how small the improvement, you are headed in the right direction. The type of reward depends on your interests but here are a few ideas:

Purchase new exercise clothing or athletic shoes

Go to a special event-movie, play or sporting event

Get a new CD you have wanted.

It is important to also consider establishing an internal reward system - one that comes from a sense of accomplishment. Look in the mirror and congratulate yourself on a job well done - pat yourself on the back. Feel good about your ability to control your own behavior and reach an important goal.

Look in the mirror and feel good about the changes you see!

Preparing for Action

As you prepare to implement your plan, ask yourself:

- What else do I need before I begin?
  - more knowledge of how to do the exercises?
  - how to relate the principles of training to my workout?
  - an understanding of how to exercise safely and dress appropriately for all activities?
  - special equipment or clothing such as jogging shoes?
  - a support network such as friends or family who are willing to help you and remain motivated?

You may want to prepare motivational messages to yourself or "to do lists" to put on your bedroom wall or door, computer, refrigerator, bathroom mirror, etc. to serve as reminders to exercise according to your schedule.

For Your Information

Maybe you have a friend or relative who has special needs related to participating in physical activity. Consider these ideas for ways to modify games and activities.

- make the activity less vigorous
- change the boundaries
- decrease the distance to the target
- slow down moving objects
- reduce the speed of the activity

Putting the Plan Into Action

You are now ready to put your plan into action. The diagram below represents the stages which most people go through as they try to change their behavior. Each stage requires your effort and commitment. The spiral shape indicates that there may be times when you slip or have a lapse - that is normal. Just try to get back to your plan as soon as possible.

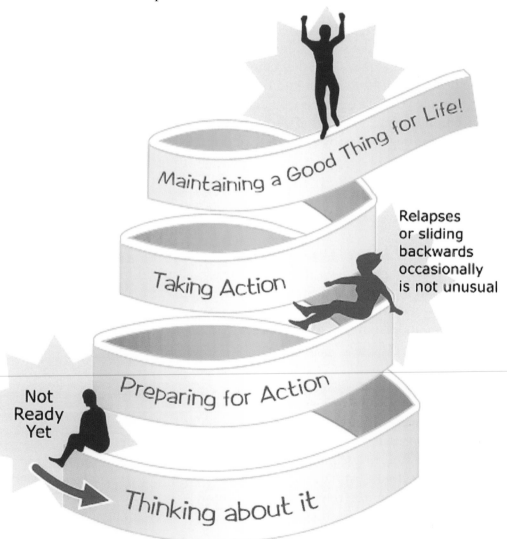

Maintaining a Good Thing for Life!

Relapses or sliding backwards occasionally is not unusual

Taking Action

Not Ready Yet

Preparing for Action

Thinking about it

Source: National Center for Disease Prevention and Health Promotion, U.S. Department of Health and Human Services, Division of Nutrition and Physical Activity. 2005.

Evaluating Sports and Recreational Activities

One way to supplement your exercise program is by including various sports and recreational activities in it. Certain activities, if performed long enough and at a high enough intensity, may contribute to an all-around fitness level, but they cannot be substituted for your planned exercise program. Participation in a fitness program can actually better prepare you for playing a sport. Think of getting fit to play a sport, rather than playing a sport to get fit.

It is very difficult to rate or evaluate the benefits to be gained from participating in a sport, because everyone has a different skill level and fitness level.

Generally, a more highly skilled person (or more fit person) can derive more value from a sport because he or she can attain a higher level of intensity and sustain it. However, the skill level of an opponent is also a factor. For example, if you are much better than your opponent in a tennis match, a long rally is not possible and you will not have to work very hard to win.

The type of activity must also be considered. Is it highly competitive or more recreational in nature? Playing volleyball in the backyard with your friends will not provide the fitness benefits that an official game between skilled players will.

Another important consideration when selecting a sports activity is what other benefits you can obtain from it. For instance, you may choose an activity because:

- your friends enjoy it.
- it is a good means of socializing.
- it helps you relax.
- it is fun.

Another factor to consider when selecting an exercise program or sports activity is the fitness component which it improves.

STRESS Stopper

Is your schedule for the week so overloaded you feel it is impossible to do it all? Make a list of everything you need to do in order of importance—identify those things which must be done this week and those which actually could wait.

Family Activity

Work with your family members to set fitness goals for the entire family. If possible, establish goals that can be accomplished together.

Did You Know?

Everyday activities which can contribute to your fitness level:
Gardening
Lawn work
Household chores
Climbing stairs
Shoveling snow
Moderate walking

Soccer and other fast-paced sports can increase cardiorespiratory fitness, coordination and agility.

For instance, does the activity contribute to better muscular endurance, flexibility or cardiorespiratory fitness? Most activities will provide benefits in more than one area, but you must select those which are best able to help you reach your goals.

The following chart categorizes a variety of activities by their health-related fitness components.

Cardiorespiratory Fitness and Body Composition

Jogging	Fast walking
Swimming	Aerobic stair climbing
Cycling	Cross-country skiing
Rowing	Aerobic dance
Step aerobics	Backpacking
Interval training	Rope jumping
Racquetball	Basketball
Handball	Soccer
In-line skating	

Muscular Fitness (Strength and Endurance)

Rowing,	Backpacking
Windsurfing	Surfing

Flexibility

Karate	Swimming
Aerobic dance	Tennis
Racquetball	Volleyball

Improving your muscular fitness can lead to better sports performance.

Are You a Good Sport?

You have probably had an opportunity to participate in some sort of sport activity either in school, at a park or in your neighborhood. Many times competitive situations bring out poor behavior. Have you ever been guilty of the following actions?

- taunting or belittling opponents
- showing disrespect to teammates, opponents or officials
- gloating after winning
- making excuses after losing

Next time you are about to demonstrate irresponsible behavior, think about the importance of being a good sport and showing respect for others. If this is a persistent problem, ask a friend to remind you when your actions are negative.

Skill-related components require very task-specific training activities. There is little crossover learning, and hereditary factors may affect the development of these components. The activities listed on this page contribute to the development of individual skill-related fitness components. To achieve a well-rounded level of fitness, you should include a variety of these activities in your exercise program.

To learn more about physical education, visit the following web sites:
www.exrx.net
www.bam.gov/fit4life

Skill-related Activities

Agility	**Balance**
Racquetball	Gymnastics
Rope jumping	Cycling
Running	Skating
Step aerobics	Fencing

Coordination	**Power**
Racquetball	Weight training
Handball	Karate
Calisthenics	Calisthenics
Judo	Judo
Rope jumping	Gymnastics
Exercise to music	Rowing

Reaction Time	**Speed**
Racquetball	Swimming
Handball	Cycling
Judo	Jogging
Karate	In-line skating
Rope jumping	

Adding a variety of sports activities to your program will improve your skill-related fitness.

Did You Know?

The Surgeon General's Report urges that "Every U.S. adult should accumulate 30 minutes or more of moderate-intensity physical activity on most, preferably all, days of the week."

Remember This ☑

The first few weeks of your program will be the most difficult. You may feel more tired as your body adjusts to the increased activity. However, within three weeks, you should start noticing improvements.

Go easy . . .

Make time . . .

Encourage yourself . . .

Add variety . . .

Join others . . .

Treat yourself . . .

Be realistic . . .

No excuses . . .

Start smart . . .

Know yourself . . .

Make it fun . . .

JUST DO IT!

Maintaining the Program

- Start slowly—do less than you think you can, progress slowly and give your body time to change and adjust.
- Make the activity a priority in your schedule. Choose a time that fits your schedule and that you can maintain. Set aside enough time for the entire workout.
- At the beginning it is best to increase duration (time) and/or the frequency of exercise rather than the intensity.
- "Listen" to your body and your feelings. Use this information to determine your rate of progression or if you need to cut back on the program.
- Avoid competing with others or pushing yourself unrealistically.
- Do it for YOU! Exercise because you have identified areas in which you want to improve—not just because someone else tells you that you should exercise. Make your own decision: What do you want? Is it important to you?

It's up to you to set your goals and accomplish them.

Evaluating Your Plan

After you have carried out the plan for at least six weeks, take time to evaluate it. Consider the following questions about your program:

- Were you able to complete the program as planned? If not, what obstacles prevented you from doing so?
- Did you really enjoy the activities? If not, which ones would you change?
- Have you noticed any changes in your health and fitness level? If so, what are they? If not, why?
- What changes would you make to improve your plan?

*F*or *Y*our *I*nformation

If you need help finding someone to work out with you, encourage other students to form a wellness club at your school. Make your school gym or weight room a wellness center.

Summary

By setting goals you are making a commitment to do something—you are taking responsibility for your own behavior. Learning to do this successfully is a skill that will benefit you throughout life.

Goal setting is a very personal activity—the goals you set must mean something to you. The reason you set goals is to motivate yourself to follow your plan. Therefore, a goal must be written down and must state exactly what you hope to achieve and the target date for reaching the goal.

It helps to establish short-term, **intermediate** and long-term goals. A suggested schedule or time frame to achieve intermediate goals helps keep you on track.

Setting goals for reaching an optimal level of fitness begins by identifying the personal fitness areas that are problems for you and those areas for which you did not achieve the health-related fitness standards. Once these areas are identified, you can set reasonable goals for improvement and plan specific activities you will participate in to achieve success. It is important to use the principles of training to guide you in establishing your plan.

By thinking through your plan and considering potential obstacles, you will be more likely to maintain your fitness program. Remember that your plan is **yours**—you can and should modify it as your needs and interests change. Be flexible and ready to adjust the plan as your situation changes.

Chapter 16 Review

Lesson Checklist

- Do you understand the process of setting goals?
- Do you know what factors you should consider in setting your individual fitness goals?
- Are you able to design a personal fitness program using the goal setting techniques described in the chapter?
- Do you have information to assist you in sticking to an exercise program when obstacles occur?

Chapter Projects

Write a response to each of the following:

1. Describe the type of things which might cause you to modify your exercise plan.
2. What specific obstacles to carrying out your plan do you anticipate and what can you do to overcome them?
3. Identify three community-based activities which interest you and are easily accessible to you. Write a paper describing the potential social, psychological and physical benefits of participating in these activities.
4. Research the resources, programs and services available through community, nonprofit organizations such as the American Heart Association, American Lung Association, American Cancer Association, etc. Develop a chart showing the opportunities available from each organization.
5. Select one type of disability (i.e.. confined to a wheelchair) and research the types of activities which are appropriate for gaining fitness. Write a report on your findings.

Behavior Change Evaluation

Review the following items to see if you have gained an understanding of fitness and wellness. On a piece of paper briefly state how you will make these changes.

- I will set realistic goals for improving my health fitness level.
- I will try to maintain my weekly schedule by overcoming obstacles that occur.
- I will periodically check my improvement and make adjustments in my exercise program.

Critical Thinking

Why is it wise to retest yourself periodically and review your activity program?

Chapter 16 Review

Test Your Knowledge

Read the questions below and select the best possible answer for each.

1. Which of the following is a reason to develop an individualized exercise program?
   a. You will never need to change it.
   b. You will avoid obstacles.
   c. You must exercise seven days a week.
   d. You will be more likely to follow it.

2. Which of the following is *not* true of an exercise program?
   a. It should emphasize skill-related fitness.
   b. It may change from time to time.
   c. It should be designed by you.
   d. It should follow the principles of training.

3. Exercise can:
   a. increase endurance
   b. help you to look and feel better
   c. increase muscle size
   d. all of the above

4. Which of the following is *not* true of a goal?
   a. It is definite.
   b. It is measurable.
   c. It is short-term.
   d. It is related to a specific time target.

5. Which group of activities would be most beneficial for developing cardiorespiratory fitness?
   a. weight training, walking, backpacking
   b. soccer, cycling, in-line skating
   c. football, racquetball, weight training
   d. judo, tennis, racquetball

6. Which of the following would have the least effect on your potential fitness gains from sports participation?
   a. your level of skills
   b. your cardiorespiratory fitness level
   c. your intensity of play
   d. age

7. Which of the following is an important guideline for selecting an appropriate fitness activity?
   a. an activity you enjoy
   b. an activity that requires special equipment
   c. an activity that must be done in groups
   d. an activity that is easy to do

8. Which of the following is true of sports activities?
   a. They are excellent for health-related fitness.
   b. They have little fitness value for the highly-skilled person.
   c. They are of great fitness value to the poorly-skilled person.
   d. Their value depends on a number of factors.

Becoming a
Wise Consumer

17

Chapter Topics

- Consumer Awareness
- Typical Advertising Techniques
- Avoiding a "Rip-off"
- Spotting a Quack
- Recognizing Health and Fitness Fallacies
- Drugs and Fitness
- Purchasing Equipment
- Joining a Fitness or Health Club

Chapter Objectives

After completing this chapter, you will be able to:

- Identify the differences between facts and fallacies as related to numerous health and fitness products and services.
- Spot a quack and avoid being ripped off or buying fads.
- Determine the accuracy of marketing claims promoting fitness products and services.
- Consider the factors related to the selection, purchase, care and maintenance of physical fitness equipment.
- Evaluate a fitness center before joining.

Key Words

anabolic steroids	diuretics	quacks
androstenedione	elliptical trainer	quackery
consumer	fact	rip-offs
creatine	fad	
dehydration	fallacy	

Suggested Physical Activities

Do a series of workouts using a variety of exercise equipment: rower, stair climber, stationary bike, ski machine, etc. If this equipment is not available at your school, check with a local YMCA, YWCA, health club, community college or university.

Healthy People 2010 Goals

◆ Help individuals of all ages increase life expectancy and improve their quality of life.

Use the *Personal Fitness for You* Student CD for:

◆ Lab 17-1: Consumer Awareness
◆ Lab 17-2: Identifying Potential Rip-Offs
◆ Chapter Practice Test
◆ Chapter Study Guide
◆ Chapter Crossword Puzzle
◆ Vocabulary Flash Cards
◆ Chapter Power Point Review

It is important to be a wise consumer.

Have you, or has someone in your family, every purchased a product that was advertised with many claims about its greatness only to find that it really didn't live up to those claims? Did you feel cheated, deceived and "ripped-off"?

Unfortunately, this may happen to you (and millions of others) again and again. The basic problem is that there is no local, federal or state government agency that approves or verifies claims in advertising before they are printed or broadcast. Agencies can take action only after the advertisements appear. Most of the time this is after people are already victims of the false claims. Who loses in this situation? The **consumer**, the one who purchases or uses goods or services, is the loser. You are a consumer. To avoid buying useless or harmful products you must be a wise consumer.

Consumer Awareness

The burden and responsibility to become better consumers is on us. A wise consumer:
- takes the time to learn about products and services before selecting them.
- reads advertisements carefully and with a critical view in order to spot **fallacies** (a false or mistaken claim—the result of inaccurate information).
- is careful not to buy every **fad** (a passing style or fashion—one that will soon be out of date) that appears on the market.
- is aware of **quacks** (individuals who represent harmful and/or useless practices as beneficial).
- knows how to identify information in articles, books, newspapers and other media that is **fact** (a reality or certainty), not just an advertising scheme.

Becoming a wise consumer is more than avoiding the purchase of worthless products. It is avoiding the purchase and use of potentially dangerous products.

Americans waste huge sums of money on useless and unneeded health products and services. These products can contribute to health problems, and they delay the use of products that could be beneficial to the individual.

People want to believe in miracles, the quick fix, the easy cure. We are constantly searching for the simple solution and shortcuts to health and fitness. As a wise consumer, you will learn to recognize that many of these shortcuts are **rip-offs** (being cheated by exchanging something of value, usually money, for something worthless).

Typical Advertising Techniques

In order to protect your health and wealth, consider some of the techniques advertisers rely on.

Does the product or service claim to be:

- a special or secret remedy?
- good for almost everything?
- available from only one source with payment in advance?

Does the seller:

- use case histories and testimonials from grateful users (especially celebrities and athletes) or the "hidden camera" commercial which actually uses actors and actresses to portray the average citizen?
- use the peer pressure approach— "Everybody is using it..." "Most doctors recommend...." "All the best athletes use..." are the common phrases?
- use the patriotic approach—pictures of flag, country, family and children?
- use the medical or scientific appeal— the advertisement shows individuals in a lab or clinical setting—terms such as "doctor tested," "hospital tested," or "studies show" are commonly used?
- offer to save you time and money?

Don't be fooled by advertising techniques.

- use scare techniques—implying that unless you use this product you will get a particular illness or disease?
- promise you will look better and younger—it will restore energy, improve your attractiveness, allow you to lose weight quickly, remove wrinkles, etc?
- appeal to your concern for the underdog—"We are number two—but we try harder" is a familiar example?
- appeal to your desire to look more "masculine or feminine"—sometimes this is a subtle implication that the product will do this?
- use thoughts of the "good old days"—this "return" to the good feelings of the past will occur if you buy records or other products associated with a particular time period.
- use words such as "miracle," "natural" or "secret?"
- claim it will help the environment or is a natural or organic product?
- offer a money-back guarantee—most have a clause stating that you also must adhere to a comprehensive health and fitness regimen?

As a wise consumer, you should read all advertisements carefully. Look beyond the words, pictures and music to reveal the hidden message or psychological approach that is being used to sell the product to you. Look for misleading and inaccurate statements.

Avoiding a "Rip-off"

Because of the increased awareness and concern for health and fitness, there are products on the market which claim to help improve your health. As a wise consumer be aware of the techniques used to sell these products so that you can identify which products are beneficial and avoid those which are merely "rip-offs."

If an offer is too good to be true, it probably is.

A good technique you, the consumer, can use to avoid being "ripped-off" is to develop a questioning attitude. Ask yourself whether the claim being made sounds too good to be true—if so, it probably is. Ask yourself whether there are facts to support the claims which are being made. Seek advice from others (teachers, doctors, nurses, etc.) who might be able to help you analyze the claims being made.

Many times consumers are attracted to a new product because of an article they have read about it. In this case, it is extremely important to be able to distinguish facts from myths and false claims. Some techniques for doing this include:

Visit the following web sites:
www.acefitness.org
www.acsm.org
www.ftc.gov

- Identify the source of the report or study. Was it conducted by an objective, non-biased group or by those with a special interest in the outcome?
- What technique was used in securing the evidence? Was the study performed according to good research design?
- Are the claims justified according to the evidence collected or are they extended beyond the actual results?
- What are the credentials and background of the individuals conducting the study?
- Does the report conflict with information from another source? If so, have you resolved the areas of differences and accepted one as being more factual or current?
- Is the magazine or newspaper in which the article appears known for its accuracy and selection of factual material?

Be especially careful when making purchases on the internet.

It is especially important to use care when you are considering a purchase by mail, phone or internet. Ask yourself these questions:

- Do I really know enough about the product? Have I seen it or know someone who has used it? Do I know the quality of the product?
- Am I familiar with the company or is it just a post office box number? Will I be able to talk to someone if I have a problem?

Get the advice of someone you know and trust before making a major investment in time or money.

- What kind of guarantee is available? Does it come in writing with the product?
- Who pays for the shipping and handling? What are these charges? Are there any hidden charges?

Spotting a Quack

The quack uses worthless devices, gadgets and secret formulas (often containing only aspirin or caffeine) to treat the patient. The reason quacks exist and flourish in America is because of ignorance. It is difficult to know the difference between a legitimate expert and one who lacks the credentials but sounds and acts like one. In addition, many people who have serious (even incurable) diseases will seek any alternative cure that may offer some hope.

A quack may try to sell:

- a product said to be endorsed by the Federal Drug Administration (FDA). It is against the law to state that the government endorses any nonprescription drug or medical device.
- a nonprescription drug that claims to cure cancer or arthritis.
- vitamin and mineral supplements that will cure a variety of illnesses.
- a product that is endorsed by *Consumer Reports*—this magazine does not allow the use of its name in the marketing of a product.

Be able to recognize language related to **quackery** (representing harmful and/or useless practices as beneficial). Watch for these words in advertisements:

amazing	new discovery
breakthrough	home cure
instant	scientifically based
secret formula	quick
natural	technology
painless	European

As a wise consumer, you should take the time to investigate the background of the person offering the product or treatment. Good sources of information include:

- a doctor, pharmacist or other health professional
- a local consumer protection office
- the Better Business Bureau
- a local office of the Food and Drug Administration
- if it is a mail order, your local postmaster or the Postal Inspector Service.

Recognizing Health and Fitness Fallacies

Consumer magazines may be a good source of reliable information about a product or service.

Nutritional Fallacies

Consumers should be especially knowledgeable about claims made on food labels. Many manufacturers attempt to attract buyers by using words that are "in"—those that are associated with health and fitness. Such words include "natural," "no preservatives or additives," "low-fat," etc.

While some such words are indications of important nutritional information about the product, others are used only to attract the unsuspecting buyer. The consumer must understand that some words on food labels are not defined or restricted by government regulations; therefore, these words can be used on any product.

To find out the real nutritional value of a product read the list of ingredients which appears on the label. These items are listed in order from greatest amount to least. Individuals concerned about excessive fat, salt or sugar a product may contain should read the nutritional information on the label.

Product packaging can be very misleading. Read the fine print to get the facts!

Many manufacturers take advantage of current health concerns, such as **osteoporosis** (a thinning of the bones which contributes to bone fractures, especially in older people), to sell worthless or questionable products. Be especially careful of such claims and do not try to diagnose and "treat" yourself. Consult a medical professional, if you are considering a special product.

Follow the recommendations for sound nutrition (see Chapter 8). Be aware of claims which are unproven and may be harmful.

Nutrition Myths:

- *Eating sports bars or power bars and other foods such as honey, sugar or sweets just before a competition or a workout provides a burst of quick energy.* This is not true. It takes the body one to four hours to digest food. Energy for activities comes from food that is already digested and stored in your muscles.
- *Natural vitamins have special benefits over synthetic vitamins.* Naturally occurring and manufactured vitamins have identical chemical structures.
- *Supplements relieve stress.* Stress tablets are a marketing scheme. No supplement can relieve stress. Use the techniques described in Chapter 10 to manage stress.

Read the list of ingredients on the label to find the nutritional value of a product.

Nutritional Supplements

Many advertisements make claims about how certain nutritional products can help you achieve personal fitness and wellness. It is important to look at the facts and evaluate what each of these supplements does.

• Bee Pollen: This supplement is a mixture of bee saliva, plant nectar and pollen. It is supposed to increase energy levels and enhance performance. To date, there is no scientific evidence to support these claims.

• Ginseng: This is an extract from the ginseng root which is supposed to protect you from tissue damage. However, such claims cannot be confirmed by scientific evidence.

• Spirulina: This substance is a microscopic blue-green algae which is hailed as a great source of protein, however, to increase your protein intake you would be better off eating lean meats and legumes.

Other supplements such as brewer's yeast, DNA or DHEA do not improve athletic performance. Some of these may even be harmful to your performance and health.

Amino acid supplements are also very popular. Some athletes believe that using amino acids increases muscle mass and strength without the use of steroids. Physiologists agree that more long-term studies of amino acid supplements are needed before health risks can be determined. Eating a healthy, balanced diet, which includes proteins such as milk, chicken and fish, will provide your body with adequate amounts of amino acids.

Two nutritional supplements currently receiving a lot of attention because of their use by athletes are creatine and androstendione. **Creatine** is a legal, over-the-counter powder. The claim is that it will boost the energy supply in muscles so that more intense weight lifting - and thus more muscle mass - should be achieved.

Eating a healthy diet high in proteins is the best way of providing the body with adequate amounts of amino acids.

Androstenedione is a testosterone-building agent that comes in capsules and tablets. It is also an over-the-counter supplement. The tablet gives a one-hour boost in testosterone which helps create muscle mass and promote recovery after injury.

Since these substances are classified as dietary supplements, they are not regulated by the FDA unless substantial life-threatening safety issues arise. However, you should be aware that many sports groups (NFL, NCAA and International Olympic Committee) have banned them and that there are risks and dangers associated with these substances.

Some irregularities associated with creatine are:

- fatigue
- behavior change
- heart problems
- muscle cramps
- dehydration

Possible side effects of androstenedione are:

- breast enlargement
- testicular atrophy
- acne
- liver damage

Remember This ☑

Foods promoted as "natural," "organic" or "health foods" may not provide any special benefits. For instance, natural vitamins (made from foods) are not any better than synthetic vitamins (produced in a lab).

For Your Information

Three excellent sources of reliable nutrition information are:

- *Tufts University Newsletter*
- *University of California-Berkeley Wellness Letter*
- *Harvard Health Letter*

Check your school or city library for copies.

Weight Control Fallacies

Spot Reducing

As you learned in Chapter 9, fat cannot be removed from specific areas by doing exercises for the muscles in that area. For example, doing crunches does not cause a loss of fat in the abdominal area. When we exercise, fat is lost from deposits throughout the body. You cannot spot reduce. Any device claiming to spot reduce is a gimmick.

Body Wrapping

The claim that "body wrapping" helps dissolve cellulite and tighten skin is quackery. The two most popular "wrapping" substances are plastic wrap and ace bandages. Sometimes a cream is used with the plastic wrap, and the ace bandage may be soaked in a warm solution of wintergreen or menthol. These substances produce a warm or cool feeling to the skin convincing the individual that a tightening effect is taking place.

You may wonder, if body wrapping does not work, why do user testimonials claim to lose several inches in their body measurements? Have you ever worn a tight elastic cuff or band? When you removed it, did you notice an indentation in your skin? Body wrapping squeezes the body fluids either upward or downward, so the area that was wrapped appears to be smaller. The wrapped area will slowly return to its normal size after the pressure is removed.

Advertisers may also manipulate measurements. The measuring tape may be moved higher or lower, the measurements may be taken at different angles, or the measuring tape may be pulled tighter.

Rubberized Suits

Another claim is that rubberized or plastic suits will help you lose weight. This type of clothing causes excessive loss of water (**dehydration**) and is particularly dangerous when used in hot, humid weather. This attire does not aid in weight reduction, only in water loss, which is temporary. The best clothing for exercising is loose, comfortable, absorbent and reflects the sun.

Massage

Another fallacy is that massage will help you lose weight. Massage, whether by machine or masseur, will help to increase circulation and may promote relaxation, but has no value in removing fatty tissue or in developing physical fitness.

Vibrating Chairs and Belts

Perhaps you have seen advertisements which claim that vibrating chairs or other devices can help you lose weight.

> ## Remember This ☑
> Passive exercise devices do not work. You cannot lose weight, spot reduce, increase muscular strength or endurance by performing an exercise that does not involve muscular contraction.

Using hot tubs does not help you lose weight.

For Your Information

Saunas, hot tubs and steam baths are not effective for weight loss and will not prevent or cure bruises, backaches, colds, arthritis or bursitis.

According to the sellers, these devices reduce weight, firm muscles and even improve posture. In actuality, however, the only things these devices really do is promote relaxation.

Saunas and Hot Baths

Steam baths, saunas and hot tubs remove body fluids. Rapid and excessive fluid loss can cause dehydration and abnormal mineral loss. Therefore, these do not cause a true weight loss and can be potentially dangerous. Drinking fluids returns weight to normal.

Electric Muscle Stimulators

Electric muscle stimulating devices cause an electric current to go to the muscle and make it move. This does not increase your fitness or cause a loss of weight and can also be dangerous.

Motorized Exercise Devices

Any device that does the work for you cannot contribute to your fitness, cause any caloric expenditure or produce a weight change.

Weighted Belts

Weighted belts worn around the waist, hips or thighs cannot help you reduce weight and may even be harmful.

Drugs and Fitness

Anabolic Steroids

Many athletes are looking for a quick way to build muscle mass and strength. Taking anabolic steroids is not a safe way to do this. **Anabolic steroids** are synthetic versions of the male hormone testosterone (the primary male sex hormone). These hormones can assist in developing muscle mass; however, there are many dangers of using such drugs.

Steroids can cause:

- cancer of the liver
- increased blood pressure
- decreased testicular size
- decreased sperm production
- liver failure
- increased body hair
- menstrual irregularities
- increase potential for disease
- complexion problems (oil glands enlarge and secrete more frequently)
- increased risk of injury (connective tissue cannot strengthen as fast as muscle tissue)
- increased level of aggressive behavior

While most people understand the negative effects of steroidal abuse, unfortunately, it is still a popular choice among athletes. Intelligent athletes stay away from steroids. Some athletes use steroids for short periods of time, believing that they will not harm their bodies; however, health related problems from steroid use may not show up for many years after their use. Lyle Alzado, a former NFL great in the 1980s, died from brain cancer which he believed was directly attributed to his use of steroids. Steroids are not worth the risk!

Taking pills is not a safe way to gain strength or lose weight.

Appetite Suppressants

Drugs which suppress the appetite are of little value, cannot and should not be used for long periods of time, can be habit-forming, and may cause unhealthy side effects such as constipation, insomnia, dizziness, depression, nausea and increased heart rate.

Remember This ✓

Cellulite is just another word for fat. To lose fat (cellulite), exercise and monitor your calorie intake.

Diuretics (Water Pills)

Some people mistakenly believe that their excess weight is due to water accumulation. However, taking **diuretics**, drugs that increase the urine production and thus the loss of water by the body, is very dangerous. Diuretics may:

- upset the body's chemical balance (especially minerals such as potassium)
- cause circulatory disorders leading to fainting, low blood pressure and weakness
- cause increased pulse rates and decreased work efficiency
- cause blood clotting problems during menstruation
- cause kidney problems

> **Remember This ☑**
>
> There are no quick fixes or miracle solutions for health and fitness. Millions of dollars are spent each year on exercise and weight loss gimmicks that don't work. If you decide to buy, make an informed, intelligent decision.

Purchasing Equipment

At some time, you may be interested in purchasing exercise equipment for your home use. Of course, it is important to make a wise selection from the many choices available on the market. The following items can contribute to improved health and fitness:

- Cross-country ski machines
- Stair climbers
- Rowers
- Stationary bicycles
- Treadmills
- Free weights and benches
- Step aerobics boxes
- physioball

Optional exercise devices you may wish to consider:

- Workout watch (runner's watch)—provides elapsed time, split times, countdown timer, alarm and sweep second hand
- Heart rate monitor—the best monitors of your pulse during exercise are chest straps or wristwatch combinations

> **Remember This ☑**
>
> **Exercise Equipment Questions**
>
> - What type of workout will I get?
> - Does the equipment enable me to use the overload principle? How do I adjust for frequency, intensity and duration?
> - Can I follow the principle of progression?
> - Is the equipment safe for me?

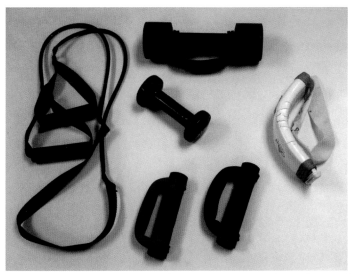

Hand weights and tubing are low cost items which can be used in home workouts.

- Pedometer—enables you to track the number of steps, distance walked and calories burned
- Hand or wrist weights

Once you purchase exercise equipment, take care of it. Store it in a place that is dry to prevent rust, mildew and other types of deterioration. Follow all manufacturer recommendations for maintenance and cleaning. Replace worn parts regularly.

There are several benefits to buying home equipment:

- It's convenient—you can use it anytime even while watching television or reading.
- It may be more comfortable to exercise indoors.
- Bad weather does not stop you from exercising.
- No waiting in line to use equipment at a health club.
- It can help you stick to your exercise program and to stay on schedule.
- No excuses!

There are many sizes and types of exercise balls.

Guidelines for Purchasing Exercise Equipment

When purchasing exercise equipment, follow these guidelines:

- Don't be in a hurry. Shop around and avoid buying on the spur of the moment. Shop at a specialty store or a good sports store with a competent sales staff. Try the equipment before buying. Be careful when ordering from a catalog or magazine ad.
- Buy only quality equipment. Rather than saving a few dollars, wait until you can afford better equipment.
- Make certain it is equipment you will continue to use.
- Make sure you have a convenient place to use and easily store the equipment.
- Make certain the equipment will help you meet your fitness goals. Don't be misled by false claims or advertising hype.
- Determine if the equipment needs to be assembled and if so, can you assemble it yourself or will you need assistance?
- Decide which features you really need and can afford.
- Purchase equipment with a warranty. Find out if it can be serviced locally.

Remember This ☑

When purchasing a weight machine make sure that all critical joints are welded, not bolted, and that no key parts are made of plastic.

Home Weight Machines

Lifting, pushing and pulling exercises using weight resistance machines enable you to build and tone different muscle groups. Doing a continuous series of different strength and endurance exercises in quick succession for a set amount of time (circuit training) can even provide some aerobic benefits.

Buyer Tips

Safety:
- Adequate padding around plastic and metal parts is important.
- Moving parts should be sturdy.

Features:
- A wide range of resistance settings are available.

Try It:
- Does the machine feel comfortable during the workout?

Stationary Bicycle

Stationary bicycles offer a good non-impact aerobic workout with little stress to the knees. They are especially excellent for those overweight who might be harmed by excessive walking or jogging.

Buyer Tips

Safety:
- The seat and resistance should be easy to adjust.
- A recumbent or reclining bike reduces strain on the lower back.
- It should have pedal clips to prevent the feet from slipping.

Features:
- Some models offer arm pumping handlebars—this burns more calories and works the arms and shoulders.
- A speedometer, odometer and tension control should be within easy reach.
- Stationary bikes are available in three types:
  Single action—works only the legs
  Dual action—has a handle that you pump back and forth for an upper body workout;
  Recumbent (reclining)—works the buttocks and back of the legs (hamstring muscles) by sitting back on the seat and pedaling with the legs in front of the body.

Try It:
- Does it have a smooth pedaling motion?
- Is it easy to adjust the seat, workload, etc.?
- Is the seat comfortable?

Treadmill

Treadmills offer the opportunity to walk or run indoors in a safe comfortable environment at any time. They provide an aerobic workout as well as important lower body muscle tone.

Buyer Tips

Safety:
- Surface should have give to absorb the shock—a hard surface puts strain on the legs.
- Some have a safety key or code to start it. This is an especially good feature if there are small children around.

Stationary bikes are a low impact, non-weight bearing workout with little stress on the joints.

Treadmills provide an aerobic workout and tone the lower body.

Features:
- Inclined motorized tracks are best. (Walking briskly uphill is an excellent aerobic workout.)
- 1 1/4 to 1 1/2 horsepower motor is best.
- Handrails should be able to support your weight.
- Models with computerized displays for speed, distance, time, calories burned and heart rate are available.

Try It:
Test the actual model before buying.
- Is it wide enough and long enough?
- Is the range of speed suitable to your workout (up to 5 m.p.h. for walkers and up to 10 m.p.h. for joggers)?

Rowing Machines

Vigorous rowing is one of the most effective aerobic workouts and calorie burners. In addition, rowers strengthen arms, back, shoulders and abdominal muscles.

Buyer Tips
Safety:
- Make certain the seat supports the lower back.

Features:
- Electronic control panels offer program options and display time, stroke count, strokes per minute, calories burned and tempo.
- There are two basic types of nonelectric rowers—hydraulic and wind resistance. The wind resistance type provides a more natural feel, similar to electric rowers.

Try It:
- Glide back and forth on the seat to make sure it moves smoothly and feels comfortable.
- Make certain the electronic control panel is easy to understand and control.
- Look for durability, quietness and smoothness.
- There should be no squeaking or feeling of dragging.

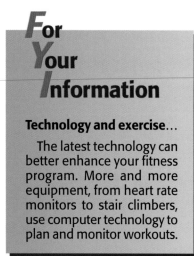

For **Y**our **I**nformation

Technology and exercise…

The latest technology can better enhance your fitness program. More and more equipment, from heart rate monitors to stair climbers, use computer technology to plan and monitor workouts.

Rowing machines offer a non-weight bearing aerobic workout and strengthen the arms, back, shoulders and abdominals.

Stair Climbers

Stair climbers provide a good aerobic workout and also strengthen leg (especially the hamstrings and calves), hip and buttocks muscles.

Buyer Tips

Safety:

- People with knee problems should check with a doctor before using a stair climber.
- It may be difficult for those with balance problems.
- Climber should not wobble as you step rapidly.

Features:

- Handrails should be within reach.
- Step platforms should be sturdy.
- Should be easy to operate resistance settings and controls.
- There are two different models: steps that move independently of each other so you control the step height; and steps that are linked to ensure the full stepping range.
- Some have preset programs and even measure aerobic capacity and fitness level.
- Some models have moving hand grips that work your upper body.

Stair climbers provide a good aerobic workout, but may be stressful on the knee joints.

Try It:
- Be certain you feel comfortable using the machine.
- Can you adjust it to your needs?

Elliptical Trainer

Elliptical trainers combine the motion of stair stepping with cross-country skiing, providing a low impact workout. Some devices also include poles that can be maneuvered with the arms while the legs are in motion.

Buyer Tips:

Safety:
- Make certain the equipment is properly fitted for your size and range of movement.
- If motorized, look for a safety turn-off control.
- Make certain the unit is very sturdy and stable.
- Side rails should be included and provide balance.

Features:
- Pedals with a textured, "non-slip" surface and high curved ridges will prevent your feet from sliding.
- Look for a unit that allows you to adjust the stride length.
- Some units are motorized but make certain you have the proper power supply in your home.
- Check to see if the trainer needs to be calibrated.
- If it has a control panel, check the type of information it provides.

Try it:
- Be certain stride length is correct for your leg movement range.
- Can you maintain a comfortable upright posture rather than leaning forward?
- Learn how to use the programming features.

Elliptical trainers provide an excellent low-impact workout.

Ski Machines

Ski machines simulate the activity of cross country skiing and provide a total workout without heavy impact. The poling motion builds upper body strength while the leg movement builds leg muscles and tones the lower back.

Buyer Tips

Safety:
- Arm motions should be smooth—not tight or jerky.
- Stride should be comfortable—don't overstride.
- It may take some practice to learn to coordinate arm and leg movement.

Features:
- Machines come with either independent (unlinked skis) or dependent (linked skis with one ski sliding forward as the other goes back) leg motion.
- Machines have either skis with stirrup-like attachments and cables which the arms pull back and forth or ski-like tracks with platforms that slide with poles on the side. The first model gives a better workout.
- Some have control panels which display distance, time and speed of movement. Some also monitor heart rate and calories burned.
- Some have programmed resistance settings to repeat the same workout.
- Vinyl hip support pads are available with some models.
- Some machines have variable incline features to simulate uphill skiing and they also work the thigh muscles.

Ski machines provide an upper body workout as well

Try It:
- Try machines with both dependent and independent leg motion to see which is best for you.

Water Exercise Equipment:

- Kickboards: Most boards are made of Styrofoam and are used by beginners and experts to help develop a strong kick (and leg muscles).
- Hand paddles: Many types are available for wearing on the hands and practicing the pulling action of the arm stroke. To avoid elbow problems, use either small or medium-sized hand paddles.

A variety of equipment is available to enhance water exercise.

- Pull Buoys: These devices are held between the thighs and are used to keep the legs afloat without kicking. This allows the swimmer to concentrate on arm action and developing upper body muscles. Most buoys are 6-8 inch cylinders of Styrofoam held together by nylon cord. Buy one that is right for your leg length, amount of buoyancy needed and comfort.

Body Composition Scale

There are several new products that may not only measure your body weight but determine your body fat percentage as well. Some even give you recommended calorie intake and percentage of muscle and water. Check the internet for a listing of these new scales.

Joining a Fitness or Health Club

Sometime in your life you may become interested in joining a fitness or health club. Before you decide to join a fitness club, answer the following questions:

- Are there possible alternatives? Have you considered walking or running in a park, a shopping mall, a parking lot, a parking garage, the beach or even a school yard?
- Is the facility conveniently located and close to your home? How will you get there?
- Does the club offer devices to build strength (such as weight machines) and opportunities to improve cardiorespiratory fitness (such as a lap swimming pool, treadmill or stationary bicycle)?
- Have you checked the Better Business Bureau for complaints?
- Have you carefully read the contract for undesirable clauses such as high interest rates, waivers of liability, noncancelable clauses, or holder in due course clauses (this allows the establishment to sell your promise-to-pay contract to a collection agency)? None of these is in your best interest.
- Are you a self-motivated person or do you have to be encouraged or motivated to exercise?
- Have you visited the club during the hours you would probably use it? Look for overcrowding and whether the members appear satisfied.
- Have you checked the qualifications of the instructors and managers? Do they know what they are doing? What are their exercise habits? Are the instructors certified trainers by a group such as American College of Sports Medicine, American Council on Exercise, or National Strength and Conditioning Association?

Make sure the health club has equipment that you will enjoy using.

Family Activity

If a family member or friend is considering a membership in a health club, share your knowledge with them. Offer to visit the facility with them to help them evaluate equipment and programs.

When you join a health club, read the contract carefully.

For **Y**our **I**nformation

Cultural Variations

Are fitness centers and health clubs as popular in other cultures as they are in the U.S.? Interview several people from different cultures to answer this question.

- Do they offer classes and programs for fitness such as step aerobics, spinning, stress management.

You should make every effort to become a knowledgeable, wise consumer. Do not be taken in by products that claim to do the work for you or promise miraculous results. There are many good programs and products to choose from—make certain you follow the guidelines in this chapter when making your decisions. Strive to participate in fitness activities outside of this class. Make fitness a part of your daily life—take responsibility for making healthy choices.

Make fitness a part of your daily life.

Summary

As a consumer, it is important to your health and for your budget to make wise decisions. Although this is not always an easy responsibility, use the guidelines for avoiding rip-offs and understanding advertising claims presented in this chapter to assist you.

Make certain you know the differences between facts, fads, quackery and fallacies—especially related to health and fitness. Before you invest in a product or service, review the wise consumer's checklist.

Because of increased awareness and concern about health and fitness, there are numerous exercise and health products on the market. As a wise consumer, select only those that can truly assist in obtaining optimal fitness.

Portfolio Idea

Becoming a Wise Consumer

Record the results of this activity in your personal portfolio or follow instructions from your teacher.

Keep a log for one week of advertisements you hear or see on television, radio, magazines and newspapers related to health, nutrition, and fitness products. Then respond to the following questions.

◆ Reflect on the accuracy and reliability of the information provided. For each advertisement, describe why you feel the information was or was not accurate and reliable.

◆ Was evidence presented to support its claim of developing health, nutrition, or fitness? Describe why or why not?

◆ What is the most important thing you learned from this activity?

Chapter 17 Review

Lesson Checklist

- Do you know the wise consumer guidelines?
- Can you spot a quack or avoid a "rip-off"?
- Can you make wise decisions about exercise and nutrition products?

Chapter Projects

With three other students, prepare a community fitness directory. Include a listing and description of exercise, health or fitness facilities in your community. Start with the facilities at your own school.

Behavior Change Evaluation

Review the following items to see if you have gained an understanding of fitness and wellness. On a piece of paper briefly state how you will make these changes.

- I will read all ads carefully and look for misleading and inaccurate claims.
- I will ask questions and do a thorough study before making a purchase.
- I will not be fooled by claims for special devices, drugs or supplements to improve my health and fitness.
- I will remember that there is no quick fix or easy way to health, wellness and fitness. I must maintain a healthy lifestyle.

Critical Thinking

Based on what you have learned about consumer awareness, describe how you and your family would go about selecting a piece of exercise equipment for your home.

Chapter 17 Review

Test Your Knowledge

Read the questions below and select the best possible answer for each.

1. How can you become a wise consumer?
   a. Listen carefully to commercials on television.
   b. Critically read magazine advertisements.
   c. Ask questions before buying.
   d. All of the above

2. When deciding whether to join a fitness club, you should consider:
   a. the qualifications of instructors and managers
   b. whether current members seem satisfied
   c. whether it includes opportunities for developing cardiorespiratory fitness as well as strength
   d. all of the above

3. Which of the following can help you determine if a product's claims are true?
   a. You are guaranteed your money back if not satisfied with the product.
   b. A famous football player endorses the product.
   c. The advertisement appears in your favorite movie magazine.
   d. The product claims are justified based on facts collected by an unbiased authoritative source.

4. Spot reducing:
   a. cannot be done
   b. only works with exercise
   c. only works with special equipment
   d. takes a long time to work

5. Which of the following can lead to dangerous dehydration of the body?
   a. massage
   b. wearing a rubberized suit while exercising
   c. using a vibrating belt
   d. all of the above

6. Which is effective in promoting fitness?
   a. anabolic steroids
   b. diuretics
   c. protein supplements
   d. none of the above

7. Which is an effective way to lose weight?
   a. rubberized suit
   b. vibrating belt
   c. sauna
   d. exercise

8. When buying exercise equipment, which is *not* an essential factor to consider?
   a. equipment features
   b. fitness benefits offered
   c. electric controls
   d. durability, comfort and ease of use

9. Which can help you avoid a rip-off?
   a. a questioning attitude
   b. thinking through your decisions
   c. consulting someone else
   d. all of the above

10. A fallacy is:
    a. a useless practice
    b. a false claim
    c. a passing fashion
    d. a certainty

Lifetime Personal Fitness

18

Chapter Topics

- The Personal Fitness Challenge and You
- Evaluating Your Progress
- Your Changing Body
- Potential Health Problems
- Fitness and Wellness Career Opportunities
- Wellness and Fitness Forever
- The Decision Is Yours

Chapter Objectives

After completing this chapter, you will be able to:

- Evaluate your progress in achieving the healthy fitness zone for the health-related fitness components.
- Identify the changes which occur in the body over the years.
- Describe potential health problems which can affect your fitness.
- Identify a variety of fitness and wellness career opportunities.
- Describe the importance of one's lifestyle choices to the attainment of lifetime fitness.

Key Words

anabolic steroids   osteoporosis
behavior modification

Suggested Physical Activities

Select the activity you have most enjoyed during this class and do it at least twice during the week.

Healthy People 2010 Goals

- Improve health, fitness, and quality of life through daily physical activity.
- Reduce illness, disability, and death related to tobacco use and exposure to secondhand smoke.
- Reduce tobacco use by adolescents.
- Reduce initiation of tobacco use among children and adolescents.
- Increase tobacco use cessation attempts by adolescent smokers.
- Increase adolescents disapproval of smoking.
- Reduce the proportion of adolescents who report that they rode, during the previous 30 days, with a driver who had been drinking alcohol.
- Increase the age and proportion of adolescents who remain alcohol and drug free.
- Reduce steroid use among adolescents.
- Increase the proportion of adolescents who disapprove of substance abuse.
- Increase the proportion of adolescents who perceive great risk associated with substance abuse.

Use the *Personal Fitness for You* Student CD for:

- Lab 18-1: Evaluation of Your Health Fitness Improvement
- Chapter Practice Test
- Chapter Study Guide
- Chapter Crossword Puzzle
- Vocabulary Flash Cards
- Chapter Power Point Review

The Personal Fitness Challenge and You

This text has presented you with the information you need to accept the personal fitness challenge and achieve lifetime personal fitness. To achieve and maintain your optimal fitness level, remember the following points which have been presented in this textbook.

- Fitness and wellness provide important benefits.
- Even moderate activity is beneficial.
- Conduct periodic self-evaluation of the health-related fitness components.
- Exercise safely.
- Use your knowledge of the health-related fitness components and the type of activities which contribute to their improvement to achieve lifetime personal fitness and wellness.
- Follow the principles of training to gain greater benefits from an exercise program.
- Use your knowledge of the basics of nutrition to maintain a healthy diet.
- Plan your diet using the guidelines of the MyPyramid Food Guide.
- Be aware of your body composition and manage your weight.
- Identify your stressors and implement strategies for stress reduction.
- Designing and following a personal fitness program is a lifelong pursuit.
- Follow the guidelines for being a wise consumer.

Accept the fitness challenge—the decision is yours!

Use your knowledge of the MyPyramid Food Guide to maintain a healthy diet.

Evaluating Your Progress

Retake the health-related fitness tests described in Chapter 4 and compare your results to those at the beginning of the course. Use the test results form in Chapter 4 to note the changes in your test results.

Based on the results of your retests, identify changes which may be needed in your exercise program and/or lifestyle to maintain or achieve the healthy fitness zone. Refer to the chapters for each health-related concept to learn what you can do to modify your exercise program.

For instance:

- If you are still below the healthy fitness zone in the cardiorespiratory fitness area, make sure you are doing aerobic activities 3 to 5 times a week for 20-60 minutes and elevating your heart rate to the target heart rate zone.
- If your muscular fitness scores are still below an acceptable range, look at the type of muscular strength and endurance exercises you are doing. Have you followed the principles of overload, progression and specificity in your muscular fitness exercises?
- If your flexibility ratings are not in the healthy fitness zone, perhaps you are not stretching enough or your method of stretching is incorrect. Are you stretching daily or at least 2-3 times a week and holding your stretches for 15 to 30 seconds?
- If your body composition rating is not in the healthy fitness zone, consider some of the factors, such as exercise habits, eating pattern, types of foods eaten, etc., which you may need to change.

As your lifestyle and activity preferences change, continue to reexamine your choices and make necessary modifications. The fitness assessments you have learned in this class can be used throughout your life; however, the healthy fitness zone standards will change as you get older.

WEBSITE

To learn more about fitness, visit the following web sites:
www.fitness.gov
www.diabetes.org

Aerobic activities will help you improve your cardiorespiratory fitness.

Exercise can help delay the signs of aging.

Remember what works today may not work later in life, but you can apply the basic principles of training throughout your life.

Your Changing Body

After age thirty, the body generally goes through a series of changes. Of course, to a large extent, the rate and degree of these changes is dependent upon how well you have taken care of your body, your lifestyle, heredity and environment. Many of the signs of aging can be delayed with a healthy lifestyle. The most common changes which occur are:

- Skeletal muscles may lose some of their strength.
- The circulatory system may become less efficient.
- The skin may become wrinkled.
- Hair turns gray.

Surprisingly, some people become more physically fit as adults than when they were younger, because they understand the need to adopt a lifestyle that promotes fitness and wellness. They make exercise a priority in their schedule and exercise regularly. They are aware of what they eat and eat more healthful meals. They have gained a measure of control over the tensions and stresses in their life.

Your potential health and wellness as an adult is often determined by lifestyle choices you make now.

Did You Know?

Approximately 1/3 of all causes of preventable death in the U.S. are related to complications of alcohol abuse.

Potential Health Problems

Throughout life we have many choices in regard to our activities and what we will eat and drink. As you learned earlier in the text, your behavior is the key to your health and fitness. Use the information that follows to help you make good lifestyle choices.

Alcohol

The effects of drinking alcohol vary depending on the amount of alcohol consumed. The diagram below illustrates potential effects on various parts of the body

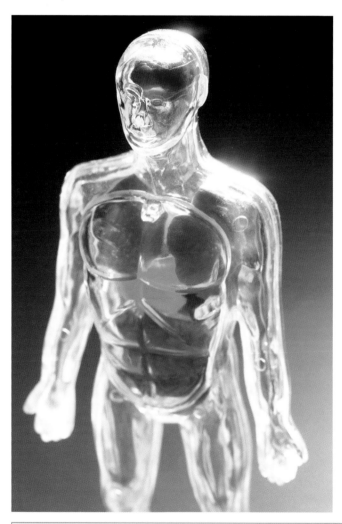

Brain:
- becomes less efficient in activities requiring alertness.

Heart:
- may beat abnormally
- force of contractions may decrease

Blood Vessels:
- capillaries dilate and carry internal heat to the skin which creates an illusion of warmth

Liver:
- excess alcohol causes cirrhosis and scarring which leads to reduced functioning

Stomach:
- inflames the stomach lining

Reproductive Organs:
- in men, can cause impotence
- in woman, can increase the risk of birth defects

Kidneys and Bladder:
- increases water loss and can lead to dehydration

Muscular Coordination:
- several drinks can affect the cerebellum which controls muscular coordination (that is why drinking and driving is a dangerous idea)
- speech may be slurred

Are there any benefits from moderate drinking? Studies show that moderate drinking (no more than two drinks per day) may have some protective effect against heart attacks and stroke. The reason for this benefit appears to be alcohol's effect on the HDL cholesterol level. Alcohol raises this "good" cholesterol that helps keep the arteries free of dangerous plaque build up. However, it is not recommended that non-drinkers start using alcohol or that drinkers increase the amount they drink. There are other ways to raise HDL levels.

Alcohol Facts:
- Alcohol is a depressant, narcotic drug and not a stimulant.
- Alcohol has very limited food value and contributes approximately 7 calories per gram.
- Alcohol inhibits the body's ability to use vitamins and calcium.
- The amount of alcohol in one drink is the same for:
  12 ounces of beer
  5 ounces of wine
  1.5 ounces of distilled liquor
- Alcohol is processed (burned off) at a rate of two hours for each drink.
- Women have less tolerance than men for the same amount of alcohol even if they weigh the same as men.
- Wine coolers may look like mere juice, but they have just as much alcohol as a 12 ounce beer.
- Drinking increases the risk of injury from car crashes, falls, burns, drowning and suicide.

These individuals should not drink alcoholic beverages:
- women who are pregnant or trying to conceive
- individuals who plan to drive or engage in activities that require attention or skill
- those using prescription and over-the-counter drugs
- individuals who cannot limit their drinking to a moderate amount
- children and adolescents

The amount of alcohol is the same for 5 oz. of wine, 12 oz. of beer and 1.5 oz. liquor.

Tobacco Use

Three million people around the world die each year from smoking-related diseases. Cigarette smoking is the major cause of illness, disability, and death in the U.S. In addition to heart disease, tobacco is also a major cause of lung, mouth, throat and other cancers; emphysema; chronic bronchitis; chronic pulmonary disease and strokes.

When a person smokes,
- nicotine and over 1,000 toxic compounds are released into the bloodstream. These substances can damage the arterial walls, which allow cholesterol to be more easily deposited thus forming atherosclerotic plaque.
- the risk of the formation of blood clots, which can cause complete blockage of a blood vessel, increases.
- heart rate increases.
- blood pressure increases.
- HDL (good) cholesterol levels decrease.

People who chew tobacco or smoke pipes or cigars also increase their risk of heart disease. Toxic chemicals are absorbed through the mouth and are transported through the bloodstream. Incidences of mouth and throat cancers are much greater for these individuals. The U.S. Surgeon General has stated that nicotine is as addictive as heroin and cocaine.

Osteoporosis

Osteoporosis is a condition in which the bones lose so much calcium content that they become weak and may break easily. When osteoporosis occurs the bones are "thinned out" from the loss of calcium and protein. The bones are the same size but the walls of the bone become thinner and the holes in the spongy bone become larger. A report by the *Physician and Sportsmedicine* magazine estimates that approximately 1.2 million fractures occur each year as a result of osteoporosis.

Even secondhand smoke can be a problem.

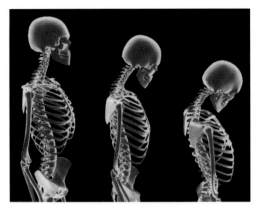

Osteoporosis causes the bones to collapse, your spine shrinks and the back curves in a "C".

Remember This ☑

Soft drinks prevent the absorption of calcium-rich foods—so drink them in moderation!

Early symptoms of osteoporosis include a loss of height, back pain or soreness and a slight curvature of the upper back. Factors believed to cause osteoporosis include:

- small bones
- lack of calcium in the diet
- lack of exercise
- tobacco use
- deficient estrogen after menopause
- race (white and Asian races are most susceptible)

Osteoporosis primarily affects women over the age of fifty. Women's bones are smaller and lighter than men's, so a greater part of a woman's total bone is lost than a man's. Women also lose bone faster than men do, especially after menopause (when menstruation stops). The reason for this is that at menopause the ovaries stop producing estrogen and the levels of estrogen in the body decrease. Estrogen protects against bone loss.

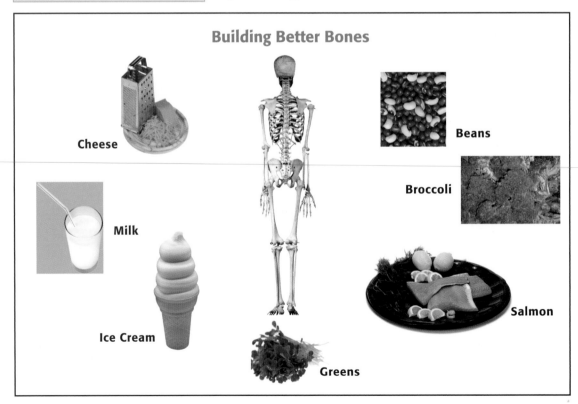

Building Better Bones

Cheese

Beans

Broccoli

Milk

Ice Cream

Salmon

Greens

Preventing Osteoporosis

Now is the best time to build better bones. The largest deposits to strengthen your bones occur between the ages of 6 and 18. What you do now is essential for good bone health. Here are some things you can do:

- Diet: If the calcium in the blood falls below a certain level, the body will replace it with calcium from the bones. Calcium protects the bones by slowing the rate of bone loss. Women need 1000 mg. of calcium per day before menopause and 1500 mg. after menopause. Vitamin D can aid the absorption of calcium from the stomach. A vegetarian diet is very healthy for the bones. Eating too much protein can lead to excessive bone loss.
- Exercise: The bones must be used to keep them healthy and strong. Walking, aerobic exercise to music and jogging help slow the rate of bone loss and may also start the growth of new bone.
- Avoid Risks: Since cigarettes, alcohol and caffeine increase bone loss, use of these substances should be limited or stopped. Some prescription drugs such as thyroid medications, diuretics, corticosteroids for arthritis and anticonvulsants can also increase the rate of bone loss.

Cancer

A study by Harvard School of Public Health showed that 30 to 40 percent of all cancers could be avoided by changing lifestyle and eating habits. Keys to lowering cancer risk include:

- eating a plant-based diet
- maintaining moderate weight
- exercising

It is clear that we can affect our chances of getting cancer by making positive changes in how we live and the foods we eat.

For Your Information

One 8 oz. glass of milk provides about 300 mg. of calcium.

Did You Know?

Two of the most avoidable causes of cancer are smoking and alcohol consumption. Totally eliminating these substances could help avoid 1/3 of all cancers.

Source: Presidents Council on Physical Fitness & Sports June 1995.

Fitness and Wellness Career Opportunities

It is quite possible that once you experience the exhilaration of participating in fitness activities, you may develop an interest in working in a health fitness career.

Do you have a personal commitment to health and fitness for yourself and others? Are you dedicated and willing to undertake the education and preparation necessary to succeed in a health and fitness career? Do you have leadership skills to motivate others? Are you a physically fit role model for those with whom you would work?

Some of the career opportunities available include:

Athletic Trainer
Corporate Fitness Instructor
Dance Exercise Instructor (Aerobics Instructor)
Dietitian
Exercise Physiologist
Fitness/Wellness Center Director
Health Club Exercise Program Director
Health Educator
Health Fitness Instructor
Medical Doctor
Nautilus and Weight Training Instructor
Occupational Therapist
Personal Trainer
Physical Educator
Physical Therapist
Sports Nutritionist
Sports Physician
Sports Sociologist
Yoga Instructor

Ask your physical education teacher or school guidance counselor for additional information about these career possibilities.

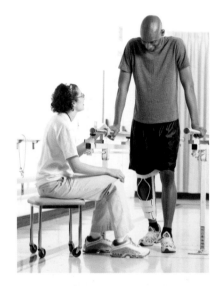

There are many opportunities for a career in fitness.

- What are your feelings about activities and exercise now? Have you changed any of the negatives to positives?
- Do you feel good about the progress you have made?
- Do you know what will work for you now and how to modify it in the future?

One of the keys to continued success in achieving lifetime personal fitness is the ability to adjust and modify your goals based on your current situation. What works for you today may not work in the future. In this course you have learned how to evaluate your level of fitness and how to make healthy diet choices. Continue to use this information to guide you everyday.

This process of permanently changing behavior that is destructive or negative to positive behaviors that will lead to better health and well-being is **behavior modification**. Hopefully, you have already learned to develop a behavior modification program by following the suggestions in this text for including regular physical activity in your daily schedule. You will need to remember these strategies throughout your life as your personal health needs change.

You can improve your health and wellness by remembering the activity pyramid, the principles of training and the keys to good nutrition.

Go for it!

Getting fit and staying fit depends on:
- Self motivation—Do it because you believe it.
- Time Management—Make exercise a priority in your schedule.
- Commitment—Make fitness a priority.
- Enjoyment—Find activities that you will continue to do because you enjoy them.

Include regular physical activity in your daily schedule for the rest of your life.

Maintaining personal health is a matter of individual initiative. In the United States, there is not a comprehensive system of truly preventive health care. Yet many health problems result, to a large degree, from things which are controllable—things you can do something about. The evidence is clear that how you live determines to a great extent how long you live and how well you live. The decision to be healthy and fit is within your grasp. Establish a lifestyle which enables you to achieve your highest potential for well-being.

Studies show that the vast majority of deaths due to cardiovascular disease are "premature" since they occur in relatively young individuals. These deaths are clearly connected to negative lifestyles and habits such as lack of exercise, poor diet, smoking and high stress. Many have called these the diseases of choice, because they relate to the way people choose to live their lives. Don't let the choices you are making now contribute to these early diseases and death.

It is difficult to make lifestyle changes when you are currently feeling "okay"—and when the real benefits are long-term and not immediately noticeable. The human body is able to absorb large amounts of abuse and neglect without any overt signs of harm for many years, and this misleads people into thinking that what they are doing is all right. Most people seem to think that these changes can be put off until tomorrow. Unfortunately, by the time tomorrow arrives, it may be too late.

Are you getting 30-minutes of activity at least 5 days a week?

Remember to keep modifying your activity plan, use the *My Activity Plan* from the *Personal Fitness for You* student CD to make plans for your future lifestyle and activities.

The Activity Pyramid

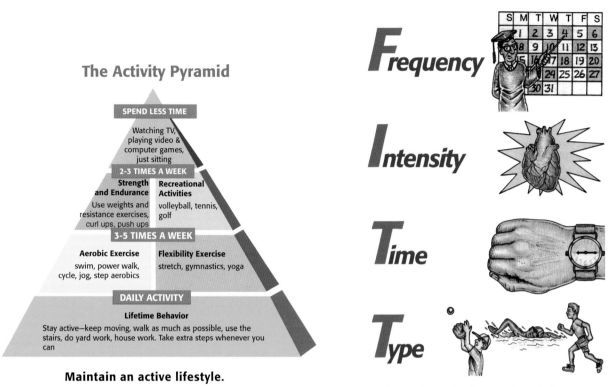

SPEND LESS TIME
Watching TV, playing video & computer games, just sitting

2-3 TIMES A WEEK

Strength and Endurance
Use weights and resistance exercises, curl ups, push ups

Recreational Activities
volleyball, tennis, golf

3-5 TIMES A WEEK

Aerobic Exercise
swim, power walk, cycle, jog, step aerobics

Flexibility Exercise
stretch, gymnastics, yoga

DAILY ACTIVITY

Lifetime Behavior
Stay active—keep moving, walk as much as possible, use the stairs, do yard work, house work. Take extra steps whenever you can

Maintain an active lifestyle.

Frequency

Intensity

Time

Type

Follow the principles of training to reach your health fitness goals.

The Keys to Good Nutrition

Follow the Dietary Guidelines

Use MyPyramid Food Guide

Read Food Labels

Use the keys to good nutrition to improve your eating habits.

Are You Making Responsible Decisions?

In life you may be tempted to do things which do not contribute to fitness or wellness. Use what you have learned in this course to make responsible decisions.

The Decision Is Yours

As you grow into adulthood, you will experience many changes in your body. The activities you choose to participate in now may not be appropriate as you get older. For instance, rigorous gymnastics, wrestling and football may be inadvisable for most middle-aged and older adults. Other sports and activities, such as golf, sailing and racket sports, lend themselves to lifetime participation. It is a good idea to start acquiring the skills for participating in these sports now.

Wellness is always important. Regardless of your age, you can enhance the quality of your life. Fitness activities are beneficial for people of all ages. However, as you grow older, you may need to adjust the kind, amount and timing of exercise to make certain it is compatible with your needs, interests and capabilities.

As you leave high school and either go on to college or a career, there is a possibility that exercise and fitness will have a lower priority in your life and you may become "too busy" to exercise. Your dietary habits may also change. If you become responsible for preparing your own meals, you may be tempted to consume more processed foods, high calorie foods and greater quantities of alcohol. This combination of physical inactivity and failing to eat nutritionally sound meals, may lead to obesity and other health problems.

Use what you have learned about fitness in this course to prevent this from happening. Just as the gains you have achieved in this course have been worth the investment to help you feel and look better now, continue to accept the personal fitness challenge for the rest of your life. In order for these fitness and wellness gains you have made to be effective and to serve as preventive medicine, they must be lifelong. Make a personal commitment now.

You have a choice—the physically active life which has documented benefits or the inactive life with all the problems associated with it. Choose the active life!

Summary

Use what you have learned in this course to help you achieve your optimal health. What is important is the quality of each day of your life. The goal is to feel the best you have ever felt in your life now, not just the distant future. It will take action and sacrifice on your part to improve your lifestyle. Why not start today to make the healthy choice? Do it not just to live longer, but to enjoy each day to the fullest and to look and feel better! The decision is yours!

Choose the Active Life!

Chapter 18 Review

Lesson Checklist

- Do you know how to revise your fitness program based on the results of retaking the fitness tests?
- Can you identify physical changes that occur as people get older?
- Do you understand the special health problems which can affect your fitness?
- Can you list some of the fitness and wellness career opportunities?
- Can you describe the lifestyle choices necessary for lifetime fitness?

Chapter Projects

Write a response to each of the following:

1. After examining the Healthy People 2010 Goals presented throughout the text, identify three that are important to you and why.
2. Using the information you have learned in this course, write a dialogue trying to convince a friend to develop a fitness program.

Behavior Change Evaluation

Review the following items to see if you have gained an understanding of fitness and wellness. On a piece of paper briefly state how you will make these changes.

- I know how to revise my exercise program based on lifestyle changes.
- I will be able to recognize physical changes that occur as I get older and make appropriate adjustments in my exercise program.
- I will make personal lifestyle choices which enable me to achieve lifetime personal fitness.

Critical Thinking

Describe what you feel are the most important things you have learned in this course that will enable you to attain a goal of lifetime personal fitness.

Chapter 18 Review

Test Your Knowledge

Read the questions below and select the best possible answer for each.

1. As people age:
   a. cholesterol increases
   b. skeletal muscles lose strength
   c. flexibility is reduced
   d. all of the above

2. Which of the following is true of alcohol?
   a. beer contains more alcohol than wine
   b. alcohol is a stimulant
   c. women have less tolerance than men for the same amount of alcohol
   d. all of the above

3. A condition in which the bones become weak and may break easily is:
   a. asthma
   b. osteoporosis
   c. diabetes
   d. arthritis

4. To lower your risk of cancer:
   a. eat a plant-based diet
   b. exercise
   c. maintain a moderate weight
   d. all of the above

5. Which of the following is not related to the development of osteoporosis?
   a. lack of exercise
   b. tobacco use
   c. lack of calcium in diet
   d. large bones

Glossary

A

Abdominals: The group of muscles forming the supporting wall of the pelvic and abdominal regions.

Achilles Tendon: The tendon connecting the heel bone and calf muscle.

Adequate Intake (AI): An interim RDA which is used because scientific data isn't strong enough to recommend an RDA.

Adrenaline: A hormone secreted by the body in response to stress; prepares the body for "fight or flight."

Aerobic Capacity: A term which means the same as cardiorespiratory fitness – the ability to perform muscle, dynamic, moderate to high intensity exercise for prolonged periods.

Aerobic Exercise: Continuous exercise using large muscle groups that keeps the heart rate in the target zone.

Agility: The ability to start, stop and move the body quickly and in different directions.

Alarm Stage: The first stage of stress in which the stressor is recognized and adrenaline is released.

Alveoli: Tiny sponge-like air sacs found in the lungs. They are responsible for the rapid exchange of air in the blood.

Amino Acids: The building blocks of protein.

Anabolic Steroids: Synthetic versions of the male hormone, testosterone.

Anaerobic Exercise: Exercise which is so intense the body cannot supply the amount of oxygen needed during the workout.

Androgens: Hormones that promote the growth of muscle tissue.

Anemia: A condition occurring when the blood does not have enough red blood cells or the cells do not contain enough hemoglobin.

Anorexia Nervosa: An eating disorder, primarily of young women, in which there is an extreme and irrational fear of gaining weight that can lead to starvation dieting.

Antioxidant: The body's natural defense mechanism against free radicals which cause cell damage.

Aorta: The large artery that carries blood from the heart to be distributed throughout the body.

Artery: A blood vessel that moves blood away from the heart.

Assertive Behavior: A means of coping with stressful situations by following one's own basic beliefs.

Asthma: A condition marked by labored breathing, often accompanied by wheezing and attacks of coughing or gasping.

Atherosclerosis: A buildup of plaque and narrowing on the inside of arterial walls.

Atria: The top two of the four chambers of the heart. The atria receive blood from the veins and force it into the ventricles.

Atrophy: When a muscle becomes smaller because of non use.

B

Balance: A kind of coordination which allows you to maintain control of your body while stationary or moving.

Ball and Socket Joint: A joint in which the rounded head of one bone fits into the cup-like cavity of another bone and permits movement in any direction.

Ballistic Stretch: When the muscle is stretched by a bouncing or jerky movement.

Basal Metabolic Rate (BMR): The rate at which your body burns food and nutrients to perform minimal bodily functions while at rest.

Behavior: The way a person conducts himself or herself; the factor most responsible for determining total fitness.

Behavior Modification: The process of permanently changing behavior that is destructive or negative to positive behaviors that will lead to better health and well-being.

Beta carotene: A plant product which is converted to Vitamin A in the body.

Bioelectrical Impedance Analysis: A method of determining body fat percentage which measures electrical resistance encountered in the body.

Biomechanics: The study of human motion and the effect forces have on the body.

Blood Pressure: The force of the blood against the walls of the blood vessels.

Blood Sugar: The concentration of glucose in the blood.

Blood Vessels: A series of tubes which distribute blood to all tissues of the body.

Body Composition: The relative amount of body weight that is fat weight and lean body weight (tissue, bone and muscle).

Body Mass Index (BMI): A measurement of your body composition, calculated by using height and weight.

Body Wrapping: A process in which the body is wrapped, usually in plastic wrap and/ or ace bandages, often presented as a way of firming the body and losing weight.

Bronchi: One of two tubes through which air travels from the trachea to the lungs.

Bronchioles: The smaller branches of the bronchi through which air travels through the lungs.

Bulimia: An eating disorder characterized by binge eating and purging by vomiting or laxatives.

C

Caliper: See Skinfold Caliper.

Caloric Expenditure: Burning of calories through activity; usually compared with caloric intake to determine whether fat or weight loss will occur.

Caloric Intake: Calories taken in by the body.

Calorie: A measurement of the potential energy of food.

Capillaries: The smallest of the body's blood vessels which carry oxygen and nutrients to the body cells and pick up waste products - serve as bridges between the arteries and veins.

Carbohydrate: The major source of energy for the body.

Carbon Dioxide: The waste gas created during the respiration process and exhaled by the body.

Cardio: A word which means "heart."

Cardiovascular: Relating to the heart and blood vessels.

Cardiovascular Fitness: The ability of the body to do vigorous activity over a long period of time.

Cardiorespiratory System: Composed of the heart, blood vessels, and respiratory system.

Carotid Artery: The large neck artery that is often used to count pulse rate.

Cartilage: Firm, elastic connective tissue.

Cellulite: Term frequently used to describe lumpy fat deposits.

Cellulose: Plant fiber that is non-digestible.

Cholesterol: A waxy, fatty-like material used by the body in a variety of chemical processes.

Circuit Training: Refers to a series of exercise stations that combine a variety of exercises such as weight training, flexibility, and aerobic exercises.

Complete Protein: A protein food which has all the essential amino acids needed by the body.

Complex Carbohydrate: Carbohydrates which are stored in the body and broken down slowly, thus providing energy over a longer period of time. Grains and vegetables are examples.

Concentric Contraction: A muscle contraction in which one end of the muscle remains stationary while the other end pulls and turns the bone about the joint. Also known as a shortening contraction.

Consumer: One who uses and/or purchases goods or services.

Contract and Relax Stretching: Contracting a muscle before it is stretched. The person stretching performs an isometric contraction, while a partner provides resistance. Also called PNF stretching.

Cool-down: The tapering off period after completing the conditioning phase of training. It usually consists of walking, slow jogging and stretching.

Coordination: The ability to do a task integrating movements of the body and different parts of the body.

Coronary Arteries: The blood vessels that supply blood to the heart.

Cramp: A muscle spasm.

Creeping Obesity: Gradual weight gain triggered by the aging process.

Criterion-referenced Test: A test based on public health research that sets a standard by which to measure an individual's test scores.

Cross-training: The combination of two or more types of exercise in one workout or using different exercises alternately in successive workouts.

D

Dehydration: When body tissues lose fluids, particularly water.

Diabetes: A condition caused by a breakdown in the body's ability to regulate sugar metabolism.

Diaphragm: The muscle separating the chest and abdominal cavity.

Diastole: The relaxed phase of the heart's contraction during which the heart chambers are filled with blood.

Diastolic Pressure: The blood pressure between beats when the heart is relaxed.

Dietary Reference Intake (DRI): Recommended nutritional guidelines for optimal health.

Distress: Stress brought about by negative events.

Diuretic: Drugs that increase urine production and the loss of water by the body.

Dominant: The more effective of a pair of body parts; for example, the dominant hand is the one used most frequently and most efficiently.

Duration: Overload principle that refers to the length of a training session.

E

Eccentric Contraction: A muscle contraction which involves a gradual release of the contraction; often termed a lengthening or negative contraction.

Ectomorph: Thin, slender body build with lack of muscle contour.

Elasticity: The ability of a muscle to recover its original size and shape after use.

Electrolytes: Electric conductors such as sodium, potassium, and calcium, which are found in the body and are sometimes depleted due to heavy exercise and sweating.

Emphysema: A disease of the lungs in which the person is unable to take in enough oxygen.

Endomorph: Heavy, rounded body type with limited muscular development.

Endorphins: Substances produced naturally by the body, available for release during periods of extreme stress or pain.

Endurance: Being able to do a continuous activity and to resist fatigue.

Enriched: When nutrients that are destroyed in processing are added back to a product.

Environment: The conditions which surround us; the cultural and social conditions that influence the life of the individual.

Essential Amino Acids: Substances making up protein which must be supplied each day by the food we eat.

Estimated Average Requirement (EAR): An amount of nutrient needed by specific groups of people (such as pregnant women).

Eustress: Stress brought about by positive events.

Exercise: Planned, structured, and repetitive bodily movements performed to maintain and improve physical fitness.

Exhaustion Stage (of stress): The third level resulting from prolonged stress; may lead to various stress-related illnesses.

Extension: The lengthening movement of muscles around a joint.

F

Fact: Something that is a reality or certainty.

Fad: A practice or an interest followed with great enthusiasm, usually for a short period of time.

Fad Diet: A diet that depends on one food, a special combination of foods, or eliminating (or depending upon) only one major food group.

Fallacy: A false or mistaken idea; often the result of deception or inaccurate information.

Fasting: A deliberate program of not eating.

Fast-twitch Muscle Fiber: A muscle fiber having a low capacity to use oxygen and the ability to contract fast. These muscles are used for short and intense bursts of action.

Fats: Food substances that provide body energy and have the ability to be stored.

Fat Weight: Weight which is not muscle, bone, tendons, ligaments, internal organs or water.

Fat-soluble Vitamin: A vitamin which can be stored in fat deposits in the body (Vitamins A, D, E and K).

Fiber: The structural part of plants which is neither digested nor absorbed by the body; serves as an intestinal "house cleaner."

"Fight or Flight": Refers to the decision one makes when faced with danger or stress - whether to face the situation or run from it.

FITT: Letters to help remember the overload factors: frequency, intensity, time and type.

Fatty Acids: The basic building blocks of fats. They include saturated, unsaturated, and trans fatty acids.

Flexibility: The ability of a joint and muscle group to move through a maximum range of motion.

Flexion: The bending movement of muscles around a joint.

Fracture: The breaking of a bone.

Free Radical: A molecule or atom that has an extra free-floating electron (one without a matched pair) that can damage cells.

Frequency: How often - that is, the number of times per day or week - an activity is performed.

G

Gender: A person's sex (male or female).

Glycemic Index: A method of comparing foods based on how quickly the foods are digested into glucose and absorbed; and therefore how much they cause the blood sugar to rise.

Goal: Something you wish to achieve; may be short-term, intermediate, or long-term.

Gram: A metric unit of mass and weight.

H

Hamstrings: The large muscle group at the back of the upper leg.

HDL: See High-density Lipoprotein.

Health: A state of complete physical, mental and social well-being.

Health-Related Fitness: Those aspects of fitness vital to well-being: cardiovascular endurance, muscular strength, muscular endurance, flexibility, and body composition.

Heart Rate: The number of times a heart beats or pumps per minute.

Heat Cramps: A sudden cramping of the muscles caused by excessive loss of body fluids.

Heat Exhaustion: A body condition usually caused by lack of fluids and excessive heat. Symptoms are paleness, weakness, heavy perspiration and skin cool to the touch.

Heatstroke: A serious condition resulting from prolonged exposure to high temperatures and the body being unable to cool itself. Symptoms include dry, flushed skin, high body temperature, and high pulse rate.

Hemoglobin: The part of the red blood cell that contains iron and gives the cell its color.

Heredity: Qualities and potentialities genetically passed on by one's ancestors.

High Blood Pressure: See Hypertension.

High Density Lipoprotein (HDL): A fatty acid that holds a greater amount of protein, is heavier, and contains less cholesterol than low density lipoproteins. Generally considered to be "good" cholesterol.

Hinge Joint: A joint which permits only limited movement (such as the knee).

Homeostasis: The internal balance of the body.

Hyperflexibility: Slack, overstretched ligaments caused by improper exercises or injuries and result in too much motion in a joint.

Hypertension: When blood pressure is usually higher than normal, exceeding 140/90.

Hypertrophy: The increase in muscle fiber size as a result of strength training.

Hypothermia: A serious condition in which body temperature falls below normal.

I

Ideal Body Weight: The best weight for a person when body fat percentage is kept within an acceptable range.

Imagery: Mental images; a process helpful in dealing with stressful situations.

Individuality Principle: The principle of training that states that a training program must be based on an individual's goals and objectives for physical activity and fitness.

Intensity: Placing an increasingly greater workload on the body.

Intermediate Fast-Twitch Fiber: A type of muscle fiber used in activities of high intensity and moderate duration.

Intermediate Goals: Goals which can serve as milestone events along the way to achieving your long-term goals.

Interval Training: Alternating periods of exercise at high intensity with periods of light exercise or rest.

Isokinetic Training: Training in which the length of the muscle changes while the contraction is performed at a constant speed. The machine provides maximum resistance throughout the entire range of motion.

Isometric Contraction: A static muscle contraction against an immovable resistance. The muscle length remains constant while muscle tension increases. An example of isometric training is pushing against a wall.

Isotonic Contraction: A muscle contraction involving shortening and lengthening of the muscles and movement at a joint.

J

Joint: Where two or more bones meet and form a junction.

L

Lactic Acid: A body waste product found in the muscles and tissues.

LDL: See Low Density Lipoprotein.

Lean Weight: Body weight composed of muscle, bone, tendons, ligaments, internal organs and water.

Legumes: Vegetables from a specific family of plants; most common are peas and beans.

Lifestyle: The way a person conducts his or her daily life.

Ligament: A strong band of connecting tissue that holds bone to bone.

Lipid: A fatty substance such as cholesterol, the fatty acids or triglycerides.

Lipoprotein: When fats (lipids) combine with protein so as to become soluble for transportation in the blood.

Long-term Goals: Goals which involve major changes in lifestyle or behavior and take a longer time to achieve.

Low Density Lipoprotein (LDL): A fatty acid that holds larger molecules than high density lipoproteins (HDL). Generally linked to increased chances of cardiovascular disease.

M

Maturation: Age, physical development, body type, weight and readiness to learn.

Maximal Oxygen Uptake (Max VO$_2$): The amount of oxygen used by the body during exercise. Generally considered to be the best measure of cardiovascular endurance.

Maximum Heart Rate: The highest heart rate capable by the human body.

Meditation: The process of focusing one's thoughts on something specific, often for the purpose of relaxing or reducing stress.

Mesomorph: Athletic, muscular body build with prominent bone and muscle development.

Metabolism: All body processes that allow the cells to function.

Migraine Headache: A severe headache often accompanied by nausea and vomiting; may be triggered by stress.

Minerals: Nutrients occurring naturally and found in many foods. Calcium, phosphorus, potassium, sodium, and iron are among the minerals needed by the body.

Moderate Activity: Medium intensity exercise.

Monounsaturated Fats: Fats, usually in liquid form, found in vegetable sources; olive and canola oils are examples.

Muscle: Bands of fiber which enable the body to move.

Muscle Fiber: The basic unit of the muscular system.

Muscular Endurance: The ability of a muscle group to continue muscle movement over a length of time.

Muscle Imbalance: Occurs when one muscle group is worked much more than the opposing muscle group thus becoming much stronger.

Muscular Strength: The amount of force that can be exerted by a single contraction of the muscle.

MyPyramid Food Guide: A plan developed by the U.S. Department of Agriculture to help you choose foods and amounts that are right for you.

Myth: An idea or belief, sometimes widely accepted, which often proves false.

N

Negative Coping Strategies: Methods of dealing with stress that are harmful to a person; for example, using alcohol or drugs.

Negatives: Eccentric muscle contractions.

Nutrients: Substances which promote growth and help the body to function. The six basic nutrients are carbohydrates, protein, fats, vitamins, minerals, and water.

Nutrition: The study of food and its use by the body.

O

Obese: When a person has an excess amount of body fat.

Obesity: Having an excess amount of fat on the body.

Obliques: Thin, flat muscles that form the middle and outer layers of the lateral walls of the abdomen.

Omega 3 Fatty Acids: A type of fat that may help to improve triglyceride level and lower blood pressure.

One Repetition Maximum (1 RM): The most weight you can properly lift through the full range of motion one time.

Optimal Fitness: The highest potential of an individual to be fit; varies from one person to another.

Osteoporosis: A thinning of the bones which contributes to bone fractures.

Overfat: Having more fat than you should as determined by skinfold measurements.

Overload Principle: One of the principles of training which determines the effectiveness of a training program. Overload relates to making increased demands upon the body.

Overtraining: Participation in any physical activity at very high intensity levels or for unusually long periods of time.

Overweight: When one weighs more than a prescribed weight thought to be desirable.

Oxidation: Cell damage caused by free radicals.

Oxygenated: Mixed or combined with oxygen, as when the red blood cells combine with oxygen in the blood.

P

Pectorals: The muscles which connect the upper arms and shoulders to the chest.

Percent Daily Value (%DV): Recommendations on food labels based on the Daily Value Recommendations for key nutrients for a 2,000 calorie diet.

Percentage of Body Fat: The percentage of body weight made up of body fat.

Personal Best: The best performance you as an individual have achieved.

Physical Activity: Bodily movement that is produced by the contraction of skeletal muscle and that substantially increases energy expenditure.

Physical Fitness: The ability to attain certain physical attributes and a state of physical well-being.

Physiological: Dealing with the processes and functions of the body.

Plaque: A buildup of fatty deposits inside the arteries.

Plasma: The fluid part of blood.

Plateau: A period in which one's performance remains stable and shows little change.

Polyunsaturated Fats: Fats, usually in liquid form, found in vegetable sources; safflower and corn oil are examples.

Pooling (of blood): Accumulation of blood in the lower extremities which can result in dizziness or faintness.

Positive Coping Strategies: Methods of dealing with stress that result in benefits to the body; for example, exercise.

Power: The ability to combine strength and speed in a movement.

PRICE Method: The recommended method of treating injuries: protect the area, restrict movement, ice the area, use compression, and elevate the area.

Principle: A rule or method of conduct.

Principles of Training: The guidelines for achieving improvement-progression, overload, specificity, regularity, and individuality.

Progression: Gradual increase in exercise or activity over a period of time.

Progressive Muscle Relaxation: A progressive program of relieving tension from all body muscles, by tensing and relaxing muscles group by group.

Protein: The basic building block of the body; used to repair, replace and build body cells.

Psychological: Dealing with the processes of the mind.

Pulse: The regular throbbing in the arteries caused by contraction of the heart.

Q

Quack: An individual who represents harmful and/or useless practices as beneficial.

Quackery: Representing harmful and/or useless practices as beneficial.

Quadriceps: The large group of muscles located in the front of the thigh.

R

Radial Artery: The artery on the inside of your wrist where the pulse can be counted.

Range of Motion (full): The ability of a body joint to move to its full limit without undue stress.

Rate of Perceived Exertion: The assessment of the intensity of a workout compared to how you feel.

RDA (Recommended Daily Allowance): Recommendations for levels of nutrients needed by the general population daily.

Reaction Time: The time required to start a movement after being alerted to the need to move.

Recommended Dietary Allowance (RDA): Recommendation for the amount of a nutrient that is necessary to meet the nutritional needs of almost every healthy person in a specific age and gender group.

Recovery Heart Rate: A measurement after strenuous exercise indicating the rate at which the heart beat returns to normal.

Recreational (activities): Pleasurable and enjoyable activities.

Red Blood Cells: The blood cells which transport oxygen and carbon dioxide.

Regularity Principle: The principle of training based on the concept that you must perform physical activity on a regular basis.

Repetitions (Reps): The number of repeated lifts or movements performed.

Resistance Stage: The second stage of stress in which physical symptoms become more pronounced and the body tries to adjust to the stressor.

Respiratory System: The body system responsible for transport and exchange of gases such as oxygen and carbon dioxide between the lungs, blood, and tissues.

Resting Heart Rate: A measure of the heart rate following a period of inactivity.

Rip-off: Being cheated or exploited by exchanging something of value (usually financial) for something worthless.

Risk Factors: Those things which affect your chances of developing a disease or a health problem; for example, smoking.

S

Saturated Fats: Fats, usually in solid form, mainly found in animal sources; butter and lard are examples.

Sedentary: Inactive; a sedentary lifestyle is one in which most time is spent sitting or lying down, rather than physical activity.

Septum: The wall of muscle separating the right and left chambers of the heart.

Set: In weight training, a group of successive repetitions without rest.

Set Point: Your normal weight when you are not attempting to control it.

Shin Splints: An injury or inflammation of the lower leg, usually resulting from running on hard surfaces.

Short-term Goals: Goals which usually take a relatively short time to achieve (usually weeks or months).

Skill-Related Fitness: Those aspects of fitness which form the basis for successful sports participation-agility, balance, coordination, power, reaction time, and speed.

Skinfold: A fold consisting of a layer of fat and a layer of skin; used to determine body fat percentage.

Skinfold Caliper: A device used to measure skinfold body fat obtained by pinching the skin.

Slow-twitch Muscle Fiber: A type of muscle fiber having a high capacity to use oxygen, but slow contractile ability. These fibers are used most in long endurance type activities.

Sociological: Relating to social needs and problems.

Sodium: A mineral commonly referred to as salt; needed by the body but, consumed excessively, can cause health problems.

Somatotype: Body type related to your frame size and distribution of fat and muscle tissue.

Specificity: Improvement will only occur in that fitness area each exercise is designed to improve. For example, participating in stretching exercises will improve flexibility but will not improve muscular strength.

Speed: Ability to move one's total body quickly from one point to another.

Spot Reducing: Attempting to lose fat in only one area of the body. This is not effective.

Spotter: Someone who assists the weightlifter.

Static Contraction: When the muscle remains in partial or complete contraction without changing its length.

Static Stretch: The slow and gradual movement of muscle and joint through a range of motion. The stretch position must be reached and held for several seconds.

Steady State: When a balance between supply and demand of oxygen is reached.

Steroids: Compounds said to increase muscle mass but having many negative effects on the body.

Stitch in the Side: A sharp pain in the side often resulting when one first begins a conditioning program.

Strength: The degree of force a muscle can exert.

Stress: The response of the body to any demand made upon it.

Stressor: Something which creates stress.

Stress Test: A test designed to evaluate the response of the cardiovascular system to strenuous exercise.

Stretch Reflex: A muscle spasm which prevents the muscle from overstretching.

Stroke: Occurs when the blood supply is cut off to a part of the brain.

Supplement: Something which is added; for example, extra vitamins may be taken as a supplement to the diet.

Systemic: Refers to the left side of the heart, which sends blood to all systems of the body.

Systolic Pressure: The highest force exerted by the blood against the arterial wall.

T

Target Heart Rate: The most desirable rate at which the heart should be beating to achieve a cardiovascular training effect.

Tendon: Tissue that attaches muscle to bone.

Tension Headache: Headache caused by muscle contractions in the head and neck, usually triggered by stress.

Testosterone: A hormone which is partially responsible for muscle development.

Time: Refers to the duration of the exercise training session.

Tolerable Upper Limit (UL): The safe upper limit for nutrients.

Toxic: Poisonous.

Trachea: The windpipe.

Training: The procedure of systematically preparing a person in the most efficient manner to perform strenuous activity and to recover from that activity as quickly as possible.

Training Effect: The physiological results from performing vigorous fitness activities.

Training Heart Rate: The pulse rate per minute required to produce significant changes in cardiovascular fitness.

Trans fatty acids: Unsaturated fatty acids which contain partially hydrogenated vegetable oils that can raise LDL and total cholesterol.

Triceps: The large muscle along the back of the upper arm.

Triglycerides: Fatty particles that transport fat in the blood.

U

Underweight: Being more than 10% below the ideal weight for one's bone structure and height.

Unsaturated Fat: A liquid type of fat that does not solidify at room temperature.

V

Vascular: Term used to refer to the blood vessels.

Veins: The blood vessels that move blood from the outer parts of the body back to the heart.

Ventricles: The two bottom chambers of the heart.

Vigorous activity: High intensity exercise.

Vitamin: An organic substance required by the body to use and absorb nutrients.

W

Warm-Up: The beginning phase of the training session in which the body is prepared for a workout.

Water-soluble Vitamin: A vitamin which dissolves in water; B Vitamins and Vitamin C are examples.

Wellness: Quality of life which includes intellectual, physical, emotional, spiritual, and social fitness.

White Blood Cells: The blood cells that defend the body against infection.

Bibliography

The following are excellent resources to obtain additional information about health, fitness and wellness. The organizations listed are leaders in the area of health and provide excellent on-line information as well as publications which can be ordered on their website.

American Council on Exercise
Information provided: Get Fit, Fit Facts, Health and Fitness Tips, Healthy Recipes, an Exercise Library with basic to advanced workouts in all fitness areas.
www.acefitness.org

American College of Sports Medicine
Information provided: Guidelines for Exercise Testing and Prescription, Health and Fitness tips, Guidelines for Aerobic Activities, Fit Society newsletter.
www.acsm.org

American Heart Association
Information provided: Get the Facts, Heart Healthy, Recipes, Active Living Everyday, Healthy Eating Everyday, Controlling Cholesterol, Exercise and Fitness, Health Tools.
www.americanheart.org

The Cooper Institute for Aerobics Research
Information provided: Health Tips, Extensive Health Information on a variety of topics, recipes, nutrition tips, on-line newsletter.
www.cooperaerobics.com

Healthfinder
Information provided: Links to health information resources, health library, health news, on-line medical dictionary, encyclopedia and journals.
www.healthfinder.gov

The International Fitness Association
Information provided: Library of exercises including weight training and step aerobics, Fitness Manual, Stretching book, and other on-line books.
www.ifafitness.com

National Heart, Lung and Blood Institute
Information provided: Health Assessment tools, Recipes for Healthy Eating, publications which can be received on-line.
www.nhlbi.nih.gov

The President's Challenge
Information provided: Physical Activity and Fitness Awards Program, Activity Log, Fitness Calculators, Active Lifestyle information for the family.
www.presidentschallenge.org

President's Council on Physical Fitness and Sports
Information provided: Physical Activity Fact Sheet and numerous publications.
www.fitness.gov

U.S. Department of Agriculture
Information provided: links to MyPyramid, the Dietary Guidelines for 2005, and other information on food and nutrition.
www.usda.gov

U.S. Department of Health and Human Services
Information provided: Public health reports including the Healthy People 2010 Goals.
www.os.dhhs.gov and www.healthypeople.gov

Index